Telecommunications Competition

AEI Studies in Telecommunications Deregulation
J. Gregory Sidak and Paul W. MacAvoy, series editors

TOWARD COMPETITION IN LOCAL TELEPHONY
William J. Baumol and J. Gregory Sidak

TOWARD COMPETITION IN CABLE TELEVISION
Leland L. Johnson

REGULATING BROADCAST PROGRAMMING
Thomas G. Krattenmaker and Lucas A. Powe, Jr.

DESIGNING INCENTIVE REGULATION IN THE
TELECOMMUNICATIONS INDUSTRY
David E. M. Sappington and Dennis L. Weisman

THE FAILURE OF ANTITRUST AND REGULATION
TO CREATE COMPETITION IN
LONG-DISTANCE TELEPHONE SERVICE MARKETS
Paul W. MacAvoy

UNIVERSAL SERVICE:
COMPETITION, INTERCONNECTION, AND MONOPOLY IN THE
MAKING OF THE AMERICAN TELEPHONE SYSTEM
Milton L. Mueller, Jr.

TELECOMMUNICATIONS COMPETITION:
THE LAST TEN MILES
Ingo Vogelsang and Bridger M. Mitchell

Telecommunications Competition

The Last Ten Miles

Ingo Vogelsang
Bridger M. Mitchell

The MIT Press
Cambridge, Massachusetts
London, England
and
The AEI Press
Washington, D.C.
1997

Published by

The MIT Press
Cambridge, Massachusetts
London, England

HE
7781
.V64
1997

and

The AEI Press
Washington, D.C.

Library of Congress Cataloging-in-Publication Data

Vogelsang, Ingo
    Telecommunications competition: the last ten miles / Ingo Vogelsang,
Bridger M. Mitchell
        p.   cm. — (AEI studies in telecommunications deregulation)
    Includes bibliographical references and indexes.
    ISBN 0-262-22050-4 (alk. paper)
    1. Telecommunication—Deregulation—United States.
2. Competition—United States. 3. Telecommunication—Deregulation.
4. Competition. I. Mitchell, Bridger M. II. Title. III. Series.
HE7781.V64 1996
384'.041—dc20   96-27952
                                                                       CIP

Printed in the United States of America

To Julia and Bianca, and

Kristin, Morgan, and Jed,

who will benefit most from telecommunications competition

Contents

Foreword

DRAMATIC ADVANCES IN COMMUNICATIONS and information technologies are imposing severe strains on a government regulatory apparatus devised in the pioneer days of radio and are raising policy questions with large implications for American economic performance and social welfare. Before the passage of the Telecommunications Act of 1996, one was compelled to ask, Is federal and state telecommunications regulation impeding competition and innovation, and has that indeed become its principal if unstated function? Is regulation inhibiting the dissemination of ideas and information through electronic media? Does the licensing regime for the electromagnetic spectrum allocate that resource to its most productive uses? Now that the 1996 act is in place, is it likely to correct any of those ill effects?

Ingo Vogelsang and Bridger M. Mitchell's study directly analyzes the most pivotal of the issues raised by the 1996 act—competition in the last ten miles of the telephone network. It shows that the arrival of effective competition will be the culmination of dramatic technological, regulatory, and market changes. This work is one of a series of research volumes addressing those questions commissioned by the American Enterprise Institute's Telecommunications Deregulation Project. The AEI project is intended to produce new empirical research on the entire range of telecommunications policy issues, with particular emphasis on identifying reforms to federal and state regulatory policies that will advance rather than inhibit innovation and consumer welfare. We hope that research will be useful to legislators and public officials at all levels of government, and to the business executives and, most of all, the consumers who must live with their policies. The volumes have been written and edited to be accessible to readers with no specialized knowledge of communication technologies or economics; we hope they will find a place in courses on regulated industries and communications policy in economics and communications departments and in business, law, and public policy schools.

Each volume in the Telecommunications Deregulation Project has been discussed and criticized in draft form at an AEI seminar involving federal and state regulators, jurists, business executives, professionals, and academic experts with a wide range of interests and viewpoints, and has been reviewed and favorably reported by anonymous academic referees selected by the MIT Press. I wish to thank all of them for their contributions, noting, however, that the final exposition and conclusions are entirely the responsibility of the authors of each volume.

I am particularly grateful to Paul W. MacAvoy, Williams Brothers Professor of Management Studies at the Yale School of Management, and J. Gregory Sidak, F. K. Weyerhauser Chair in Law and Economics at AEI, for conceiving and overseeing the project's research and seminars, and to Frank Urbanowski, Terry Vaughn, and Victoria Richardson of the MIT Press for their support and steady counsel in seeing the research to publication.

CHRISTOPHER C. DEMUTH
President, American Enterprise Institute
for Public Policy Research

Acknowledgments

PREPARATION OF THIS VOLUME has benefited from an analysis of competition and equal access in U.S. local telephone markets, conducted by Leland L. Johnson and the present authors with the support of France Telecom, and from joint work by Pablo Spiller and one of the present authors on the regulation of British Telecom. Additional material is drawn from Ingo Vogelsang, *The Interaction of Federal and State Regulation in U.S. Telecommunications*, a study sponsored by WIK; *Network Interconnection in the Domain of ONP*, a study we prepared for the European Commission jointly with colleagues at WIK and the European-American Center for Policy Analysis and RAND; and *Expanded Competitiveness and Regulatory Safeguards in Local Telecommunications Markets*, an affidavit filed by the present authors in support of a motion to vacate the Modification of Final Judgment, the agreement reached between the U.S. Department of Justice and AT&T on January 8, 1982. The authors also very much thank the following regulators, colleagues, and friends for information and advice on this project: Sanford Berg, Steve Brenner, Ken Gordon, Dale Hatfield, Raymond Lawton, Paul MacAvoy, Karl-Heinz Neumann, Greg Sidak, Dennis Taratus, an anonymous referee, and participants in an AEI workshop.

INGO VOGELSANG
BRIDGER M. MITCHELL

About the Authors

INGO VOGELSANG is professor of economics at Boston University. He is internationally known for his work on economic regulation, telecommunications pricing, price caps, and privatization of public enterprises.

Professor Vogelsang is a coauthor with Dr. Mitchell of *Telecommunications Pricing: Theory and Practice* (Cambridge University Press 1991) and of the comprehensive 1994 study, *Network Interconnection in the Domain of ONP*, for the European Commission. He is the author of six other books and numerous articles in industrial organization, utility regulation, public enterprises, and privatization.

Professor Vogelsang's international consulting experience is extensive and includes assignments with the World Bank, the German Ministry for Posts and Telecommunications, the Science Center in Berlin, and the European Commission. In the United States he consults to telecommunications and energy regulatory bodies and leading industry participants.

Professor Vogelsang holds a doctorate in economics from the University of Heidelberg and a postdoctoral degree from the University of Bonn.

BRIDGER M. MITCHELL is a vice president of Charles River Associates and director of its California office, where he specializes in the economic analysis of the telecommunications, computer, information, and energy industries.

Previously, Dr. Mitchell taught economics at Stanford University and the University of California at Los Angeles and held the position of senior economist at the RAND Corporation. His international experience includes residence at the Science Center in Berlin and the European-American Center for Policy Analysis in Delft, the Netherlands. He has consulted to the European Commission, the World Bank, regulatory authorities in Hong Kong, Mexico, and Peru, and numerous legal and commercial clients.

Dr. Mitchell is the author of numerous articles and six books, including *Telecommunications Pricing: Theory and Practice* and *Network Interconnection in the Domain of ONP*, both coauthored with Professor Vogelsang. His research encompasses major regulatory issues involving telecommunications pricing, competition and equal access in telephone markets; the interconnection of telecommunications networks; the structure of international telephone rates; and carriage of broadcasting programming on cable television systems. He has developed pioneering models of the cost structure of a cable television firm and the incremental costs of local telephone networks. Dr. Mitchell has also worked extensively on health insurance financing, energy demand, and utility rate structures.

Dr. Mitchell holds a Ph.D. in economics from the Massachusetts Institute of Technology and an A.B. in economics from Stanford University.

1

Introduction

AROUND THE WORLD the telecommunications sector is in the throes of a decades-long transformation. Nothing shows this more vividly than the passage by Congress of the Telecommunications Act of 1996, the first complete overhaul of the Communications Act of 1934.

The telephone network has traditionally been organized as a regional or national monopoly, supplied by a single, vertically integrated firm. In the United States the American Telephone and Telegraph Company (AT&T) for many years supplied telephones, switchboards, local service, long-distance service, and private lines. In most other countries a public posts and telecommunications (PTT) monopoly provided equivalent domestic services. The replacement of this monolithic market structure by a wide range of suppliers, some highly specialized and others integrated or linked to related markets, is well underway. The new telephone and telecommunications firms compete at all levels of the network, from customer and network equipment to voice and information services.

Whereas the first twenty years of competition in U.S. telecommunications services were dominated by long-distance services, it is local services competition that may well dominate the next twenty. Local competition appears today as contentious as long-distance competition was in the early 1970s. Once again the main issue is cross-subsidization of local residential services, and new entrants still attack by picking the ripest cherries in the local market. But otherwise the issues—and especially the players—are now very different. The entrants undermine the very basis for cross-subsidies and ultimately seem to be competing for the business that is currently claimed to receive those subsidies. Instead of one monolithic and vertically integrated Bell System, the new local competitors face a market of seven or fewer regional Bell operating companies, a multiregional GTE Corporation, and many small local exchange companies (LECs). And whereas in the 1970s AT&T faced competition mainly from what was then a tiny startup company called MCI, local service incumbents today are under attack from a host of entrants, ranging from small but financially well-backed competitive access providers, cable television companies, electric utilities, and cellular carriers to the mighty AT&T itself.

That continuing restructuring of the telecommunications industry is driven by fundamental changes in technology and by equally basic developments in public regulation of telecommunications markets. Fiber optics, digital electronics, and wireless technologies are enabling new suppliers to offer communications services, and public policy has been shifting away from cost-based regulation and toward promotion of competitive markets. Most of the fundamental changes in market structure occurred first in the United States or the United Kingdom.

In this book we try to capture the effects of those changes in the market for local telecommunications services. Our main subjects are the LECs as actors facing new types of competition. The book's focus, broadly speaking, is on competition within the local access and transport areas (LATAs) defined by the 1982 consent decree that divested AT&T of its local operating companies. Thus, we are dealing not with a single local market—the "last mile" to the final consumer—but rather with a set of possibly many markets, covering roughly the last ten miles to the consumer. In each of those markets a LEC is the dominant firm, as measured in the first instance by the LEC's share of total sales in a given market segment, or by the LEC's market power: its ability to raise its price without losing its customers. The competitive arena includes most of the services that LECs now offer, and in particular interconnection services—those that link one network with another—offered to (and by) the new competitors. Related markets, such as the cable television market, interest us to the extent that cable television companies want to enter markets dominated by the LECs, and to the extent that the LECs in turn want to enter the cable market.

THE SCOPE OF THE LOCAL TELECOMMUNICATIONS MARKET

Consumers obtain access to the public switched telephone network today by means of conventional telephone lines or cellular radio links. The number of telephone access lines is the most comprehensive single measure of access points in a network. In 1993 LECs reporting to the Federal Communications Commission (FCC) accounted for 138 million switched access lines.[1] Residential subscribers accounted for 69 percent of switched access lines nationwide, businesses for 30 percent, and public telephones for just 1 percent. Cellular telephones provide additional points of local access. At the end of 1995 U.S. cellular operators reported 33.8 million subscribers.[2]

The number of lines serves as a rough indicator of the number of telephone network subscribers. Some residential users and many businesses have multiple lines. For many larger businesses, lines consist of trunk connections to the customer's own private branch exchange (PBX) equipment, which can support many separate lines within the customer's premises. The seven regional Bell operating companies supply 81 percent of switched access lines nationwide; their share of the national market is disproportionately urban, and they supply 85 percent of the switched lines of business subscribers.

At the end of 1993 there were also eleven million special access lines reported to the FCC. Those facilities, which typically carry much larger volumes of traffic than switched access lines, enable business customers that are heavy users of telephone services to connect directly to interexchange carriers (IXCs), the companies that provide long-distance service from one LATA to another. Special access is concentrated in areas served by the regional Bell companies, which account for 92 percent of all special access lines.[3]

1. The FCC statistics exclude some small, independent local exchange carriers. More inclusive estimates of access lines are reported in BRIDGER M. MITCHELL & TENZING DONYO, UTILIZATION OF THE U.S. TELEPHONE NETWORK (RAND MR-436-EAC/WIK) (Mar. 1994).

2. CELLULAR TELECOMMUNICATIONS INDUSTRY ASSOCIATION, 1996 WIRELESS INDUSTRY SURVEY RESULTS (Mar. 25, 1996).

3. FCC, STATISTICS OF COMMUNICATIONS COMMON CARRIERS 1992/3

The vast majority of telephone calls are placed to nearby telephones. As reported by the LECs, "local" calls are those billed under local exchange tariffs. The geographic extent of the local calling area varies by state and by carrier, but broadly speaking it encompasses the last ten miles to the customer. In 1993 a total of 447 billion local calls accounted for 85 percent of all switched telephone calls. Other calls to nearby locations—so-called intraLATA toll calls—accounted for an additional 5 percent.

Interexchange toll calls account for the remaining 10 percent of switched calls. Access to IXCs is through switched and special access lines supplied by the LECs and by facilities provided by competitive access suppliers. In 1992 the interstate switched access revenues of fifty-six large carriers reporting to the FCC totaled $11.2 billion, and special access revenues were $2.5 billion; total intrastate access revenues were $6.6 billion.[4] Competitors of the LECs are estimated to have received revenues of $279 million from dedicated access in 1994, and self-supply of long-distance services by end users has been valued at $480 million.[5]

The statistics reported by the FCC and by trade organizations exclude customers' self-supply of telecommunications services. Many organizations have sizable private networks, including on-premises systems attached to PBX switches, and citywide and long-distance networks linked by private lines or by carriers' virtual private network services. Those networks are typically interconnected with the public network, so that the same system can both route intraorganization calls and reach the general public.

OVERVIEW OF THIS VOLUME

The last ten miles to the consumer is a telecommunications landscape shaped by regulatory history, technological advance, and commercial innovation. Those trends intersect repeatedly in many variations. We have organized our analysis by providing, in the

---

(1993) at table 3–10.

4. *Id.* at table 7–2.

5. *RBOC, LEC, and ALT/CAP Market Shares*, 3 CONN. RESEARCH REP. COMPETITIVE TELECOMM. (June 1, 1995).

next four chapters of the book, a review and analysis of market developments in local telecommunications, the technology of local telephone networks, and the regulation of that sector. We then take up the experience with competition, in two detailed chapters that examine the growth of local competition in the United States, a chapter that summarizes the first federal order establishing regulation guidelines for local competition, and a complementary chapter in which we analyze the parallel experience in the United Kingdom. In the final chapter we resurvey from a broader perspective the landscape we examined in the earlier chapters, and we assess the prospects for continued expansion of competition.

Chapter 2 begins the analysis by surveying the landscape on which telecommunications networks are erected, with particular attention to the opportunities for integration of supply within a single provider, on the one hand, and competitive supply of components of local services, on the other. The dynamics of that changing landscape are driven by advances in technology and market entry by many types of firms. Chapter 3 then provides a general overview of the technology of the local telephone network and the types of access that users and competitors are seeking.

Chapters 4 and 5 are devoted to the economic regulation of telecommunications. Chapter 4 delineates the federal, state, and judicial regulatory structures that now govern that sector, and chapter 5 focuses specifically on the regulation of the LECs.

Chapters 6 and 7 analyze the actual experience with competition in local markets. Chapter 6 is concerned with wholesale telecommunications markets, in which suppliers of services procure access to the local network. It was here that significant rivals to the LECs first materialized. We devote particular attention to interconnection to local networks. The conditions for interconnection have been the repeated focus of regulatory proceedings because they are fundamental to the nature and extent of market entry. Chapter 7 considers entry and competition in local exchange retail markets. Here, too, regulatory developments are sculpting the competitive landscape. The IXCs are gaining access to the outer reaches of the LECs' markets (short-distance toll calls), and carriers are unbundling their network elements to allow access by competing local providers. The extremely popular new wireless services and new suppliers will increasingly substitute for traditional calling over telephone lines. For their part the LECs are also seeking to enter markets outside their traditional franchise, to supply video distribution and long-distance services.

In early 1996, when this book was essentially finished, Congress acted to revamp the Communications Act of 1934.[6] The main purpose of the new legislation is to open markets further while safeguarding competition against the market power of incumbent carriers. A number of provisions of the Telecommunications Act of 1996[7] only indirectly concern local competition in telecommunications. They cover cable television rates, ownership of broadcast stations, and minors' access to indecent material sent over the Internet. Several items are highly relevant here, however. The regional Bell operating companies, until now barred from offering interLATA toll services by the 1982 Modification of Final Judgment that resulted in the AT&T divestiture,[8] will be allowed to enter those long-distance markets, provided they can show that facilities-based entry by competitors for local switched services has developed in their service territories.

The FCC has already acted on some of the provisions of the new act that are particularly vital to local competition. In its "Implementation of the Local Competition Provisions in the Telecommunications Act of 1996,"[9] the FCC specified rules under which telecommunications carriers can interconnect with incumbent local exchange carriers, buy unbundled network elements from them, and acquire discounted retail services from them for resale. That decision came after the other parts of our book were completed

6. Communications Act of 1934, 76 Stat. 419, 15 U.S.C. 21, 47 U.S.C. 35, 151–609.

7. Telecommunications Act of 1996, Pub. L. 104–104, 110 Stat. 56 (Feb. 8, 1996).

8. United States *v*. American Tel. & Tel. Co., 552 F. Supp. 131 (D.C.C. 1982) (text of the decree), *aff'd sub nom.* Maryland *v*. United States, 460 U.S. 1001 (1983); United States *v*. Western Electric Co., 569 F. Supp. 1057 (D.D.C. 1983) (approving the plan of reorganization).

9. Implementation of the Local Competition Provisions in the Telecommunications Act of 1996, First Rep. & Order, CC Dkt. 96-98 (Aug. 8, 1996).

and set. We thought it too important, however, to leave out and have provided a description of that order in chapter 8.

The transformation of the telecommunications sector is hardly confined to U.S. markets, and therefore in chapter 9 we turn to the United Kingdom, where competition in local telecommunications is also proceeding rapidly. The development there of price-cap regulation was an important innovation, and Britain has been at the forefront of entry by mobile and cable television providers into local markets.

The concluding chapter assesses the rapidly changing local telecommunications landscape in light of the preceding chapters' analysis and ventures some views about future developments. Continuing advances in technology are likely to increase the opportunities for successful entry into local telephone service markets by suppliers in related markets and by specialized providers. Regulation's role will continue to evolve, away from detailed prescription of rates and services to a focus on the structure of interconnection arrangements and elimination of entry barriers.

Telecommunications policy continues to change at a breathtaking pace, and other developments will occur in the near future that we cannot cover here. We do not believe, however, that they will alter our main conclusions. In time, we expect a mature local telecommunications sector to emerge in which both wholesale and retail markets are competitively structured and a variety of firms contest the last ten miles to the customer.

RELATED VOLUMES IN THIS SERIES

Developments in telecommunications markets are often as interconnected as the services themselves, and several of the topics touched on in the present study form central elements of other volumes in the AEI Studies in Telecommunications Deregulation series. William J. Baumol and J. Gregory Sidak[10] analyze rules for pricing access to local networks. Leland L. Johnson[11] focuses on

---

10. WILLIAM J. BAUMOL & J. GREGORY SIDAK, TOWARD COMPETITION IN LOCAL TELEPHONY (MIT Press and AEI Press 1994).
11. LELAND L. JOHNSON, TOWARD COMPETITION IN CABLE TELEVISION

the scope for competition in video services between cable television and local telephone carriers. David E. M. Sappington and Dennis L. Weisman[12] deal with the interaction between incentive regulation and competition. Paul W. MacAvoy examines the state of competition in long-distance markets.[13] The interested reader will find in those and other volumes rich sources of additional detail.

(MIT Press and AEI Press 1994).

12. DAVID E. M. SAPPINGTON & DENNIS L. WEISMAN, DESIGNING INCENTIVE REGULATION FOR THE TELECOMMUNICATIONS INDUSTRY (MIT Press and AEI Press 1996).

13. PAUL W. MACAVOY, THE FAILURE OF ANTITRUST AND REGULATION TO ESTABLISH COMPETITION IN LONG-DISTANCE TELEPHONE SERVICES (MIT Press and AEI Press 1996).

2

The Local Telecommunications Landscape

THIS CHAPTER SURVEYS the major features of the landscape within which local telecommunications services are provided: the technical organization of telephone networks, advances in technology that are making competition possible, the different types of providers that have entered the field, and transformations in the structure of the market. We begin by introducing our analytical framework, which centers on the issue of interconnection between networks, and we use that framework to characterize the horizontal and vertical relationships between telecommunications firms.

The discussion necessarily uses a number of technical and specialized industry terms, the most important of which appear in the glossary.

ANALYTICAL FRAMEWORK

Local exchange carriers hold dominant positions in their home telephone markets. The prospects for effective competition turn on interconnection with the LECs' local facilities. Potential competitors invariably require access to some components and services of the local network. By using those facilities, a new competitor can specialize in those market segments where competition is viable and avoid having to construct a complete, stand-alone network to contest portions of the LEC's business. Interconnection with the local network thus lowers an otherwise extremely high barrier to entry, and the terms of that interconnection are the key to creating the structural conditions for effective competition.

For most of the history of telecommunications, interconnection has meant connection among carriers operating in locally, regionally, or nationally distinct markets. Interconnection served primarily to extend the geographic reach of one carrier's network into another carrier's territory. Today a new dimension of interconnection arises from the desire of one telecommunications carrier to use the facilities and services of another carrier in the same region or market.

Although interconnection can also benefit the dominant incumbent carrier, a LEC that retains control over access to most customers will generally have incentives to limit the availability and the terms of interconnection to retain a competitive advantage. Thus, policy toward interconnection must be a central preoccupation of the regulatory authority concerned to achieve the benefits of competition.

A single LEC's telecommunications network contains a large number of interfaces at which components can be interconnected. An integrated network carrier manages those connections internally, by coordinating its staff and by establishing specifications for its external suppliers of components.[1] Rather than strive to duplicate the incumbent's entire range of network facilities and services, competitors aim to compete by supplying selected services and components on their own and purchasing the rest from the incumbent carrier. We examine here the multiply connected web of components that make up a telecommunications network from three complementary perspectives: the services delivered, the hierarchy of production, and the points of interconnection.

Layers of Service Provision

Network relationships may be represented in terms of a series of service provision layers (figure 2–1):

---

1. The carrier and its suppliers sometimes rely on international technical standards to define some or all aspects of an interface. More often, carriers have modified those standards or developed proprietary interface requirements to be met by all of its suppliers.

- The bottom layer—the network infrastructure—provides capacity (bandwidth). That infrastructure is built up from rights-of-way and transport facilities (cables, radio links, and satellite facilities). It includes the transport facilities of different entities such as telephone carriers, cable television distribution companies, and television broadcasters.
- The technology at the second layer provides the routing of circuits, messages, and signals through the infrastructure. It consists of network switches and control facilities. Network services at that level include voice telephone service, switched and packet data services, and television distribution.

FIGURE 2–1

THE LAYERED MODEL OF TELECOMMUNICATIONS AND INFORMATION
SERVICES PROVISION

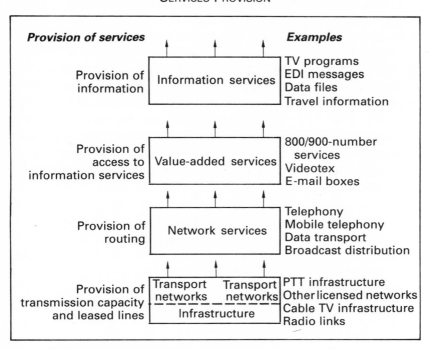

NOTE: EDI, electronic data interchange.
SOURCE: Arnbak, Mitchell, Neu, Neumann, and Vogelsang, with the collaboration of N'Guyen and Ickenroth (1994).

- At the third layer, networks provide access to value-added services: information or communications services that individual users can select, such as credit-card calling, 800-number service, videotex, and e-mail boxes.
- Finally, the top layer consists of the information transported over the network, such as data files, travel information, and television programs.

The Network Hierarchy

The layered network model of figure 2–1 can be expanded into three dimensions to show more explicitly the range of possibilities for competitive provision of resources. Figure 2–2 depicts such a three-dimensional *interconnection space* with four service planes. Competitive facilities or services offered at a given layer by different telecommunications entities appear as duplicated symbols in that layer. To distinguish between competing providers at each layer, each of the four layers is extended horizontally into a service plane. In each service plane the (potential or real) competitors are spaced apart in one dimension (front to back), while the perpendicular dimension (left to right) in each plane indicates the hierarchical distance to the end user in the delivery chain of network components. In this hierarchy the delivery chain consists of the user terminal, the access network, the local network, the trunk network, and the international network.

In the lowest plane, that of infrastructure, the facilities of a telephone carrier are potentially integrated from the supply of terminal equipment up to the national frontier, at which an international gateway switch connects to another national carrier. The second plane represents network routing and switching capabilities, which are tightly integrated into a telephone carrier's traditional network. Value-added services, such as calling-card and information services (directory assistance, weather, etc.), and the information content itself appear in the two highest service planes of the figure.

FIGURE 2–2
INTERCONNECTION SPACE FOR COMPETITIVE TELECOMMUNICATIONS
AND INFORMATION SERVICES PROVISION

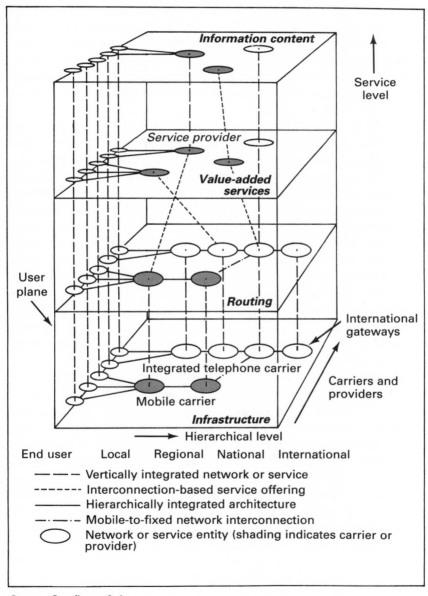

SOURCE: See figure 2–1.

Points of Interconnection

The points of potential interconnection between telephone carriers and other service providers are central in determining the opportunities for local competition. Strong new technological and economic forces are prying open the network interfaces that have traditionally been internal to the LEC and creating new relationships between the various providers of telecommunications. For example, in the lowest (infrastructure) plane in figure 2-2, an independent mobile carrier (indicated by shaded ovals) is shown interconnected to the LEC's infrastructure at an intermediate level in the switching hierarchy. The interconnection is indicated by the dashed line connecting to a tandem or regional switch. The LEC may also supply some of the routing services needed for mobile calls. Consequently, in the second plane the mobile operator is shown interconnecting its signaling facilities with the LEC's signaling network. As another example, the figure also shows independent service providers in the top two planes interconnected to the LEC for routing and infrastructure services. Obviously, that interconnection space contains an abundance of internal interfaces where network components belonging to a single telecommunications firm might be interconnected. Selecting the best path of internal interconnections is a classic economic problem faced by all telecommunications firms in their continuing engineering processes of procuring equipment from vendors and reconfiguring the network so as best to respond to market needs.

Under classic conditions of monopolistic supply of telecommunications resources, telecommunications organizations encompassed within their perimeters much of the interconnection space depicted in figure 2-2. One national carrier supplied all infrastructure components, from the international gateways at the far right of the bottom plane down to and often including the end user's terminal equipment at the far left of that plane. AT&T occupied that role in most areas of the United States and interconnected with independent operating companies that served predominantly rural and smaller urban communities. Initially, only a few external interconnection interfaces existed: the international gateways (transit switches at the highest hierarchical level) and, later, interfaces for user terminal equipment. As a result of that history, those "perimeter" interfaces have become the most widely standardized. In similar fashion, the local network was vertically integrated and supplied both routing capability and value-added services.

VERTICAL AND HORIZONTAL RELATIONSHIPS

Telecommunications firms use many types of communications technology to supply markets. Economies of scope and scale lead firms to integrate "vertically" in two separate dimensions: over two or more service layers and over hierarchical levels of network switching and control. Similar economies provide incentives to integrate "horizontally" across geographic areas as well as across nonsubstitutable services such as cable television distribution and switched voice telephone services. In arriving at those arrangements, firms are driven by market demands and customer needs and are not necessarily constrained by the hierarchy of technical relationships that govern a network. For example:

• Typically, a firm will integrate two or more technological layers within its own organization to better serve market needs and to realize economies of scope by reducing costs it would otherwise incur from using separate suppliers or technologies at each layer. AT&T before its divestiture was the leading example of such vertical integration, operating at all layers of figure 2–2 to provide voice telephone service and information services. Traditionally, other telecommunications suppliers, including cable television and broadcast services, have also been vertically integrated.

• Integration of network components can also occur across the hierarchy of relationships determined by proximity to the final user. Before the *Carterfone* decision in 1968, AT&T integrated all elements of the chain from the terminal up to international services. User terminal equipment was subsequently unbundled (that is, made available separately from other services), and since AT&T's divestiture in 1984 local switching and long-distance services have been supplied by separate firms. Most recently, firms have begun to provide local access in competition with the dominant LECs.

• Finally, users themselves may be multilevel entities. Users demand access to the network. In addition, they may supply for themselves some of the telecommunications services they consume, such as PBX switching and private networks, and they may, in addition, offer value-added services and so-called intelligent network services (described in chapter 6) to others.

Thus, technology makes it possible to supply telecommunications services in a wide variety of ways. There are a large number of potential interfaces and points of interconnection between carriers. Economic factors including economies of scale, economies of scope, and product differentiation, together with regulatory provisions governing unbundling and pricing, rather than strictly technical factors, will determine where carriers and service providers seek to interconnect. The technology of telecommunications networks is compatible with the existence of vertically integrated, horizontally integrated, and specialized carriers. But fundamental changes in the basic technologies that support telecommunications are now altering the longstanding comparative advantage of vertically integrated firms. Economies of specialization are giving some suppliers advantages in producing at a single layer of the hierarchy. Meanwhile, developments in transport capacity, switching, and computer control are enabling suppliers to integrate horizontally and to supply formerly separate networks or services by using common infrastructure and software facilities. Yet, at the same time, highly integrated firms are also finding it profitable to split up some cellular, cable, and information services operations into separate business organizations.

Changes such as those are redrawing the boundaries of telecommunications organizations. Even as some existing firms are vertically disintegrating and new firms are supplying single components within the vertical chain, others are horizontally integrating across distinct types of networks. Those new organizational relationships have several implications for competition in the local exchange. Some key interfaces that were formerly managed within the firm or network are now points at which two firms meet in both technical and commercial relationships. Moreover, the LEC now has a new set of customers: telecommunications entities that both purchase some network services from it and compete with it to supply services to final consumers.

The changing organizational relationships between firms may correspond to entirely new paths through the interconnection space in figure 2–2: between two end users, for example, or between an information service provider and an end user. Generally, such new paths represent innovative technical relationships in terms of external interface standards, management of network security and integrity, allocation of service quality levels, and so forth. New interconnection paths also involve entirely new economic transactions between organizations, with costs and benefits yet to be determined.

ACCESS AND BOTTLENECKS

The LEC is the principal supplier of access to telecommunications networks and services. Access is to be viewed from two complementary standpoints (figure 2–3). From the perspective of the user, the local telephone network provides access to a full panoply of telecommunications services, including local telephone calls, long-distance calls, information services, and connection to data networks and eventually to video and other broadband services. From the perspective of the network carriers and service suppliers, the local network provides access to customers: businesses and individuals at home and on the road.

Whenever a competitor, so as to produce and distribute its own service, requires as an input a resource that the dominant supplier produces or controls and that the competitor is unable to produce on its own, a "bottleneck" is said to exist (we examine the economic characteristics of bottlenecks in chapter 4). For true competition to occur, would-be competitors must secure access to the essential resource. Despite the technical possibilities for multiple paths in the interconnection space, the LEC controls several resources that may be essential to competitors. Access to those resources then requires interconnection to the LEC's network. For most competitors, there is no technical alternative to obtaining, through interconnection, one or more of the following bottleneck resources from the LEC:

• *Access to small end users*. The traffic volumes of most residential subscribers and many small business users are too small to require more than one access line. An alternative carrier would find it prohibitively costly to supply a second line to such users to

FIGURE 2–3
RELATIONSHIP OF ACCESS PROVIDERS TO NETWORK CARRIERS AND USERS

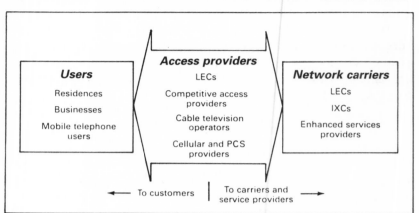

terminate calls originating on its network. The costs of inter-connection with the LEC are far lower.

• *End-office switching.* For a carrier (such as a cable television network) that competes with the LEC in providing local distribution to end users, the costs of supplying local switching may greatly exceed the costs of interconnection to LEC switching.

• *Numbering.* Telephone numbers are essential to providing access to end users. In most networks, numbers provide network routing information as well as subscriber addressing. New carriers are better able to compete for customers if subscribers can avoid the inconvenience of changing their telephone numbers when changing carriers.

• *Intelligent network services.* Creation and management of new services will require access to intelligent network services. To obtain quality of service comparable to that enjoyed by the LEC itself, competitors will require interconnection to the control and database facilities of the LEC's intelligent network. On the second plane of the interconnection space, the intelligent network concept is closely bound up with the signaling systems required to provide routing through the dominant network. Carriers are inclined to invoke that relationship and to assert the need to protect network integrity to deny or restrict interconnection to their intelligent networks. That then gives them a competitive advantage on the third and fourth planes in the interconnection space, where modern value-added information services are located.

Control over bottleneck resources, if undeterred by regulation, gives the LEC great power to tilt the competitive playing field to its advantage. Ensuring equal access to the LEC network is a continuing challenge to public policy, which we address in chapters 4, 6, 7, and 8.

THE VARIETY OF TELECOMMUNICATIONS SERVICE PROVIDERS

The following distinct types of telecommunications service providers operate in today's marketplace:

• Local exchange carriers provide telecommunications services to end users within the boundaries of local access and transport areas and provide access to those end users for other service providers. In the United States the largest LECs are the seven regional Bell operating companies (the regional carriers created upon AT&T's divestiture) and GTE Corp. In addition, there are hundreds of small, independent LECs operating predominantly in rural areas. Following passage of the 1996 Telecommunications Act, reorganization of those operating companies can be anticipated.[2] Four of the regional Bells have announced merger plans—SBC Communications Inc. with Pacific Telesis Group and Bell Atlantic Corp. with NYNEX Corp.[3]

• Interexchange carriers provide long-distance services between LATAs and have recently begun providing intraLATA long-distance services in a number of states.

• Cellular operators provide mobile telephone services in designated areas (see chapter 7).

---

2. Telecommunications Act of 1996, Pub. L. 104-104, 110 Stat. 56 (Feb. 8, 1996).

3. *SBC, Pacific Telesis Plan First Bell Company Merger in Wake of New Telecom Law*, TELECOMM. REP., Apr. 8, 1996, at 1; *Proposal to Merge Bell Atlantic, NYNEX Raises Questions About Fate of Competition*, TELECOMM. REP., Apr. 29, 1996, at 1.

•   Enhanced services providers supply various value-added network services, such as information services and answering services.[4]

•   Competitive access providers provide alternatives to the local loop (the final connection to the end user) for IXCs, enhanced services providers, and large end users. They also provide leased-line services between their customers. They are direct competitors of the LECs.

In addition, cable television companies and paging companies are about to emerge as telecommunications service providers. Personal communications services (PCS) systems, now under construction, will increase substantially the number of access providers now that the Federal Communications Commission has auctioned off additional radio spectrum for that service. Finally, telecommunications equipment manufacturers supply ever more sophisticated customer premises equipment, which can substitute for a range of services formerly provided elsewhere in the network. The equipment manufacturers have also been important for the regulatory setup, in particular because of vertical integration (AT&T, the dominant IXC, is also the largest equipment manufacturer)[5] and because the regional Bell operating companies have been barred from equipment manufacturing by the 1982 Consent Decree.

ADVANCES IN TECHNOLOGY

Technological developments have reduced barriers to entry in the LECs' markets and expanded the range of competition, increasing

---

4. The Modification of Final Judgment uses the notion of information services providers, which for most purposes are identical to enhanced services providers. United States *v.* American Tel. & Tel. Co., 552 F. Supp. 131 (D.C.C. 1982), *aff'd sub nom.* Maryland *v.* United States, 460 U.S. 1001 (1983).

5. AT&T is in the process of undergoing a second divestiture by spinning off its equipment manufacturing and computer subsidiaries. The manufacturing company is now named Lucent Technologies. AT&T, 1995 ANNUAL REPORT (1996).

the effective number of suppliers of such services as message taking, customer-premises switching, and voice access, as well as video delivery and access to IXCs. The thrust of the principal technological changes that have occurred since the divestiture of AT&T has been to reduce the compartmentalization of formerly separate telecommunications markets. No single firm competes across the board in every market supplied by a LEC. Rather, advances in technology along many fronts have brought competition from many different sources. Several examples illustrate the range of this competition:

• The message-taking service market is supplied by customer-owned answering machines, voice mailbox services supplied by the LECs and independent vendors, independent telephone answering services, and radio paging services.
• The market for customer-premises switching is supplied by numerous vendors of PBXs and by Centrex service supplied from the LECs' central offices.
• Voice access to the public switched network is supplied by the LECs' wireline loops and by cellular telephone carriers. Cable television operators are supplying switched voice access abroad and have applied for authorization in U.S. markets.
• Access to IXCs is supplied by the LECs over switched and dedicated lines, by competitive access providers over high-capacity fiber-optic cable, and by other access providers using rooftop-mounted microwave links.
• Video services are delivered by conventional broadcast television, satellite direct broadcast, cable television, and soon by the LECs' local loops using data compression and digital transmission technology.

Frequently, the LECs' competitors are able to add a new service to their existing lines of business and to reap economies of scope from sharing of facilities and staff. Combined with service based on the latest technology, this places them in a strong position to compete effectively.

Of the many technological advances that have affected telecommunications markets, three broad developments are profoundly altering the LEC marketplace in particular: fiber optics, wireless telephony, and digital electronics.

Fiber Optics

In the decade following the AT&T divestiture, fiber-optic technology has matured, and fiber-optic cable has become the preferred medium for high-capacity telecommunications transport. Fiber-optic cable was first introduced by the IXCs on high-density, intercity routes. Competitive access providers then brought fiber optics into metropolitan markets. By constructing networks with a ring architecture that provided two separate paths from the customer to a node of the fiber network, those firms could offer high-capacity services with increased reliability against outages. Meanwhile, in urban residential areas cable television operators are replacing much of their coaxial cable distribution networks with fiber-optic facilities.

Fiber-optic facilities today have very high capacity. For users with high traffic volumes and for traffic aggregated into high-density routes between network nodes, fiber optics is ordinarily the low-cost transport technology. Once the cable is installed, the cost of additional circuits is low and principally involves adding electronic multiplexing units.[6]

Deployment of fiber-optic cable technology has proceeded rapidly since the AT&T divestiture. From 1985 to 1993, the IXCs increased the mileage of fiber-optic cable deployed by 459 percent.[7] During the same period the miles of fiber optics deployed by the LECs grew by 1,365 percent.[8] As a result, the total fiber-optic capacity of the LECs is now more than twice that deployed by the IXCs.[9] In total, the seven regional Bell companies increased

6. BRIDGER M. MITCHELL, INCREMENTAL COSTS OF TELEPHONE ACCESS AND LOCAL USE (RAND Corp., R-3909-ICTF 38-41)(1990).

7. FCC, INDUSTRY ANALYSIS DIVISION, FIBER DEPLOYMENT UPDATE, table 2 (Apr. 1994).

8. *Id.* at table 6.

9. The statistics reported by the LECs combine fiber-optic lines that connect users and IXCs with those that connect the LECs' own central and tandem offices.

their miles of fiber installed by 26 percent during 1993 alone, to a total of 6.3 million miles.[10]

That same year competitive access providers increased their installed fiber-optic capacity in urban areas by 87 percent, to a little over 240,000 miles.[11] Those providers have used fiber-optic cables to serve three related markets: to provide transport between IXC nodes, to bypass the LECs and supply end users with direct access to the IXCs, and to provide private lines connecting end users to each other for voice and data networks.

Competitive access providers have access to the same fiber-optic technology as the LECs. They have therefore been well positioned to compete vigorously in local markets by introducing the latest technology, focusing on selected business users with high communications volumes, and building large-capacity facilities at low per-circuit costs. Incumbency does not bestow cost advantages in that market. Thus, because of their competitors' sunk costs, the LECs are unable to drive out entrants.

Fiber-optic cable technology has largely eliminated distance as a factor in the cost of providing switched services. The traditional LEC copper-wire pair technology requires a star architecture, with a local switching office located within a few miles of subscribers. A competitor seeking to enter a local market, if it chose the same architecture, would need to establish switching centers throughout the community and would experience a significant cost disadvantage because it would achieve a lower rate of penetration than the LEC in any one switching area. Fiber-optic technology enables the new entrant to transport calls to a distant switch at very low marginal cost and thus to economize on switching facilities and associated buildings. In particular, because of their switching facilities and existing customer relationships, the IXCs may be able to enter local markets at low cost once they are authorized to do so.

10. FCC, *supra* note 7, at table 6.
11. *Id.* at table 14.

Wireless Telephony

Wireless local telecommunications services are the second major technology that has developed since AT&T's divestiture. Wireless services are providing rapidly growing competition to the LECs' services in local markets.

Cellular Telephone Service. The FCC gave final authorization to cellular service in 1982, and the first systems became operational in 1984. Demand for cellular service has been intense. The number of subscribers has increased by 40 percent or more per year and reached almost thirty-four million in December 1995.[12]

To date, under FCC regulation U.S. cellular telephone service has been supplied by two carriers in each serving area (except in lower density communities) by using analog transmission in the 800 megahertz (MHz) bands. The available frequencies are reused by dividing the service area into a large number of low-power transmission cells, arranged so that adjacent cells use different frequencies to avoid interference with each other. A mobile cellular user who "travels" from one cell to another is detected by the system's control electronics, and the user's mobile terminal is automatically directed to switch to frequencies used by the new cell.

Advances in digital radio technology and the limited capacity of the current analog systems have spurred cellular system operators to plan to introduce digital transmission systems. Carriers will use one of two distinct digital, multiple-access technologies—time-division and code-division—that are expected to achieve a three- to twentyfold increase in the effective capacity of a given band of radio frequencies.[13]

Cellular service initially developed as a premium telephone service emphasizing portability and mobility. Cellular telephony, because of its higher prices than fixed telephone service and limited capacity to expand, has been considered by the MFJ court (the court that oversees implementation of the Modification of Final Judgment

12. CELLULAR TELECOMMUNICATIONS INDUSTRY ASSOCIATION, 1996 WIRELESS INDUSTRIES SURVEY RESULTS (Mar. 25, 1996).
    13. TELEPHONY, Jan. 10, 1994.

in the AT&T divestiture) to be a separate market.[14] But declining costs of radio terminals, the greatly increased capacity made possible by digital technology, and the entry of new types of wireless suppliers can be expected to reduce prices and broaden service offerings to the point that wireless services will compete directly with fixed-line telephone service for basic service.

Personal Communications Services. The potential capacity of wireless systems has been greatly increased through the FCC's award, by competitive auctions, of a total of 120 MHz of radio spectrum for PCS. Many of those systems will provide radio coverage to small, low-power mobile terminals through microcells serving office buildings or neighborhoods. Within the supplier's network the microcell antennas will be linked by transmission facilities provided by cable television operators, competitive access providers, the LECs, and microwave radio operators.

The licensing procedures established by the FCC provide for six blocks of channels that allow as many as six PCS operators in a single market. A wide variety of wireless services are likely to be offered, including voice telephony, fax and data communication, two-way paging, and wireless PBXs. Two additional channel blocks, totaling 40 MHz, will also become available for unlicensed PCS applications.

The substantially expanded capacity of existing cellular systems that will result from second-generation digital technology, together with competition from the entry of PCS, will intensify competition in the wireless services market and lead to increased quality and variety and to lower prices. If the recent 45 percent annual rate of expansion is maintained, at least 85 million subscribers, a number exceeding half of all fixed local loops in service in 1992, will be using wireless telephone services by 1999.

14. United States *v.* Western Electric Co., Trade Cas. (CCH) ¶¶ 69,177, 64,450 (D.D.C. 1990).

Digital Electronics

Continuing advances in digital computers, software, and information processing are the third major technological development that is reducing market barriers and increasing competition in LEC markets.

Common-Channel Signaling. In the decade since AT&T's divestiture, common-channel signaling technology has been added to the major U.S. interexchange and local telephone networks to control the routing and accounting of calls, manage network resources, and support the supply of information services. Common-channel signaling transmits those signals on a shared channel that is separate from the circuits that carry telephone conversations. The system that is today's international standard, Signaling System 7 (SS7), is a digital packet-switched network connected to a telephone carrier's telephone switches. The largest IXCs now manage their networks with SS7 technology, and the LECs are in the process of extending SS7 capability to local exchanges. At the end of 1991, 53 percent of LEC access lines were connected to SS7-equipped switches. At the end of 1995 the LECs and major independent companies were scheduled to serve almost all lines in urban areas by SS7 switching.[15]

Widespread deployment of common-channel signaling makes it possible for a service provider to separate the functions of supplying and processing information from the supply of the telephone connection itself. Databases can be stored in high-capacity regional and national depositories, and the software needed for intelligent network services can be supplied by independent vendors. As chapter 6 discusses in greater detail, that unbundling of basic network service from information processing has been promoted by the adoption of open network architecture requirements, with the consequence that the LECs face competition from a wide variety of information service providers.

15. FCC, MONITORING REPORT, May 1993, at 460.

Data Compression. Fundamental improvements in the technologies of data coding and data compression have enabled telecommunications suppliers to increase the capacity of traditional circuits and to reduce the time and cost of transporting messages. Compression of video signals, combined with advances in signal coding, has resulted in the development of asymmetrical digital subscriber line (ADSL) systems. That technology enables a network operator to simultaneously transmit a telephone call, a television program, and user responses over a single pair of copper wires. ADSL will allow the LECs to compete in video distribution with cable television operators by using their existing copper-wire distribution plant to deliver video service to most of their subscribers.

Other recent advances are also increasing the capacity of twisted-pair copper local loops. High-bit-rate digital subscriber line (HDSL) systems now provide bidirectional capacity of 1.5 megabits per second to support video conferencing and high-speed data applications. The technology uses integrated circuits built into modems at the customer's premises and central office line cards.[16]

Further advances in data compression technology are likely. In January 1994 a sixteenfold digital compression technology was announced by Stevens Institute of Technology and Digital Compression Technology L.P.[17] The system could be applied to copper-wire, coaxial cable, and direct broadcast satellite channels.

High-Speed Switching. Broadband asynchronous transport mode (ATM) switches are just beginning to be deployed in the high-speed backbone segments of data networks. That technology will allow the broadband networks of cable and telephone carriers to integrate the transport and switching of all types of telecommunications services—voice, data, and video—over common broadband fiber and coaxial cable facilities. Once those switches are in place, economies of scope will enable a network operator to enter new service markets at low cost.

16. *Semiconductor Vendor Level One Has Product to Spur HDSL Deployment,* TELECOMM. REP., Jan. 17, 1994, at 29.

17. *DTC, Stevens Announce Digital Compression Breakthrough,* TELECOMM. REP., Jan. 31, 1994, at 32.

CHANGING MARKET STRUCTURES

Since the Modification of Final Judgment in the AT&T antitrust case,[18] fundamental changes have occurred in the structure of telecommunications markets. Several developments have increased the ability of firms to enter markets in which the LECs formerly enjoyed a monopoly. Entry barriers have been lowered by regulatory actions. Advances in technology have expanded the number of potential entrants and players. And substitutes for the LECs' products and services have proliferated. The potential facilities-based competitors include competitive access providers, the IXCs, cable television operators, cellular and PCS carriers, and electric utilities.[19] In those markets fast-changing business relationships and business plans are revised frequently, so that at least some of the developments we describe below will undoubtedly take a different final form.

Entry of New Firms

Competitive access providers first entered into competition with the LECs by building facilities to supply special access services (mainly transport between the IXCs' facilities and from those carriers directly to customers) and private line services to large business and government users. Since 1987, when they served only five U.S. cities, those firms have expanded rapidly; they reached more than forty cities by 1991 and seventy-two cities, including all of the twenty-five largest metropolitan areas, by 1994. In that year there

---

18. United States *v.* American Tel. & Tel. Co., 552 F. Supp. 131 (D.D.C. 1982) (text of the decree), *aff'd sub nom.* Maryland *v.* United States, 460 U.S. 1001 (1983); United States *v.* Western Elec. Co., 569 F. Supp. 1057 (D.D.C. 1983) (approving the plan of reorganization).

19. End users themselves are also potential entrants into the LECs' local markets. As described in chapter 7, users have supplied switching services to commercial and residential buildings in the form of shared tenant services. Private networks comprising leased lines provide a substitute for some local switched calls. Entry by users who are themselves telecommunications services providers is proceeding through vertical and horizontal integration as we describe later.

were at least forty-four separately managed competitive access providers, compared with about thirty just three years before. An additional thirty-six networks were under construction in 1994, and as many as forty-six more were in the planning process.[20] According to recent surveys, competitive access providers have captured at least some of the IXC access service business of between 62 and 77 percent of larger business customers.[21]

Interexchange and private line traffic is highly concentrated among a small number of users. By targeting their initial service to those large users, competitive access providers compete for a limited number of customers who make up a large fraction of the total market. Approximately 30 percent of a LEC's revenues are generated by just 1 percent of its customers.[22]

As described in chapter 6, the FCC's decisions on expanded interconnection and switched transport have substantially expanded the competitive impact of competitive access providers in the LECs' markets. As a result, such a provider can now compete for a customer supplied by LEC lines without having to build facilities to reach that customer's premises. Instead, a competitive access provider can purchase local access service from the LEC to reach its own facilities, including points of interconnection collocated in LEC switching offices.

Some competitive access providers, principally Teleport Communications Group and MFS Communications Company, now supply switched services in addition to transport services. In 1993 switched services revenues for all competitive access providers

---

20. Glenn A. Woroch, affidavit, United States *v.* Western Electric Co., Inc. and American Telephone and Telegraph Company, Motion of Bell Atlantic Corporation, BellSouth Corporation, NYNEX Corporation, and Southwestern Bell Corporation to Vacate the Decree, Civil Action No. 82-0192, at 8–9 (July 6, 1994).

21. *Ex parte* Pacific Telesis, CC Dkt. Nos. 91-141, 91-213 (Apr. 29, 1992); J. KRAEMER, TELECOMMUNICATIONS INDUSTRY PROGRAM, COMPETITIVE ASSESSMENT OF THE MARKET FOR ALTERNATIVE LOCAL TRANSPORT (Deloitte & Touche 1991).

22. Bypass of the Public Switched Network, Third Rep. & Order (May 26, 1987), at 32.

totaled $31 million. Teleport's sales of switched services increased 130 percent during that year.[23]

In 1994 Teleport supplied switched local telephone services to business customers over its own facilities in New York and Massachusetts and had the authority to do the same in the Chicago area.[24] In New York City, MFS Intelenet was then supplying local switched service with numbers that used two "NXX" codes allocated to it by order of the New York Public Service Commission. In Illinois, MFS Intelenet also has the authority to provide local exchange services to businesses in downtown Chicago. The company uses its own digital switching and transmission facilities and leases facilities and services from other carriers. It expected its typical customer to have between five and thirty-five telephone lines. MFS has been granted authority to operate in Maryland.[25] In the Grand Rapids area in Michigan, US Signal (now Brooks Fiber) had received authority to provide basic exchange and toll services where it operates a competitive access network.[26]

In late 1994 total revenues of the competitive local service industry were estimated at $620 million per year, about $160 million of which came from switched services. On the basis of large orders for switches for full-service networks, that industry has been predicted to grow to $12 billion to $15 billion before the year 2000.[27]

Entry by Vertical Integration

Besides those new entrants, well-established carriers in inter-exchange telecommunications markets are pursuing strategies to integrate their operations to obtain facilities for direct access to their

23. 2 CONN. RESEARCH REP. COMPETITIVE TELECOMM. (Jan. 1, 1994).

24. *Teleport Seeks Switched Service Authority in Michigan*, TELECOMM. REP., Nov. 21, 1994, at 18.

25. *In re* Investigation by the Commission on Its Motion into Policies Regarding Competitive Local Exchange Telephone Service, Case No. 8584, Order No. 71155, Md. Public Service Commission (Apr. 26, 1994).

26. *Teleport Seeks Switched Service Authority in Michigan*, *supra* note 24.

27. *ALTS Members Claim Public Policy "Victory," Make Case for Growth Beyond Confines of "Cap" Label*, TELECOMM. REP., Nov. 7, 1994, at 7.

customers. AT&T acquired a complete interest in McCaw Cellular Communications, the largest cellular carrier, in late 1994. The AT&T-McCaw combination now confronts all the regional Bell operating companies with wireless access competition for switched access, intraLATA long-distance, and enhanced services. MCI Communications Corp. has constructed fiber-optic rings in twenty-five local markets.[28] Local switched services will initially be offered to businesses, with the intention of eventually entering residential markets.

Entry by Horizontal Integration

Most regional Bell operating companies and some other large carriers have sought to enter out-of-region alliances with and to acquire major cable television operators. Those new business relationships provide degrees of horizontal integration that extend the activities of the LECs into other regions. Simultaneously, they alter the structure of the LEC markets in several fundamental ways. The alliances inject the participating regional Bell company into cable television markets outside the region assigned to it under the MFJ. At the same time, such alliances confront the LECs in their home regions with financially strengthened cable television operators, which are both their actual competitors in video delivery services and important potential entrants into their traditional residential local service telephone markets.

Although the largest attempted venture so far—a merger of Bell Atlantic Corp. and TCI—did not succeed, other major alliances are well established:

• U S West purchased a $2.5 billion, 25 percent interest in Time Warner Entertainment in 1993. The alliance plans to upgrade Time Warner's cable television systems to support interactive and telephone services to compete for local exchange and access services.[29]

---

28. *MCI Seeks to Be Local in Five States*, N.Y. TIMES, Oct. 4, 1994.
29. *U S West Seeks Broad Decree Waiver for Time Warner's Planned Full-Service Networks*, TELECOMM. REP., Dec. 20, 1993, at 10.

- Southwestern Bell Corp. has acquired two Washington, D.C., cable systems, in Virginia and Maryland, from Hauser cable systems.[30]
- BellSouth Corp. has acquired a 22.5 percent interest in Prime Cable.
- NYNEX Corp. has invested $1.2 billion in Viacom.[31]
- Canada's BCE Telecom International has acquired 30 percent of Jones Intercable.[32] The companies, which are already partners in a joint cable-telephony franchise in London, foresee the cable company's expanding into local exchange communications in its cable franchise areas.
- Sprint, TCI, Comcast, and Cox Cable have entered into a joint venture (Sprint Spectrum) to supply local telephone, long-distance, and wireless communications with cable services to residential and business consumers.[33]

Those new businesses can reach a large fraction of the local markets of the LECs. Television cables enter or pass 97 percent of U.S. homes and currently supply video services to more than 61 million subscribers.[34]

Cable television operators, meanwhile, are applying to state regulators to provide switched service in local communities and are conducting trials:

30. *SW Bell to Purchase Two D.C.-Area Cable Systems from Hauser Communications*, TELECOMM. REP., Feb. 15, 1993, at 9.

31. *AT&T, McCaw Cellular Defend Proposed Merger*, TELECOMM. REP., Dec. 13, 1993, at 20.

32. *Jones Intercable, Canada's BCE Add Twist to Telco/Cable TV Convergence with Deal to Form Strategic Alliance*, TELECOMM. REP., Dec. 6, 1993, at 29; Kevin Dougherty, *Bell, MH Talked About Sharing Superhighway*, FIN. POST, Apr. 14, 1994, at 3.

33. *Sprint Ventures into Partnership with Cable Company Trio*, TELEPHONY, Oct. 31, 1994.

34. NATIONAL CABLE TELEVISION ASSOCIATION, CABLE TELEVISION DEVELOPMENTS, Nov. 1993, at 1-A; PAUL KAGAN ASSOCIATES, INC., MARKETING NEW MEDIA, August 21, 1995.

• Time Warner companies provide telephone service in Kansas City, Missouri, in Indianapolis, Indiana, and in Rochester, New York.[35] Time Warner AxS has obtained authorization from the Ohio Public Utilities Commission to provide private line, nonswitched service in that state.[36] The company has applied for certification as a supplier of switched access and dial tone.

• Jones Intercable and MCI are jointly testing delivery of local and long-distance calls over two Jones cable television systems.[37] Using a "CoAccess" technology developed by Scientific-Atlanta, the system distributes both television signals and telephone service over fiber-optic cables to neighborhood points and then by coaxial cable to individual subscribers. The incoming coaxial cable is connected at the side of the house both to the homeowner's inside telephone wiring and to a coaxial cable attached to the television. The $36 million Jones-MCI trial in Virginia began delivering telephone service in October 1994 as a precursor to offering service in apartment buildings and condominiums.

• Time Warner Cable is installing a high-capacity broadband interactive network in Orlando, Florida. The service was rolled out to fifty households in December 1994. The company plans to extend service to 85 percent of Time Warner's cable network by 1998.[38] Using a hybrid fiber-optic and coaxial cable delivery network and ATM switches, the system will deliver both analog and digital video signals. The network will include support for in-building and neighborhood PCS applications.[39]

The alliances between the LECs and cable television operators reduce the barriers to entry into a LEC's market in several ways. A

35. Bill Lewis, *Bell Competitors Square Off in Data Transmission Duel,* MEMPHIS BUSINESS J., Oct. 11, 1993, at 3.

36. *Ohio Approves Time Warner AxS Application; Leaves Tough Issues for When LEC Certification Is Sought,* TELECOMM. REP., Dec. 13, 1993, at 26.

37. *Jones Lightwave, MCI Plan to Test Telephone Services over Cable TV Systems,* TELECOMM. REP., Nov. 29, 1993, at 10.

38. *Time Warner Unwraps Full Service Network,* TELEPHONY, Dec. 19, 1994.

39. *Time Warner Cable: Building Full-Service Network,* TELEPHONY, Nov. 1, 1993, at 51.

cable operator integrated with a LEC is poised to become an effective competitor in providing local exchange and network access services. Each of the announced alliances has committed large capital resources to the venture. The integrated firms expect to combine technical, marketing, and managerial expertise from the broadband entertainment market and the switched telephone service market. In offering services in competition with the dominant local carrier, the new ventures will already have access to customers over in-place physical broadband cable access facilities.

The Foreign Experience

The LECs that have been forging alliances with U.S. cable television operators have already acquired experience in combining cable television technologies with switched-voice access service in their joint ventures in foreign markets. Three LECs—NYNEX, U S West (in a joint venture with TCI), and Southwestern Bell (with Cox Cable)—now hold large cable franchises in the United Kingdom, with access to six million homes.[40] Bell Canada (BCE) and Jones Intercable also operate large cable systems in Britain. International CableTel, a subsidiary of Cellular Communications International, is rapidly installing cable television and telephone service in franchise areas in the United Kingdom covering about 1.4 million households. U.S. firms have ready access to that technology and marketing experience: in 1994 U.S. firms owned 62 percent of U.K. cable concerns.[41]

The LECs' cable television ventures in the United Kingdom are a testing ground for supplying integrated cable television and telephone services. The cable operators are expanding from initially providing residential end users with access to the two national telephone carriers, British Telecom and Mercury Communications, to providing switched service using their own switches.[42]

---

40. CABLE TELEVISION ASSOCIATION, INDEPENDENT TELEVISION COMMISSION, May 20, 1993.

41. Woroch, *supra* note 20, at 3.

42. OFTEL, Pricing of Telecommunications Services from 1997 (December 1995) (consultative document), annexes at 12.

The number of telephone lines supplied by U.K. cable companies has grown from fewer than 2,300 before 1991 to more than one million at the end of 1995.[43] The U.K. cable television experience demonstrates that competition from existing cable distribution networks can materialize rapidly.

Potential Entry by Electric Utilities

Electric power utilities are testing communications networks that will link their energy customers with telecommunications services.

• In Oregon, Electric Lightwave has been authorized to provide switched interexchange service that will connect end users to IXCs and could lead it to offer presubscribed interexchange service. The company has applied for similar authority in Washington.[44]

• In Maryland, Baltimore Gas and Electric Company is offering its business customers fiber-optic access to the IXCs.[45]

• In Little Rock, Arkansas, Entergy Corp. has been testing a pilot network to control energy appliances in the home and to provide access service to the IXCs. Applications to extend fiber-optic service to one-third of the service area could also provide local exchange and video services.[46]

CONCLUSION

The last ten miles of the telecommunications landscape are dominated by local exchange carriers, which have until recently been the sole suppliers of access and local switched telephone services. The architecture of the LEC networks, however, offers many potential points of interconnection. New technologies —especially fiber optics, wireless access, and digital

---

43. *Id.*

44. *Oregon Permits ELI to Provide Switched IX Services*, TELECOMM. REP., Jan. 24, 1994, at 7.

45. Sandra Sugawara, *A Power Play for the Information Highway?* WASH. POST, Dec. 28, 1993, at D1.

46. *Id.*

electronics—are redrawing the boundaries of telecommunications suppliers and creating opportunities for entry into local markets.

Those new players include competitive access providers, interexchange carriers, LECs from other regions, cable television operators, electric utilities, and some users themselves. The Telecommunications Act of 1996 obligates the LECs to offer all carriers interconnection to their facilities and thereby to access bottleneck resources. As a result, the new entrants have good prospects to gain footholds in the local markets and compete successfully.

The act prescribes specific guidelines for measuring the emergence of local competition and allowing the LECs to enter previously proscribed markets. Regulation will thus be a central player in the looming competitive struggle—and in the remainder of this volume. New technology, supplier integration and specialization, and regulatory controls will intersect repeatedly.

3

Network Technology and the Demand for Access

A VARIETY OF telecommunications technologies are capable of providing end users with access to switched telephone networks. Figure 3–1 depicts schematically several of those technologies and the major components that comprise the distribution system for connecting a subscriber to a network. The traditional method of consumer access is through the LEC's local distribution network, which is described in detail in the next section. Other technologies that can provide access are cellular radio and personal communications systems, cable television distribution networks, and a competitive access provider's fiber-optic ring. Table 3–1 lists the facilities that supply those components for each network technology.

Those technologies have in common a series of generic components. Proceeding from the customer, at the bottom of figure 3–1, upward into the network, those components are:

- *A customer or end-user connection.* This is the final distribution link and customer interface unit (network termination point), to which customer-premises equipment (telephone, fax machine, mobile phone, and private switches) is attached.
- *A remote terminal.* This is an intermediate interface point in the distribution link, such as a radio cell site or a cable cross-connect point, where the transmission medium changes or a cross-connection provides flexibility for provisioning service.
- *Backhaul facilities.* These are distribution facilities, including transmission equipment, that link the remote terminal to a switch or wire center.

FIGURE 3–1
A GENERIC TECHNOLOGY MODEL OF NETWORK ACCESS

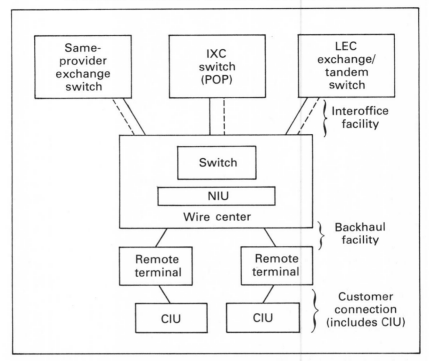

NOTE: POP, point of presence; NIU, network interface unit; CIU, customer interface unit.
SOURCE: ETI and Hatfield Associates, Inc. (1994).

- *A network interface unit.* This is a facility for interworking between dissimilar networks, for example, between cellular radio or cable television and a telephone network.
- *A switch.* This is a network node that interconnects end users, including the functionality that permits the switch to communicate with service platforms and respond to their instructions.
- *Interoffice facilities.* These consist of trunking equipment that transports calls and signaling messages between switches or to separate networks.

TABLE 3–1
TECHNOLOGIES USED FOR NETWORK ACCESS

Component	Cellular Radio and PCS	Cable Telephony	CAP Fiber-Optic Ring	LEC Network
Signaling	SS7 network	SS7 network	SS7 network	SS7 network
Interoffice facilities	LEC circuits, CAP ring	LEC circuits, CAP ring	Fiber-optic ring	LEC circuits
Switch (wire center)	Mobile switching center	Switch (head-end)	Switch (network control center)	Switch (central office)
Network interface unit	Site controller	Head-end unit	NA	NA
Backhaul facilities	Microwave or terrestrial circuits	Fiber-optic cable	Fiber-optic ring	Feeder plant
Remote terminal	Radio site	Radio frequency/optical converter	Add/drop multiplexer	Serving area interface
Customer connection	Airwaves and transceiver unit	Coaxial cable and subscriber unit	None (or ring extension)	Distribution plant (wire pairs)

NOTE: CAP, competitive access provider; NA, not applicable.
SOURCE: ETI and Hatfield Associates, Inc., "The Enduring Local Bottleneck" (February 1994).

- *Signaling facilities.* These are provided by a common-channel data network used to control the switches and interoffice facilities and to support the delivery of information services. The competitive significance of alternative technologies is that other firms, provided they can obtain interconnection to the LEC's facilities, can compete for the LEC's customers without having to duplicate all those components.

THE ARCHITECTURE OF THE LOCAL TELEPHONE NETWORK

The conventional local exchange network is depicted schematically in figure 3–2. Beginning at the subscriber's premises (at the left of the figure), the first element of the network is the terminal equipment: a telephone handset or PBX. That equipment is connected by inside wiring (conventionally in the form of copper-wire pairs, twisted together to reduce spurious signals) to the LEC network termination point. Today customer terminals and inside wiring are supplied in competitive markets, and there is unrestricted interconnection to the LEC network at point *A*, the network termination point. The terminal equipment market, characterized by vigorous competition and extensive product differentiation, includes handsets, answering machines, fax machines, personal computer boards, private exchanges, and voice mail systems. From point *A*, a "local loop" connects the subscriber to the LEC's end office (point *C*), the first point in the network at which two subscribers can be connected by a switch. In most communities the local loop is a dedicated copper-wire pair; those loops are combined into increasingly large bundles of wire pairs in a distribution network (referred to as outside plant) linking individual subscribers to the end office. Near the subscribers' premises, a small cable carries the local loops of a small number of subscribers in a single street or neighborhood to a serving area interface (point *B*). At each of those interfaces, larger feeder cables are connected to the loops to provide the connections to the wire center at the end office, where feeder cables each containing hundreds of copper-wire pairs terminate.

The LECs are replacing the larger cables in the feeder network with fiber optics, and several carriers are experimenting with architectures that bring the fiber interface to the "curb," that is, to within 50 to 100 feet of the subscriber's home or office.

FIGURE 3–2

ARCHITECTURE OF THE LEC NETWORK

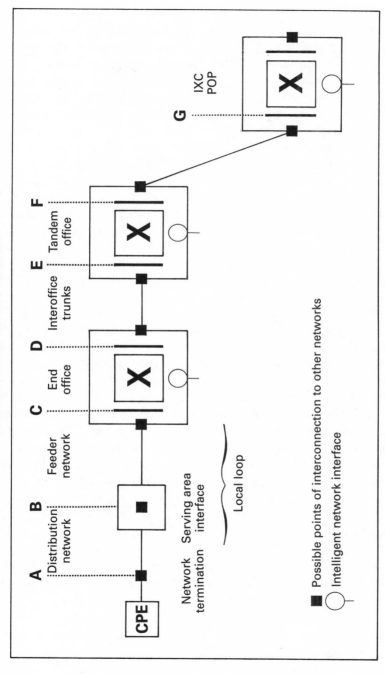

NOTE: CPE, customer premises equipment; POP, point of presence.
SOURCE: Adapted from Hatfield Associates, Inc., "New Local Exchange Technology: Preserving the Bottleneck or Providing Competition Alternatives" (April 6, 1992) (unpublished manuscript, cited in Reply Comments of MCI, FCC Docket 91-346, In the Matter of Intelligent Networks).

Alternatively, some subscribers with high communications volumes, such as larger business offices, may have a direct fiber connection from their premises to the carrier's central office.

Interconnection at those intermediate points in the distribution system is not yet open to competing suppliers, even though it would be demanded by, for example, a personal communications service's radio microcell that could serve the area of subscribers now connected through the LEC distribution plant. The microcell could interconnect to the network at a serving area interface.

At the end office the subscriber line terminates at the subscriber's main distribution frame (point *C*). That is the next potential point of interconnection. Access to that "lineside" interface to the local switch would be necessary for a competing local transport carrier that wished to connect its own subscriber to the local switched telephone system. That interface was opened to competition by the FCC's 1993 expanded interconnection order, which we examine in chapter 6.

From the main distribution frame the subscriber's line is connected to the local switch (represented by the *X* between points *C* and *D*).[1] The switch can connect two subscriber loops to complete a local call within the area served by that switch. For calls to more distant subscribers, the switch establishes a circuit on an outgoing trunk to reach another switch in the network. Interoffice trunk facilities terminate at a "trunkside" interface of the end office, at the trunk main distribution frame (point *D*), from which they are connected to the switch (or to another cross-connect device). Trunks, which may consist of copper-wire or fiber-optic cable or of microwave radio links, carry aggregated traffic (a number of calls simultaneously) or high-volume data between switching nodes.

The trunk main distribution frame provides the point of interconnection for IXCs, enhanced service providers, and competitive access providers; the IXCs typically purchase access under a "feature group" tariff (discussed in chapter 6) that provides voice-grade transport, answer supervision and other associated signaling, and automatic number identification.

---

1. In the case of a private line, the line connects to a cross-connect device, from which it is connected to another dedicated line.

In the LEC network, interoffice trunks connect an end office (point *D*) to a tandem office (point *E*) and switch (as shown), to another end office, or to the point of presence of another carrier (point *G*). Tandem switches are used to switch traffic that has been aggregated from several LEC central offices or the points of presence of several IXCs. The tandem switch is frequently located in the same building with one of the end-office switches. In the case of a tandem office, trunk terminations at the distribution frames of the tandem switch (points *E* and *F*) are additional interconnection points.

A competitive access provider could serve high-volume business subscribers with a fiber-optic cable that it interconnects to the LEC network. To do so it would collocate its own cable termination equipment in the LEC end office; that equipment would then be connected to the LEC switch through the main distribution frame. A cellular radio system connects the antennas at its cell sites to its mobile telephone switching office, using either lines leased from the LEC or another transport provider or its own cable or microwave facilities. That office is then interconnected to the LEC network by trunks that terminate at either the tandem office (*E*) or the end office (*D*).

Control of calls and access to essential data within the LEC network depend on a network signaling system, and the provision of information services therefore requires some access to LEC signaling. The LECs are converting from in-band signaling, in which voice messages and signaling information travel on the same circuits, to a separate digital signaling system (signaling architecture is discussed in chapter 6). The system that currently serves as the international standard, Signaling System 7 is a distributed processing, packet-switched network with well-defined interfaces. Those interface points, designated by small circles within the switches in figure 3–2, provide for logical or programmatic (as opposed to physical) interconnection with the LEC network. For example, through a service control point interconnected to the SS7 network, an independent information services provider could operate a database that would be accessible to the LECs, IXCs, and consumers with digital access lines. Another enhanced service provider could access a LEC database by using defined SS7 messages independent of a telephone call.

THE DEMAND FOR ACCESS TO THE LOCAL NETWORK

Demands for access to the telephone network are highly varied—reflecting the diverse needs of users and the great versatility of the telecommunications infrastructure in meeting them. Demands can be classified in many ways: by type of traffic (voice, data, video), by technical measure of volume (bandwidth, speed), by type of user (residence, business, or government, or urban versus rural), and so forth. LECs have been the predominant and often sole supplier of access services for all of those purposes. But, as described in chapter 2, a wide variety of competitors are already beginning to enter many of those markets by using new technologies and alliances with firms in related markets.

As entry into the local telephone market accelerates, public policy choices concerning the regulatory structure and market organization of the network naturally focus on the boundaries at which customers and firms meet. For those purposes it is most useful to classify demands for access in two ways:

•   Firms can demand access according to the major points at which facilities can be physically interconnected. On either side of each interface a different entity could, in principle, provide the relevant telecommunications equipment.

•   Firms can demand access according to the logical organization of information and the control of network facilities. Again, on either side of the control and software interfaces a different entity could provide services and exert operational responsibility.

Below we describe the major points of physical and logical interconnection to the LEC network, both those already established and those under discussion. Some of those interfaces (for example, attachment of customer terminal equipment) are fully open, whereas others (for example, basic control software in the local switch) are completely closed, but most are in various stages of examination by U.S. regulatory authorities.

Physical Interconnection to the LEC Network

Physical interconnection of facilities to the LEC network has been established, or is requested, for various types of service suppliers. Figure 3–3 illustrates several varieties of interconnection. Their demands for access may be grouped according to the point of interconnection in the LEC's network into several major categories.

Interconnection with Customer Premises Equipment. Two examples of this type of interconnection are shown in figure 3–3. In the first, the end user connects inside wiring at his or her premises to terminal equipment attached to the LEC local loop (point 1 in figure 3–3). In the second, the end user connects a private switch (PBX) to trunk-termination equipment of the LEC or an alternative local carrier at the user's premises (point 2).

Outside Plant Interconnection at the Serving Area Interface. Again the figure illustrates two examples. In the first, a distributor provides the connection to the end user, for example by cable or radio (point 3). In the second, an alternative local network, with feeder and distribution cable, transports its traffic from a serving area interface to the LEC wire center by LEC feeder cable (point 4).

Interconnection at the Subscriber Main Distribution Frame. In the first of two examples shown, a competitive access provider supplies all feeder and distribution connections to end users and interconnects copper-wire or fiber-optic facilities to the lineside interface of the LEC switch (point 5). In the second a service supplier uses the LEC's feeder and distribution cables for its own services but needs access to the distribution frame to connect to those cables at the switch (point 6).

Interconnection at the Trunk Main Distribution Frame. A transport provider supplies transport from the trunkside interface of the LEC switch to some other entity, using multichannel copper or fiber-optic facilities. The transport entity may itself provide competitive local switching and distribution (point 7). Alternatively, the LEC or a transport provider connects the trunkside interface of the LEC

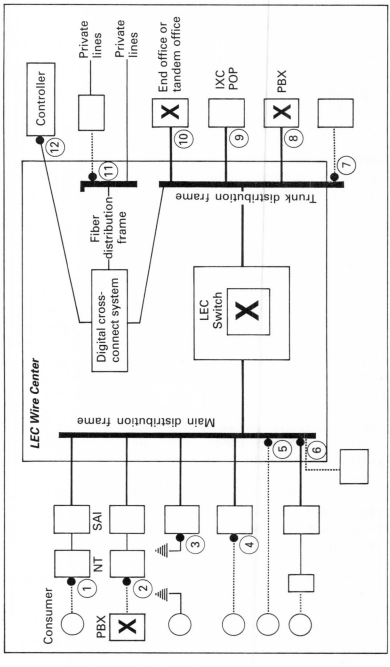

FIGURE 3-3
TYPES OF PHYSICAL INTERCONNECTION TO THE LEC NETWORK

NOTE: NT, network termination; SAI, serving area interface; POP, point of presence.

switch to PBX switching at the end user's premises (point 8), to transport to an IXC's point of presence (point 9), or to another LEC end office or tandem office (point 10).

Interconnection at a Fiber Distribution Frame. A transport provider supplies private line services and interconnects fiber-optic cable to the LEC's fiber distribution frame (point 11), or interconnects its control equipment to the LEC's digital cross-connect system to allocate bandwidth on fiber-optic cables (point 12).

Logical Interconnection to the LEC Network

A rather different perspective on network interconnection is gained by viewing carriers and service providers as suppliers of functions that control communications pathways and access to information. That focus emphasizes the "logical" aspect of a communications network, that is, the flow and control of information, regardless of how it is accomplished over physical facilities. As telecommunications networks become more thoroughly controlled by computer hardware and software, it is expected that the IXCs, competitive access providers, and information services providers will compete to supply those functions and to demand access to logical interface points in the LEC network. In figure 3–4 those logical functions are schematically related to the physical telecommunications resources.

Viewed in that way, the local network can be described in terms of several types of logical network objects:[2]

- A *switch* in this context may be described as the functionality to connect an end user with another end user or with a resource element, including the functionality to communicate with service platforms and respond to their instructions. Call control capability is included within the switch's connection to the end user's lines, to recognize that action by a service platform is needed

2. Information Industry Liaison Committee, Issue 026 Task Group, Minutes (Sept. 2, 1993).

FIGURE 3–4
LOGICAL INTERCONNECTION TO THE LEC NETWORK

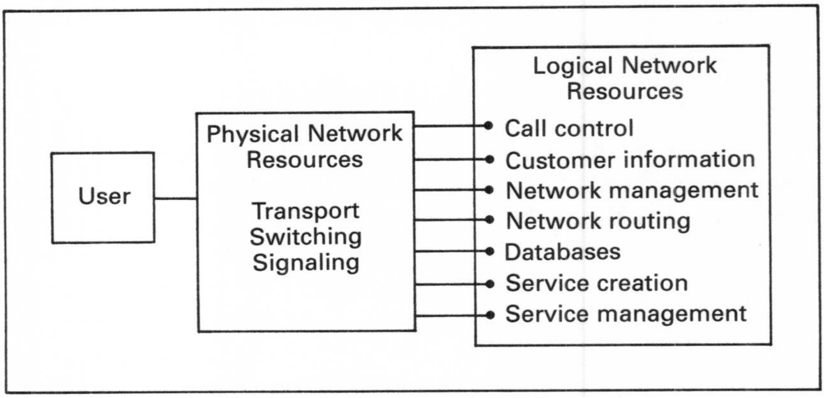

SOURCE: See figure 2–1.

to handle a call at various points throughout a call attempt.

• A *resource element* is any functionality that includes announcements, tones, or input collection (by voice or keypresses).

• A *service platform* is a facility external to a switch that receives and responds to queries from switches on how to handle calls.

• A *database* is a facility external to a switch where service-related data are stored, to be accessed in real time during call processing.

• *Service creation* is the functionality for designing, coding, and testing service logic programs.

The logical interconnection of two separate networks enables one network's (logical) resources to provide control or information to the other. For example, one network may provide a second network with access to its customer information for directory inquiries and call routing. That function is essential to making subscribers' telephone numbers "portable" between competing local suppliers. With carrier portability a consumer is able to retain the same local telephone number when changing to a different carrier. In the absence of portability, new entrants must overcome the barrier of user inertia due to high switching costs. The translation, or mapping, of demands for various types of logical interconnection onto the LEC network presents both technical and regulatory challenges that have not yet been fully worked out. We consider those issues in greater detail in chapter 6.

Conclusions

The local telephone network contains many potential interfaces and points of interconnection between carriers and service providers. That rich set of possibilities means that telecommunications services can potentially be delivered by quite different types of firms. Economic factors, including economies of scale and scope and product differentiation, rather than strictly technical considerations determine where competing suppliers seek to interconnect their networks.

The LEC networks can be unbundled at physical interconnection points at the customer premises, at intermediate points in the local loop, and at both the lineside and the trunkside termination points of the local switch. Access to those interfaces has been central to the entry of competitive access providers and will be central to the future entry of competing local exchange and wireless service carriers. As telecommunications network technology becomes more computer-driven, issues of competitive access to network resources will increasingly focus on access to the logical functions and components of the LEC networks.

In the last ten miles of the telecommunications supply chain, some elements of the LEC's physical and logical network are essential resources for nearly all potential competitors of the LECs. Regulation and competition policy will be concerned with both the technical and the economic conditions of access to those resources. The following chapters analyze many of those regulatory issues.

4

Regulation and Public Policy

LOCAL TELECOMMUNICATIONS SERVICE MARKETS have
been heavily regulated in the past. Although under the forbearance
rule of the Telecommunications Act of 1996[1] that regulation is
likely to subside in the future, existing and emerging competition in
those markets will for a time continue to be influenced by at least
some, possibly intense, regulation of dominant incumbents. This
chapter describes the regulatory procedures and institutions that
have shaped the status quo in the U.S. telecommunications industry
and will continue to shape its future. We begin by describing the
conventional rationales for regulating telecommunications services
in general and local and interconnection services in particular.

WHY REGULATE TELECOMMUNICATIONS SERVICES?

The economics literature provides two main reasons for regulating
telecommunications services. First, there are conjectured to be
sufficient economies of scale and scope in the production of those
services to make telecommunications markets natural monopolies.
Second, use of and subscription to telecommunications services are
claimed to yield two types of positive consumption externalities.
The first is known as the call externality: a caller provides benefits
to the called party, who does not pay for those benefits.[2] The

---

1. Telecommunications Act of 1996, Pub. L. 104-104, 110 Stat. 56 (Feb.
8, 1996) [hereinafter *Telecommunications Act*].
2. Conversely, the caller benefits from and does not pay for free phone
calls.

second is called the network externality: when new subscribers join the network, existing subscribers receive benefits, without paying an additional charge, from being called by the new subscribers and being able to call them.

Both the natural monopoly property and the network externality can lead to market power for an incumbent telecommunications services provider. The natural monopoly property makes monopoly the most efficient market structure. Natural monopoly is customarily said to prevail when a single firm can supply the market output at lower cost than any combination of firms. That customary definition corresponds to the normative concept that, when a natural monopoly exists, the socially optimal market structure is monopoly. Salinger[3] distinguishes from that normative concept a positive concept of natural monopoly: a natural monopoly is a situation in which monopoly is the unregulated market outcome. But the mere demonstration that a market possesses the property of normative natural monopoly does not imply that the market is a positive natural monopoly, and vice versa, the existence of a positive natural monopoly does not imply that the market possesses the property of normative natural monopoly. There are two reasons for this:

• A monopoly may be unsustainable; that is, the incumbent monopolist may be unable to keep out equally efficient entrants while at least breaking even. Although unsustainable natural monopolies are likely to be quite exceptional, unsustainability may nevertheless have been the main normative rationale for regulatory restrictions on entry in natural monopoly markets.
• The incumbent and the entrant(s) may prefer to coexist under less fierce competition, with possibly all firms' making profits. In anticipation of that, entry occurs even if the natural monopoly is sustainable.[4]

---

3. Michael A. Salinger, The Future of Local Telecommunications Networks: Will Competition Really Emerge? (1994) (paper prepared for Charles River Associates conference, Boston).

4. For an exposition of some of those cases, see Günter Knieps & Ingo Vogelsang, *The Sustainability Concept Under Alternative Behavioral Assumptions,* 13 BELL J. ECON. 234 (1982).

The fact that a market is a normative natural monopoly does not preclude entry by other firms. Natural monopolies are, however, usually accompanied by high sunk costs and other entry barriers that make entry unlikely. Similar to natural monopoly, the network externality makes a fully interconnected network the most efficient supply structure. An incumbent service provider can therefore effectively prevent entry by refusing to interconnect. That was, for example, the practice of AT&T in the early 1900s, when AT&T owned a long-distance technology far superior to that of its rivals.

Thus, according to the arguments based on natural monopoly and externality, the tasks of telecommunications regulation should be to eliminate market power and mimic the outcome of competitive markets. In addition, regulation should ensure the realization of the efficient (monopoly) market structure and help optimize with respect to the consumption externalities.

In the past few decades competition has developed in some telecommunications markets, accompanied by partial deregulation or asymmetrical regulation (where incumbents remain regulated while entrants are unregulated). Although the presence of such competition does not disprove that the market is a natural monopoly, it does call it into question. Clearly, in those areas where competition has been successful, such as long-distance services and information services, any natural monopoly property can, at best, be weak. At the same time, regulation of interconnection has taken care of those parts of the consumption externality problems caused by entry. That is extremely important because interconnection, in one stroke, creates large network externalities by providing access to potentially many new consumers. The remaining potential for additional network externalities has to be achieved through pricing and universal service policies.

As competition increases, it undermines the rationale for regulation and raises the question, Should local telecommunications services also be deregulated? Clearly, competition in those services is still in its infancy. Both the natural monopoly argument and the network externality argument appear to be stronger for local services than, for example, for long-distance services or for information services. The main reason is that, as one moves closer to the subscriber, sunk network costs per subscriber and per mile increase rapidly. To put it differently, economies of scale are an inverse function of consumers served per line. In the extreme, if only a single consumer is served, economies of scale are strongest and therefore the cost of duplication is highest. Thus, in telecommunications, the lower the network density and the shorter the call distance, the more likely it is that natural monopoly will prevail.

Are local telecommunications services now, and will they remain, a normative natural monopoly? There are good reasons to believe that the answer to both parts of this question is no.[5] First, the duplication argument only holds for consumers connected to the network by a single line. It does not hold for large business consumers, apartment buildings, and the like. Second, through interconnection, different carriers can offer access to different parts of the network without duplicating the single connection to the final consumer. Third, sunk costs do not count. Therefore, already existing parallel networks create no new inefficiency by competing with each other. That sunk-cost argument basically holds for all service providers that can offer local telecommunications in conjunction with other services for which a distribution network already exists (such as cable television). Fourth, close substitutes to local telephony have emerged in the form of wireless services. Even if economies of scale are not fully exhausted in the incumbent's network, the benefits of product differentiation may well outweigh the cost inefficiencies created by such parallel offerings.

The best way to test for the natural monopoly property is probably to let the market discover the best outcome. If, despite market entry, the market is a normative natural monopoly, some

5. This statement is backed by econometric estimates for U.S. LECs by Richard T. Shin & John S. Ying, *Unnatural Monopolies in Local Telephone,* 23 RAND J. ECON. 171 (1992), and by John S. Ying & Richard T. Shin, Viable Competition in Local Telephone: Superadditive Costs in the Post-Divestiture Period (Dec. 1994) (unpublished manuscript, on file with authors). Although that work is based on extensive empirical data, there are still conceptual and measurement problems that lead us to believe that those estimates are not yet definitive. For a critique of Shin and Ying, *see* David Gabel & D. Mark Kennet, *Economies of Scope in the Local Telephone Exchange Market,* 6 J. REG. ECON. 381 (1994).

inefficiency will be seen.[6] But that *potential* inefficiency has to be compared with the *certain* inefficiencies created by regulation of entry. Most likely, entry will occur only if the natural monopoly property no longer holds.

BOTTLENECKS AND THE ESSENTIAL FACILITY DOCTRINE

Once entry has occurred, there may still be two valid rationales for regulation. First, the incumbent operator may continue to dominate the market in such a way that consumers need protection. That need will go away as competition increases. Second, the old natural monopoly and network externality arguments may resurface in a different form. The network externality argument resurfaces in the call for interconnectivity, and the natural monopoly argument through the so-called bottleneck problem.

Interexchange carriers, competitive access providers, and enhanced services providers view access to the local exchange carrier's network as a bottleneck for their services.[7] That view has been the basis for the Federal Communications Commission's and the MFJ court's regulation of access to LEC networks. The LECs (the Bell operating companies in particular) have been required to provide nondiscriminatory access to and interconnection with nonaffiliated companies that may be their competitors.

The bottleneck rationale for regulation is closely related to the "essential facility" doctrine. That doctrine provided the fundamental underpinning for the federal government's antitrust suit against AT&T, which resulted in the MFJ, and for cases brought by MCI and Sprint against AT&T.[8]

---

6. Inefficient entry may also be due to inefficient pricing, for example, as a result of regulation.

7. For a differing view, *see* PETER W. HUBER, MICHAEL K. KELLOGG & JOHN THORNE, THE GEODESIC NETWORK II: 1993 REPORT ON COMPETITION IN THE TELEPHONE INDUSTRY (Geodesic Co. 1992).

8. For the following arguments, *see* Kevin R. Sullivan, *Competition in Telecommunications: Moving Toward a New Era of Antitrust Scrutiny and Regulation, in* FUTURE COMPETITION IN TELECOMMUNICATIONS 123–40 (S. P. Bradley & J. A. Hausman eds., Harvard Business School Press 1989), or William B. Tye, *Competitive Access: A Comparative Industry Approach to the*

The essential facility doctrine originally evolved from a 1912 case involving a railroad dispute.[9] At that time a few railroads controlled the only rail access to two bridges and a ferry over the Mississippi River into St. Louis and denied that access to their competitors. The U.S. Supreme Court decreed that the system of access lines constituted a bottleneck, and it declared denial of access to be a restraint of trade in violation of the Sherman Act.

The main elements of the essential facility doctrine are: the control of a facility by a monopolist; the inability of others, as a practical matter, to duplicate the facility; the denial of access with substantial harm to competition; and the absence of a valid business reason for not providing access. Clearly, the notion of an essential facility or bottleneck is closely related to that of (normative) natural monopoly. The second element of the essential facility doctrine spells out the natural monopoly property. The difference between a bottleneck and a natural monopoly, in our view, is that natural monopoly refers to a market or set of markets, whereas a bottleneck refers to an input for which a market may not exist or may not be meaningfully defined. The owner of the bottleneck facility is the optimal input provider, and bypass would be inefficient.

In telecommunications, the substantial harm to competition from denying access to the bottleneck is particularly manifest in the network externality that would be denied. The MFJ (described below) required local telephone companies to provide equal access to all IXCs. To achieve equal access, the LECs had to make large investments in new switching equipment for several years. Those access costs were passed on to the IXCs in switched access rates.

Essential Facility Doctrine, 8 ENERGY L.J. 337 (1987).

9. United States *v.* Terminal Railroad Association of St. Louis, 224 U.S. 383, at 411 (1912). Other decisions relevant for interconnection as a bottleneck include Otter Tail Power Co. *v.* United States, 410 U.S. 366 (1973) (control over electricity transmission network to wheel power); MCI Communications *v.* American Tel. & Tel. Co., 708 F.2d 1081, at 1132–33 (7th Cir. 1983). Phillip Areeda, *Essential Facilities: An Epithet in Need of Limiting Principles,* 58 ANTITRUST L. REV. 841 (1990), who is otherwise unsympathetic toward the practicability of the essential facility doctrine, believes that one of the few areas where it would be practical is in regulated industries. There, the regulatory agency can enforce compliance over time.

During the transition, non-AT&T carriers paid reduced access rates, and their subscribers had to dial additional digits to obtain connection.

In U.S. antitrust cases the courts have required monopolists to provide competitors with access to essential facilities, but those access rights were not easily secured. Only a few court decisions resulted in orders mandating access.[10] Moreover, the antitrust laws do not mandate absolutely equal access, but only reasonable access. Reasonableness is a weaker standard, one that would preclude undue discrimination but could allow justified discrimination, for example, due to technical infeasibility or high costs. Thus, the MFJ and the FCC, by requiring *equal* access to bottleneck facilities in telecommunications, have gone beyond the standards required by antitrust case law. The Telecommunications Act of 1996 also spells that out clearly and provides a checklist of conditions for the presence of local competition.

The bottleneck doctrine is related to monopoly leveraging theory.[11] According to that theory, a firm can leverage its monopoly power in one market into other markets where it faces competition. That can happen through price squeezes, vertical restrictions, and attempts at foreclosure by which the monopoly firm can prevent entry or induce exit in those other markets. Thus, monopoly leveraging can lead to reductions in the amount of effective competition and to distortions in the monopolist's behavior.

Monopoly leveraging does not occur in every situation where a monopoly firm in one market also competes in another market, but

10. Letter from J. Gregory Sidak, resident scholar, American Enterprise Institute, to the authors, Feb. 7, 1995.

11. For an application of monopoly leveraging theory to telecommunications, *see* David L. Kaserman & John W. Mayo, Monopoly Leveraging Theory: Implications for Post-Divestiture Telecommunications Policy (1993) (unpublished manuscript, on file with the Center for Business and Economic Research, College of Business Administration, University of Tennessee, Knoxville), and David L. Kaserman & John W. Mayo, Regulatory Policies Toward Local Exchange Companies Under Emerging Competition: Guardrails or Speedbumps on the Information Highway? (1995) (unpublished manuscript, on file with authors) and the literature cited therein.

only under certain conditions. There are two extreme cases where leveraging does not occur. The first is that in which the markets are unrelated, so that the monopolist has no possibility of extending its monopoly power to the other market. The second is that of two vertically related markets with a fixed-proportions technology, where an upstream monopolist has so much power over the downstream market that it can exercise all of that power in the monopoly alone.[12] Monopoly leveraging occurs in cases lying between those two extremes, such that it becomes profitable to use predatory techniques.[13] Monopoly leveraging may also arise if the monopoly market is regulated and the other market is not.

Fears of monopoly leveraging have been used to justify policies to keep the LECs out of long-distance markets and to regulate interconnection. Both of those policies are attempts to make more competitive the markets into which the LECs would leverage their market power. The second policy seems more precisely directed at that goal, however, because it helps competitors without excluding the LECs, whereas the first policy may actually reduce competition overall. Thus, the policy lesson from monopoly leveraging theory is that one should reduce entry barriers and other restrictions on competitors, rather than prevent the monopolist in one market from competing in another. We deal with such policies extensively in chapters 6 and 7.

Monopoly leveraging and the denial of bottleneck access thus are major concerns in the entry of competitors in local telecommunications markets. On the other hand, the existence of bottlenecks may also create opportunities for mutual dependence, cooperation, and collusion. These opportunities arise through the interconnection of noncompeting firms (for example, two firms offering complementary services, such as international operators in two different countries) or of competing firms in symmetrical situations (for example, two vertically integrated carriers with equal market shares).

12. A fixed-proportions technology is one that does not allow for substitution of one input by another.
13. In our context, predatory techniques are those that make efficient entrants exit even though the market is not a normative natural monopoly.

AREAS OF REGULATION

As long as the LECs dominate local telecommunications markets, they or their competitors are likely to be regulated in four areas:

- *Service prices.* Price regulation should reduce the opportunities for firms to exercise market power and should be efficient and equitable. The economist's view of optimal pricing under regulation has been driven by the notion of Ramsey prices, which tend to deviate from marginal costs in inverse proportions to the demand elasticities. That would translate into higher markups for basic local services than for long-distance services. Ramsey prices would have to be corrected for network externalities, so that marginal subscribers would be able to purchase basic local services at lower rates relative to inframarginal subscribers.[14] But the resulting price structure would differ substantially from the LEC price structures currently found, which are driven by political and equity considerations.
- *Entry.* The normative rationale for regulation of entry derives from the natural monopoly property. But since the regulator does not know whether that property holds, that rationale is very weak indeed. On the contrary, entry is likely to help discover the most efficient market structure. As explained above, there is a theoretical possibility that an existing natural monopoly is unsustainable, so that entry could lead to an inefficient and unstable situation. But we have not seen any empirical evidence for the prevalence of unsustainable natural monopoly in telecommunications. On the other hand, regulated price structures may well be unsustainable because of cross-subsidies.
- *Public service obligations.* The imposition of public service obligations on the LECs is largely derived from externality and equity arguments. Public service obligations include the universal service mandate—services must be provided throughout the service territory at similar rates and conditions—and are sometimes

---

14. On optimal telecommunications pricing under regulation, *see* BRIDGER M. MITCHELL & INGO VOGELSANG, TELECOMMUNICATIONS PRICING: THEORY AND PRACTICE (Cambridge University Press 1991).

expressed as a commitment by the firm to undertake certain infrastructure investments. Public service obligations have to be financed. When the financial source is another service provided by the same supplier, the result is a cross-subsidy. To the extent that public service obligations benefit only marginal subscribers, those policies should be more narrowly targeted the higher the level of subscriber penetration.

• *Interconnection.* Interconnection becomes a major issue once competition emerges in telecommunications markets. All would-be competitors of the LEC have to interconnect with the LEC to reach final customers. The terms of interconnection are therefore key to the success of local exchange competition. Two neighboring monopolists have strong incentives to interconnect voluntarily, because both are likely to benefit about equally. But the same is not necessarily true under direct competition, where the dominant firm benefits less from interconnection than do its smaller rivals. Dominant firms may actually suffer from having to offer interconnection, precisely because many of their small rivals could not survive without it.

As described in chapter 6, the main issues for interconnection are the type and the pricing of access. Theoretically, optimal pricing of access would again follow a Ramsey pricing rule, with markups of marginal costs for interconnection and retail services inversely proportional to the demand elasticities of those services.[15]

A related rule that has been proposed is the "efficient component-pricing rule."[16] Under that rule the interconnection charge is derived from the price of the retail service for which

15. Strictly speaking, the relevant elasticities are "superelasticities" that contain all cross-demand effects.

16. For an exposition of the efficient component-pricing rule, *see* WILLIAM J. BAUMOL & J. GREGORY SIDAK, TOWARD COMPETITION IN LOCAL TELEPHONY (MIT Press and AEI Press 1994). For more critical views, *see* JENS ARNBAK, BRIDGER M. MITCHELL, WERNER NEU, KARL-HEINZ NEUMANN & INGO VOGELSANG, WITH THE COLLABORATION OF GODEFROY DANG N'GUYEN & BERND ICKENROTH, NETWORK INTERCONNECTION IN THE DOMAIN OF ONP (WIK & European-American Center for Policy Analysis, Nov. 1994).

interconnection is established, by deducting any costs that the LEC avoids in providing interconnection instead of producing the retail service itself. In other words, the rule says that the interconnector, which competes with the LEC in the final goods market, should pay the resource costs for providing the interconnection plus the opportunity cost of the net revenue forgone by the LEC in the final goods market.

The efficient component-pricing rule is identical to the Ramsey rule if retail service prices are Ramsey-efficient, if the interconnector competes with the LEC on a price basis, and if the retail services supplied by both firms are identical and produced in fixed proportion to the interconnection service. Neither Ramsey prices nor the efficient component-pricing rule are very practical in that they require the regulator to have detailed information about costs and demand elasticities. Also, the efficient component-pricing rule is strictly optimal only under certain well-specified conditions, including an optimally set retail price. In practice, interconnection prices have variously been set on the basis of fully distributed costs (in the United States and the United Kingdom), on the basis of negotiations (in the United Kingdom and in international rate setting), on the basis of the efficient component-pricing rule (in the United Kingdom), or on the basis of incremental costs (in Australia). If conditions for competition in the interconnection market actually hold, both the efficient component-pricing rule and Ramsey pricing collapse to a rule of setting interconnection prices equal to marginal, or average incremental, costs.

The U.S. Approach to Telecommunications Regulation

U.S. telecommunications policy is subject to complex and sometimes conflicting tripartite authority. Provision of local telephone service is regulated in each state by a public utilities commission. At the same time the FCC exercises national jurisdiction over radio-based service and interstate services. In addition, the antitrust laws deal with issues of market power. As the prime example, for more than ten years antitrust proceedings in federal court have governed the divestiture of AT&T that took effect in 1984 and set limits and conditions on AT&T (the country's largest IXC) and the regional Bell operating companies that formerly were AT&T's local exchange carriers. The U.S. District Court for the District of Columbia, the court that issued the MFJ, has had the view that the local Bell operating companies retain bottleneck powers in most major markets. Concerned that those companies might discriminate against other suppliers, the court has maintained restrictions on the Bell operating companies that limit their opportunities to compete.

The FCC has been moving rapidly to establish policies for interstate services that affect local service competition. Those include unbundling of interconnection facilities, collocation of interconnecting carriers' equipment, and access to network intelligence. One reason for that pattern is the FCC's belief that the regional Bell operating companies and AT&T have more resources than their smaller competitors. In the same vein, the FCC is moving to undo long-established patterns of cross-subsidies and to restructure rates for services affected by competing carriers.

The state public utilities commissions are taking diverse approaches to local exchange competition and to issues of interconnection to the local network. A few largely urban states, led by New York and Illinois, have started implementing policies for competition in basic telephone service and were the first jurisdictions to require local interconnection for special access. Most others have until recently kept local exchange markets closed to entry. At the same time, however, an increasing number of states are undertaking proceedings to set policies for local competition. The Telecommunications Act of 1996 has provided strong incentives to accelerate the process.

THE HISTORY OF U.S. TELECOMMUNICATIONS REGULATION

Before examining the intersecting activities of the various U.S. regulatory institutions, we first briefly revisit key regulatory developments on the historical path to local telephone competition.

The Beginnings of Telephone Regulation

Telephone regulation in the United States began in earnest only about thirty years after the invention of the telephone in 1876. Alexander Graham Bell's original patents had expired some time previously, after which AT&T had first lost and then regained market share. AT&T had entered a period of expansion by means of mergers and refusals to interconnect, and it was during that period that regulation gained momentum. Several Southern states had started regulating telephony early on. In 1907 they were followed by Wisconsin and New York, which became the regulatory leaders. Cohen[17] sees the early involvement of the Southern states in telephone regulation as an infrastructure policy move, to promote business and industry through availability of telephone services at low rates. By 1914, thirty-four states and the District of Columbia were regulating telephony in one way or other.[18] State regulation was concerned with rate setting, common-carrier status (nondiscrimination), interconnection requirements, and licensing requirements.[19]

Federal telephone regulation started in 1910 with the passing of the Mann-Elkins Act, which empowered the Interstate Commerce Commission (ICC) to regulate telephone companies. That provision came as an amendment to an act that otherwise dealt with railroad regulation. The inclusion of telephony was, however, backed by AT&T and independent telephone companies. Up to 1934, when the ICC lost its jurisdiction over telephone regulation, the commission's regulation of that industry remained largely passive. Rather than regulate on a continuous basis, the ICC acted only upon complaints by affected parties. The commission did, however, establish a unified system of accounts and required AT&T to submit its reports and accounts.

Federal antitrust enforcement in many respects has had a more fundamental impact on telecommunications markets, especially early and late in this century, than has federal regulation of telephony. AT&T's chairman Theodore Vail, at least from 1907 onward, had promoted the nationwide integration of AT&T's network. As noted above, he achieved that largely through takeovers of independent

17. JEFFREY E. COHEN, THE POLITICS OF TELECOMMUNICATIONS REGULATION—THE STATES AND THE DIVESTITURE OF AT&T (M. E. Sharpe, Inc. 1992), at 46.
18. *Id.* at 41–42.
19. For an overview, *see id.* at 41–46.

and rival telephone companies. The independents complained against that behavior before the U.S. Department of Justice, which filed an antitrust suit charging AT&T with monopolization. Rather than lose the suit or suffer increased regulation, in 1913 AT&T entered into an agreement (known as the Kingsbury Commitment after the AT&T vice president who signed it) to interconnect with other companies for long-distance calling, to divest its holdings in the telegraph company Western Union, and to refrain from purchasing any more competing telephone companies without regulatory approval.

Since AT&T had not promised to abandon mergers with noncompeting independents, it continued to undertake such mergers, and after regulatory powers over telephone mergers and takeovers were shifted from the antitrust authorities to the ICC (by the Willis-Graham Act, passed in 1921), AT&T felt encouraged to once again engage in the takeover of competitors. In fact, as of 1934 the ICC had approved 271 out of 274 telephone company acquisitions that fell under its jurisdiction. The interests of AT&T and the independent telephone companies were only realigned after AT&T again formally abjured any further acquisitions.[20] The independents subsequently learned that they could benefit from the regulatory umbrella over AT&T, which provided for entry restrictions and cost-covering prices.[21] Thus, many independents have survived to this day.

The Communications Act of 1934

By the early 1930s AT&T, as the holding company for the Bell System, was firmly established as the dominant U.S. telecommunications carrier. It owned about 80 percent of the nation's telephones and had the only significant long-distance network. Virtually all its equipment was supplied by a manufacturing subsidiary, Western Electric. The remaining 20 percent of telephones were in the hands of hundreds of small

---

20. Richard   Gabel,   *The   Early   Competitive   Era   in   Telephone Communications, 1893–1920,* 34 L. & CONTEMP. PROB. 340 (1969).
21. COHEN, *supra* note 17, at 48–49.

independent companies that were in fact quite dependent on AT&T for long-distance services and for connections with other companies.

A combination of pressure from the states (which through a Supreme Court decision had lost, in fact if not in law, their own regulatory power over telecommunications; see the discussion of the *Shreveport* decision[22] below in our subsection, "Federal Preemption") and the fragmented nature of federal regulation at that time set the stage for major changes. The ICC had jurisdiction over common carriers for interstate services, and the Federal Radio Commission had authority over the assignment of radio frequencies. The dominance of AT&T, combined with general pressures for increased government control in the depressed economy, led to the Communications Act of 1934, which established the FCC to consolidate the relevant activities of the two agencies.

The act gave the FCC broad authority over facilities used jointly for interstate and intrastate communication but reserved to the states the right to regulate intrastate services and in particular the authority over "charges, classifications, practices, services, facilities, or regulations for or in connection with intrastate communication service of any carrier."[23] In that connection it is crucial that the act specifically states that the FCC's powers end at "local facilities and disputes that in their nature and effect are separable from and do not substantially affect the conduct or development of interstate communications."[24] That provision is the basis for the accounting separations process of state and federal assets and for the limits to federal preemption of state regulation, both discussed below. The act also provides for the creation of "Federal-State Joint Boards" to

22. Houston, East and West Texas Ry. Co. *v.* U.S., 234 U.S. 342 (1914) [hereinafter *Shreveport*].

23. Communications Act of 1934, 76 Stat. 419, 15 U.S.C. 21, 47 U.S.C. 35, 151–609, § 2(b)(1). A somewhat stronger provision applies state regulatory authority to wireline telephone exchange services "even though a portion of such exchange service constitutes interstate or foreign communication, in any case where such matters are subject to regulation by a State commission or by local governmental authority" (§ 221(b)). Section 221(b) of the act denies the FCC jurisdiction over essentially local facilities in metropolitan areas that extend across state boundaries.

24. *Id.* at § 2(b)(1).

make recommendations on issues affecting both state and federal jurisdictions and, in particular, on cost separations between them.[25]

The Consent Decree of 1956

A major concern at the time of the Communications Act and afterward was the tie between the Bell companies and Western Electric. Allegations were common that the Bell companies were paying excessive prices for Western Electric equipment and that the introduction of competition among suppliers would serve the public interest. Seeking to force the divestiture of Western Electric, the U.S. Department of Justice brought suit against AT&T in 1949. After prolonged investigation, the suit was settled under the terms of a consent decree in 1956.[26] The decree did not force AT&T to divest its equipment subsidiary. Instead it stipulated only that AT&T would confine its activities to regulated common-carrier services (telecommunications services regulated by federal or state regulatory agencies), that Western Electric would engage in manufacture of equipment solely for use by the Bell System, and that the Bell companies would license their patents under reasonable and nondiscriminatory terms to all applicants.

The rationale for confining AT&T and its Western Electric subsidiary to regulated common carriage arose from the fear of cross-subsidy: with an equipment supplier tied to its regulated telephone service, an unconstrained AT&T could, many feared, undercut other manufacturers in both domestic and foreign markets and compensate for losses there by raising prices to its monopoly telephone subscribers. Only by confining AT&T's (and Western Electric's) activities to the regulated sphere, so the argument went, could that danger of unfair competition be averted.

Shortly after the consent decree was concluded, a new concern—the prospect of competition in the long-distance market—began to emerge. In its "above 890 megahertz" decision in 1959, the FCC granted the use of radio frequencies to large private

---

25. *Id.* at § 410(c).

26. United States *v.* Western Elec. Co., 1956 Trade Cas. (CCH) ¶ 68,246 (D.N.J. 1956).

firms for the operation of microwave transmission facilities for their own use. From that opening, pressure mounted from the late 1960s to the 1970s to permit new carriers to offer the services of those facilities to third parties.

In light of those competitive developments, as well as those in the terminal equipment market, the strategy of confining AT&T to regulated monopoly markets was no longer viable. AT&T found itself operating in a mixture of monopoly and increasingly competitive markets. AT&T used every avenue available to it to make entry difficult, first by inducing regulators to disallow entry, then by refusing to interconnect, then by interconnecting slowly and with connections of lower quality, then by setting high rates for competitors' use of its network, and so on. That is an effective anticompetitive strategy, provided regulators do not interfere. Thus, AT&T must have believed either that it would get away with those practices, or at least that it could postpone and limit the amount of emerging competition. Inevitably, new complaints were voiced about AT&T's anticompetitive behavior toward long-distance newcomers, which depended on Bell's local monopoly networks to provide end-to-end service. At the same time, policy makers remained worried about the tie between the local telephone monopoly and Western Electric.

The Modification of Final Judgment

Hopes for taming AT&T's monopoly power came from a suit brought by the Department of Justice against AT&T in 1974. After years of judicial proceedings and attempted legislative solutions, that case was settled in 1982 with a Modification of Final Judgment of the 1956 consent decree.[27]

Under the terms of the MFJ, twenty-two Bell operating companies were divested from the parent AT&T (as of January 1, 1984) and organized within seven regional holding companies to

27. United States *v.* American Tel. & Tel. Co., 552 F. Supp. 131 (D.D.C. 1982) (text of the decree), *aff'd sub nom.* Maryland *v.* United States, 460 U.S. 1001 (1983); United States *v.* Western Elec. Co., 569 F. Supp. 1057 (D.D.C. 1983) (approving the plan of reorganization).

provide local telephone service. Local exchange and transport areas (LATAs) were created to mark the boundaries beyond which a Bell operating company may not carry end-user traffic. AT&T was allowed to continue providing long-distance service, and, freed of the terms of the 1956 consent decree, it was permitted to enter unregulated markets. Bell Laboratories, the Bell System's research division, was split in two. One portion, which retained the name, remained with AT&T; the other, Bellcore (the name is derived from Bell Communications Research) would serve the seven regional companies collectively. Western Electric, renamed AT&T Technologies, remained a subsidiary of AT&T. The Bell operating companies were permitted to enter unregulated markets in cases where the court was satisfied that anticompetitive behavior would not be a threat.

Three specific line-of-business restrictions were imposed on the Bell operating companies: they were not permitted to manufacture telecommunications equipment, to provide long-distance services, or to offer information services within their own telephone service territories, unless they could demonstrate that no danger of anticompetitive conduct existed.

There were three rationales for those proscriptions. First, the denial of telecommunications equipment manufacture follows the government's case against AT&T, according to which the combination of vertical integration and rate-of-return regulation had resulted in foreclosure of competing manufacturers, excessive equipment prices, cross-subsidization, and inadequate equipment quality. Second, the proscription against providing long-distance services was at the heart of the breakup. Allowing the operating companies to offer long-distance services could have subverted the MFJ's equal access requirements and could have given the operating companies incentives to put nonaffiliate IXCs at a disadvantage. Third, the proscription against providing information services was a precautionary measure, since the Bell System had not previously been active in this area. Without specific evidence supporting the need for this restriction, Judge Harold Greene based the denial on analogy with long-distance service.

Since the focus here is on local competition in the markets served by the Bell operating companies, this discussion will deal only peripherally with the line-of-business restrictions on manufacturing. But the restrictions on interexchange and information services have become highly relevant for the development of local competition.

The rationale for the settlement embodied in the MFJ rested on the notion that local service was a normative natural monopoly, whereas long-distance service was potentially competitive. Forcing AT&T to divest itself of the Bell operating companies would free it to operate in competitive markets, while the divested companies would retain the monopoly portion of the former Bell System. The problem of Western Electric as a captive supplier was solved by leaving the equipment manufacturer in the hands of the "competitive" AT&T and prohibiting the "monopoly" operating companies from engaging in competitive activities.

The Telecommunications Act of 1996

During the 1970s Congress had already been actively attempting to revamp the 1934 Communications Act. But powerful interests prevented that from happening until a large majority of both houses passed the Telecommunications Act of 1996.[28] The main purpose of that new legislation is to open markets further while protecting competition against market power of incumbent carriers and safeguarding the achievements of universal service against potential threats from competition. A number of provisions in the new legislation only indirectly concern local competition in telecommunications. They cover cable television rates, ownership of broadcast stations, and distribution of indecent material over the Internet. On the other hand, several items in the act are of great importance to local competition.

•   The regional Bell operating companies, formerly barred by the MFJ from offering interLATA toll services, are now allowed to enter those long-distance markets outside their regions immediately and will be allowed to enter long-distance markets within their regions when they can show that competition for switched services

---

28. *Telecommunications Act, supra* note 1.

is sufficiently developed in their service territories. That provision is likely to provide a major boost to local competition.

• State or local statutes that pose barriers to entry into intrastate or interstate telecommunications markets are removed or will be preempted.

• The regional Bells are required to sell local services on a wholesale basis to their competitors. That provision supersedes state legislation and regulation to the contrary.

• Telecommunications carriers now have a general duty to interconnect with the facilities and equipment of other carriers. That provision should open up local bottlenecks. It is further refined by requirements to provide access on an unbundled basis; to provide access to rights-of-way; for number portability; for incumbents to negotiate interconnection agreements in good faith; and for cost-based and nondiscriminatory interconnection charges and reciprocal compensation.

• The act establishes procedures to review universal service requirements. Those procedures leave much further work to a newly established Federal-State Joint Board and to the FCC. At the same time, the law puts some limitations on possible support mechanisms and requires quick action.

• Under a regulatory reform rule, the FCC shall forbear from applying parts of the Communications Act of 1934 that it deems unnecessary. That forbearance also preempts contrary state regulation. The FCC shall also review its rules at two-year intervals and abolish unnecessary regulations. That rule thus attempts to deregulate as competition progresses.

THE MAJOR REGULATORY INSTITUTIONS IN U.S. TELECOMMUNICATIONS

By breaking up AT&T, the MFJ created some fairly clear divisions of labor between federal and state regulation. Since then the Bell operating companies have been regulated by state public utilities commissions with respect to their local and intrastate long-distance services and intrastate access charges. They are regulated by the FCC for access they provide to the local network for the IXCs and for interstate service providers.[29] In addition, the FCC regulates spectrum allocation for (local) cellular carriers and regulates the interstate business of the IXCs, while the states potentially regulate intrastate services provided by the IXCs, in particular by AT&T. This section reviews the major institutions involved in the regulation of telecommunications in the United States.

The Federal Communications Commission

The FCC was created as a quasi-independent institution. It consists of five commissioners and a permanent staff. The commissioners are appointed for fixed five-year terms, which are usually staggered so that not all commissioners come up for reappointment at the same time. Commissioners are nominated by the president of the United States, subject to confirmation by the Senate; once confirmed they cannot usually be removed from office. The president appoints the FCC's chair from among the commissioners. A change in the presidency does not necessarily lead to a change in the composition of the commission, although it is customary in such an instance for the sitting chair to step down and resign from the commission. The chair may fill the main staff positions at will and sets the agenda for the commission, "which makes decisions on the basis of simple majority rule."[30]

The FCC has jurisdiction over radio and television broadcasting, telephony, telegraphy, cable television operation, two-way radio, radio operators, and satellite communication. As of this writing, before the predicted convergence of telecommunications and broadcasting, telecommunications is represented predominantly by two of five main sector-specific bureaus (the Common Carrier Bureau and the Wireless Telecommunications Bureau). Besides the sector-specific bureaus, the FCC has a Field Operations Bureau in charge of six regional offices. A managing director oversees the commission's internal administration. The main think tanks within

29. The Bell operating companies also provide some wholesale interexchange services for the IXCs.

30. ROGER G. NOLL & FRANCES M. ROSENBLUTH, TELECOMMUNICATIONS POLICY IN JAPAN AND THE U.S.: STRUCTURE, PROCESS, OUTCOMES (1993) (Department of Economics Publication No. 349, Stanford University).

the FCC are the Office of Engineering and Technology and the Office of Plans and Policy. The FCC staff makes first-level decisions, collects evidence for commission decisions, and prepares policy proposals for the commission.

Antitrust Division of the Department of Justice

The U.S. antitrust laws have wide applicability in all sectors of the economy. In spite of regulation they are, with few exceptions, generally applicable in the telecommunications sector. That can create some competing and sometimes conflicting responsibilities.

Prosecution of violations of the U.S. antitrust laws in the telecommunications area is primarily the responsibility of the Department of Justice. That responsibility extends to all operations that are deemed "interstate commerce." According to Noll and Rosenbluth,[31] in telecommunications that phrase is interpreted more broadly than it is in the context of federal regulation. In particular, because of network integration or interconnection across state lines, the Justice Department's jurisdiction extends to local services.

Although the primary concerns of the antitrust laws are with competition and (in a more recent interpretation) efficiency, the MFJ and its administration by Judge Greene have also demonstrated a concern for equity that is highly reminiscent of regulatory practice. An example is Judge Greene's active opposition to the subscriber line charge that the FCC wanted to institute in lieu of a contribution element in access charges.

There are two notable exceptions to the Justice Department's responsibility for antitrust issues in telecommunications:

• Responsibility for control of mergers between telephone companies still rests largely with the FCC rather than with the antitrust authorities. But mergers involving telephone companies and other firms may be taken up by either the Justice Department or the Federal Trade Commission.

31. *Id.*

• As Noll notes, "[T]he 'state action' doctrine in antitrust accords states the power to exempt from federal antitrust laws firms which are regulated by the states. In telecommunications this means that federal deregulation of a product or service may lead to reregulation by a state, including prohibitions against competitive entry."[32] The FCC can, however, preempt states from regulating (see below). Also, immunity from state antitrust action requires that the state expressly substitute regulation for competition and that the state create a relatively detailed supervision and review of the regulated market so as not to create unconstrained monopolies.[33]

Other Federal Agencies

Given the involvement of the FCC and the antitrust division of the Justice Department in telecommunications matters, the other activities of the federal government in telecommunications regulation are somewhat restricted. The president can influence the FCC through the selection of its chair and other commissioners and through presidential budget proposals (which have to be approved and can be changed by Congress).

In addition, the federal government undertakes legislative initiatives and makes budgetary proposals in the telecommunications sector. For that purpose it established the National Telecommunications and Information Administration (NTIA), an agency of the Department of Commerce that deals with telecommunications issues. The NTIA's tasks include advising the president on matters of telecommunications, developing telecommunications policies, assigning spectrum frequencies for government use, and developing international telecommunications policies in coordination with the State Department.[34] The NTIA is not directly concerned with telecommunications regulation and

32. Roger G. Noll, *Telecommunications Regulation in the 1990s*, *in* NEW DIRECTIONS IN TELECOMMUNICATIONS POLICY 11, 17 (Paula Newberg ed., Duke University Press 1989).

33. *Id.* at 17 n.2.

34. *See* Henry Geller, *Broadcasting*, *in* NEW DIRECTIONS IN TELECOMMUNICATIONS POLICY 125, 321 (Paula Newberg ed., Duke University Press 1989).

instead has recently focused on telecommunications infrastructure and on the U.S. government's legislative initiatives in that area.

State Public Utilities Commissions

All fifty states and the District of Columbia have public utilities commissions, which among other things regulate telecommunications markets. The commissions vary substantially in size, policies, and administrative and political structure. As a rule, state regulation is considerably less formal than federal regulation. State regulators also come under much less scrutiny from the courts.

A typical state public utilities commission has an internal organization quite similar to that of the FCC. The commission itself consists of three to seven commissioners, usually appointed by the governor. In fifteen states, however, the commissioners are elected directly.

State commissioners are usually independent in the sense that they have fixed terms and can be removed from office only for specific cause, such as neglect of duty, and then only by consent of the legislature. In some states, however, the formal requirements for dismissal are less severe. The legal instructions given to commissions are often vague (for example, they shall promote "just and reasonable prices" and "useful investments") but sometimes very constraining (for example, some states have prohibited entry into local exchange markets). Most commissions make decisions on a majority basis. In most states the staff of the commission plays the role of an advocate for the state in commission proceedings.

The Courts

As a general rule, regulatory decisions and rulemaking are subject to the discipline imposed by courts. In telecommunications, the U.S. Court of Appeals for the District of Columbia Circuit has jurisdiction over all final orders of the FCC and all orders of Judge Greene concerning the MFJ. As will be seen in the following chapters, the D.C. Circuit Court frequently reverses the FCC and Judge Greene. Courts are important in adjudicating conflicts not only between private parties and regulators but also between regulators of different jurisdictions. For example, state regulators have standing in federal court to bring complaints against the FCC. It has become almost standard procedure for state regulators and their joint representative, the National Association of Regulatory Utility Commissioners (NARUC), to defend themselves by filing court cases against FCC-initiated expansion of federal regulatory authority.

What has been the influence of the courts on regulatory outcomes? Court decisions must be based on the law, so that it might seem the courts would have no independent influence. Since laws are ambiguous and cases do not neatly fit their provisions, however, the courts probably do have an independent influence. Spiller and Gely,[35] for example, find that the Supreme Court's decisions reflect the ideological composition (as proxied by party affiliation) of its members and that it responds indirectly (by following the political preferences of Congress) to interest group pressures. Given the possibility of a court ruling, the influence can work directly, through actual court decisions, or indirectly, through regulators anticipating the court's reactions.

Congress and State Legislatures

Federal and state regulators can only act within the law (and then only if their rulings can be enforced in court), but Congress and state legislatures can enact new laws. A profound general implication is that those two types of legislators can counteract particular regulatory actions that are not to their liking and can discipline regulators through their control over regulatory budgets. Anticipating that possibility, regulators will therefore not deviate far from the perceived will of the legislature. A second major implication is that the regulatory setup itself can be changed through legislation. In the extreme, it appears that Congress could, if it wished, totally wipe out state regulation in telecommunications. For example, in the Omnibus Budget Reconciliation Act of 1993

---

35. Pablo T. Spiller & R. Gely, *Congressional Control of Judicial Interpretation: The Determinants of U.S. Supreme Court Labor Decisions, 1949* 23 RAND J. Econ. 463 (1992).

Congress essentially abolished state regulation of cellular telephone rates.

Whereas, in the past, the Communications Act of 1934 has given the FCC wide latitude in its decisions (it shall set "just and reasonable" rates), states sometimes constrain their regulators in various ways. For example, the state of Illinois requires the state legislature's approval of regulatory rulings. Consequently, in 1992 and 1993 Illinois was unable to preserve its innovative interconnection regime against federal preemption, simply because the Illinois legislature could not approve the ruling of the Illinois Commerce Commission within the time required.[36] Some states (Nebraska, New Jersey) have specific telecommunications laws. Until passage of the Telecommunications Act of 1996, state legislatures usually held the key when it came to allowing local telephone competition. State legislatures, however, cannot overtly constrain interstate telecommunications, in particular not in such a manner as to thwart federal regulators or Congress.

DUAL FEDERAL-STATE REGULATION

As a general principle, until now the division of labor between state and federal regulation has been between intrastate and interstate commerce, with state regulation responsible for the former and federal regulation for the latter (and for international commerce). Consequently, any individual firm will, in principle, be regulated by state regulators for its intrastate transactions and by federal regulators for its interstate transactions. But regulators at either level may choose not to regulate at all. For example, AT&T was deregulated in some states while it was still regulated by the FCC; conversely, cellular phone services were deregulated by the FCC while they were still regulated in some states.

Since telecommunications transactions and the use of capital equipment and other common cost elements can rarely be classified as purely interstate or intrastate, the division of labor between state and federal regulation is complex and contentious. It is, however,

---

36. NATIONAL ASSOCIATION OF REGULATORY UTILITY COMMISSIONERS, 1993 REPORT OF THE ADMINISTRATIVE DIRECTOR ON LITIGATION 49 (1993).

guided by certain principles, the main one being that of federal preemption. The FCC can declare that federal regulation supersedes state regulation if interstate telecommunications are materially affected. Federal preemption gained prominence during the 1970s and 1980s, as the interests of state and federal regulators diverged. Until then both the FCC and local regulators had favored cross-subsidization of the local network by long-distance rates. During the 1970s, however, the FCC backed competitive entry, which tended to undermine such cross-subsidies. But pushing back state regulation had its limits.

Federal Preemption

The principle of federal preemption in regulation was first formulated by the Supreme Court in the 1914 *Shreveport* decision dealing with railroad regulation by the ICC.[37] In that case the ICC was allowed to adapt intrastate railroad rates to the interstate rates it had already established, and so avoid discrimination against interstate traffic. That decision so greatly extended the ICC's regulatory powers that since then state regulation of railroads has all but vanished.

Although the ICC, after the *Shreveport* decision, could have completely absorbed any regulatory area it wished even if only a small portion of transactions were interstate, that principle was contained to some extent by the 1930 decision in *Smith* v. *Illinois Bell Telephone Co.*[38] That decision concerned the cost allocation procedures of the Illinois Commerce Commission. The Illinois commission had assigned all the costs of the inner-city telephone network of Chicago to intrastate traffic, largely because less than 1 percent of network traffic consisted of interstate long-distance calls. But the Supreme Court decided that in such a case a cost allocation between intrastate and interstate traffic nevertheless had to be made even if such allocation were only imperfectly feasible.[39]

37. *Shreveport*, *supra* note 22.
38. Smith v. Illinois Bell Tel. Co., 282 U.S. 133 (1930).
39. For examples that show the types of misallocation that can be created by such imperfect allocation of costs, *see* Ronald R. Braeutigam, *Analysis of*

Although the court in that case confirmed federal responsibility even where only a small amount of interstate traffic is at stake, it also postulated a division of labor between the two tiers of regulation if a cost allocation, however imperfect, is possible. The court thereby also decided in favor of the "station-to-station" method of assigning costs of long-distance calls. According to that method, the costs of a call have to be measured across the whole circuit from end to end, and therefore the usage of local plant has to be included. The competing "board-to-board" method counts only the (incremental) costs incurred between the long-distance carriers' points-of-presence (or the corresponding end offices) at both ends. Since at that time local calls were free, that decision would have meant that no local-loop costs would have been incurred by either the receiving subscriber or the long-distance caller. But subscribers at both ends would have paid for the local-loop costs of long-distance calls in their monthly charge.

As long as AT&T retained an unassailed monopoly position, the interests of the FCC and of state regulators virtually coincided, as exemplified by the fact that the FCC willingly let interstate services subsidize local services. But that situation changed between 1960 and about 1975, with the entry of new competitors. Until then the FCC had strictly opposed market entry that could have undermined the existing equilibrium. After initially being forced by court decisions into allowing entry, however, the FCC changed its position and favored further market entry. The ensuing conflict with state regulatory positions made the FCC more active in preempting state regulation.

Almost without exception, the FCC prevailed before the courts in its attempts to implement interstate interests through federal preemption. In the course of those judicial proceedings three criteria emerged for the applicability of federal preemption. First, a corresponding objective for federal regulation had to be derivable from the Communications Act of 1934. Second, state regulation had

---

Fully Distributed Cost Pricing in Regulated Industries, 11 BELL J. ECON. 182 (1980), and William J. Baumol, Michael F. Koehn & Robert D. Willig, *How Arbitrary Is "Arbitrary," or, Toward the Deserved Demise of Full Cost Allocation,* PUB. UTIL. FORT., Sept. 3, 1987, at 16.

to conflict with the achievement of that objective. Third, preemption had to be construed so narrowly that no further separation of federal from state regulation is feasible.

A major setback in the FCC's implementation of federal preemption occurred in 1986, when the Supreme Court, in *Louisiana Public Service Commission* v. *FCC,* ruled against the FCC's imposition of new depreciation rules on state regulators.[40] The Supreme Court recognized that some impediment or frustration of federal regulation caused by state regulation is a natural consequence of Congress's intention to have dual regulation in an area that is so closely interlinked.[41] Thus, wherever separation is possible and state regulation does not totally negate federal regulation, both have their place. Wherever separation is not possible, federal preemption prevails. In addition, the Telecommunications Act of 1996 gives the FCC authority to preempt states and void regulation that is in conflict with the act.

Federal-State Joint Boards

The principle of federal preemption also forms the basis for the Federal-State Joint Boards, on which state and federal regulators meet to discuss and mediate jurisdictional problems arising from their dual regulation. In keeping with the principle of federal preemption, the joint boards only advise the FCC in its decisionmaking. They achieve "joint participation without abandoning Federal superintendence in the field."[42] The FCC sets the agenda (except that certain joint boards on separations issues and on universal service, discussed below, may be required by law), but the states have the majority of votes. The boards recommend courses of action to the FCC, which the commission may accept or (as it rarely does) reject.

---

40. Louisiana Public Service Comm'n *v.* Federal Communications Comm'n, 476 U.S. 355 (1986).

41. MICHAEL K. KELLOGG, JOHN THORNE & PETER W. HUBER, FEDERAL TELECOMMUNICATIONS LAW 99, 103 (Little, Brown & Co. 1992).

42. *Id.* at 91 n.26.

The administrative setup of the joint boards is similar to that of the regulatory commissions. They consist of staff, recruited from the FCC, the NARUC, and state public utilities commissions, and of voting board members, who are commissioners of the FCC and of the state commissions.

In addition to the joint boards, state and federal regulators participate from time to time in joint conferences. Unlike the joint boards, whose purpose is to recommend decisions to the FCC, joint conferences do not make formal recommendations. The only joint conference in operation as of this writing is investigating the implementation of open network architecture (see chapter 6) and the accompanying separations process.

The functions of the joint boards include those of providing state expertise as a basis for federal decisions—the FCC has regional field offices but no local presence—and including state interests at a level other than as intervenors. Joint boards allow states to bring up problems informally with the federal regulators.

At present, there are two joint boards that exist by virtue of legislative mandate rather than at the sole discretion of the FCC. Created by a 1971 amendment to the Communications Act, the new section 410(c) of that act calls for a joint board to deal with all issues of separation of a regulated company's total costs into interstate and intrastate components. Any rulemaking proceeding that addresses jurisdictional separation of common-carrier property and expenses now has to be referred to that board, called the 80–286 Joint Board, which like the other joint boards only has the power to make suggestions to the FCC. The board derives its name from CC Docket 80–286 (Joint Board to Study Separations Manual Changes Required by Access Charge Proposal and Terminal Equipment Deregulation). The Telecommunications Act of 1996 now provides for a new board created by the FCC in March 1996 to define rules and methods to help implement universal service obligations.

Separations

A major task in the aftermath of the *Shreveport* decision was the allocation of costs between interstate and intrastate services. In particular, assets had to be divided between interstate and intrastate uses. That task is referred to in the Communications Act and is fulfilled through so-called separations.

In 1947 the FCC and the NARUC jointly developed a separations manual, which formed the basis for the federal-state cost allocation process for the next several decades. The separations process is quite complicated.[43] It is based on a uniform system of accounts prescribed for all companies under the FCC's jurisdiction. Revisions of that system were the subject of deliberations during the 1980s by a joint board established for that purpose, which was dissolved after the task was completed. With the exception of New York and Michigan (which have their own accounting standards), all state commissions prescribe FCC accounting rules. Costs and revenues are divided between regulated and unregulated services.

The separations procedures make a major distinction between traffic-sensitive and non-traffic-sensitive costs. Non-traffic-sensitive subscriber plant equipment was at first allocated between federal and state jurisdictions according to relative use (measured in minutes; an economically more correct allocation would have been by contribution to peak capacity utilization). Over time, however, the allocation was shifted more and more in favor of the local jurisdiction by increasing the interstate allocation of local plant far beyond what would have corresponded to its use. The Ozark Plan, adopted in 1970, assigned 3.3 percent of non-traffic-sensitive costs to the interstate services for every percent of actual interstate use. Thus, as the actual interstate share in minutes grew by 1983 to about 8 percent, the Ozark Plan formula caused the assigned interstate share to grow to 26 percent, at which point a decision was made to scale it back to 25 percent and freeze it there. It is questionable whether state regulators could have forced the FCC to accept a deliberately non-cost-based allocation as happened in the Ozark Plan. That it did accept such an allocation indicates that the FCC must have agreed with the underlying policy goals of the state regulators as late as 1970.

43. We give only the essentials here. A more extensive treatment is provided in, for example, JOHN D. BORROWS, PHYLLIS A. BERNT & RAYMOND W. LAWTON, UNIVERSAL SERVICE IN THE UNITED STATES: DIMENSIONS OF THE DEBATE (Mar. 94) (WIK Diskussionsbeitrag No. 124), at 34–39.

Two related sets of cost separations are those between regulated and unregulated activities and between a regulated carrier and its affiliates. The rules that govern such items are contained in the FCC's 1987 Joint Cost Order, which applies to all LECs and to dominant IXCs. Those rules were applied before jurisdictional separations, which refer only to the regulated part of a telecommunications carrier's business. Although the Joint Cost Order is not binding on the states, in practice states have little choice but to use the FCC rules at least as the starting point for their own rate-setting process.[44]

Cost separation seems to have had two major implications. One is the fixation on fully distributed costs. Although fully distributed cost allocations need not follow from cost separation, both share the same spirit (that costs can be allocated to jurisdictions), and once established, fully distributed costing is hard to reverse. The other implication of cost separation has been to shift costs away from state jurisdiction, in particular through the Ozark Plan, which resulted in the claimed cross-subsidization of local telephone rates by interstate long-distance rates. As Kellogg, Thorne, and Huber rightly observe,[45] however, that cross-subsidization was not a necessary outcome of cost separations. Had the FCC followed the same type of rate setting as the states, it would simply have covered most plant costs in fixed monthly charges. Since few subscribers, if given the option, would have declined long-distance services altogether and kept local services only, the fixed charge would have acted like a head tax, and the cross-subsidy would have become largely immaterial. The FCC's authority to set fixed rather than usage-based charges (the subscriber line charge) was specifically confirmed in the D.C. District Court's 1984 decision *NARUC* v. *FCC*.[46] On the other hand, such fixed charges might have been a political hard sell for the FCC at any time. That is borne out by the FCC's initial inability to introduce a monthly subscriber line charge that would fully replace the contribution contained in access charges to be paid by the IXCs after the AT&T breakup.

---

44. KELLOGG, THORNE & HUBER, *supra* note 41, at 438.
45. *Id.* at 449–52.
46. *Id.* at 98.

CONCLUSIONS

The traditional rationales for regulating telecommunications services have been the natural monopoly property, which would justify monopoly provision for the entire set of telecommunications markets, and the network externality, which serves to justify universal service policies. The claim that the entire telecommunications sector possesses natural monopoly properties is being convincingly challenged by successful competitive entry in parts of the telecommunications market and by empirical research on the properties of telecommunications cost functions. But that result does not preclude other parts of the telecommunications sector from being natural monopolies when viewed in isolation. Regulation may therefore be justified in certain specific areas that are deemed bottlenecks, that is, natural monopolies for specific inputs to which competitors require access. The importance of these bottlenecks is enhanced by the global network externality conveyed to all customers of such competitors. As a result, interconnection becomes the major regulatory issue for local telecommunications markets, at least as long as they are dominated by the LECs. As entry regulation subsides in the near future, regulation of the prices set by LECs and of public service obligations will persist.

As of this writing, shortly after the passage of new federal legislation, the state of local telecommunications markets has to a large extent been determined by antitrust and regulatory policies. The MFJ, an act of antitrust policy, has profoundly affected the regulatory equilibrium in U.S. telecommunications. First, the breakup of the Bell System created the current AT&T, which for its interstate business has been regulated by the FCC and for its intrastate (interLATA and intraLATA) long-distance business by state regulators. Second, the breakup created seven regional Bell operating companies, which are regulated by state regulators for local and intraLATA long-distance telephone services and by state regulators and the FCC for access and open network architecture services. Since each of the regional Bells spans several states, regional cooperation between state regulators has become a more prominent regulatory issue, which we discuss in chapter 5. Third, the MFJ placed line-of-business restrictions on the activities of the regional Bells, thereby making the MFJ court an additional regulator. In particular, the regional Bell companies have been restricted from entering interLATA long-distance services and from manufacturing telecommunications equipment, and until 1991 they were restricted from providing information services (except through a separate subsidiary). As local telephone service competition makes headway, the Telecommunications Act of 1996 will phase out the remaining restrictions.

The current spheres of influence, overlap, and contention appear to be as follows. State regulators, with passage of the Telecommunications Act of 1996, have lost some of their previous control over local and intraLATA rates charged by the LECs to other carriers. They control price and service conditions for local and intraLATA end-user services. State regulators could also, until recently, regulate services and intrastate rates charged by cellular carriers. Furthermore, state regulators have jurisdiction over intrastate interLATA services provided by the IXCs and to some extent can regulate intrastate access and open network architecture charges set by the LECs. The FCC has regulatory jurisdiction over interstate telecommunications services and some crucial jurisdiction over cellular and cable television services.[47] Most regulated telecommunications service providers are regulated by both jurisdictions, and many of them by more than one state regulator. The MFJ court quickly lost its power over the remaining line-of-business restrictions imposed on the regional Bell companies as well as its power to control mergers that involve either two regional Bells or AT&T and a regional Bell (even if only through joint ventures or small equity positions).

The relationships between federal and state regulation and between antitrust and regulation are not always harmonious. In cases of conflict, antitrust most often dominates federal regulation, and federal regulation (through federal preemption) most often dominates state regulation. Because that is not always the case, however, there is room for protracted interagency disputes and for inefficiencies created in attempts to separate spheres of influence. Although local competition primarily appears to be intrastate in

47. Although cable television is a local service, it usually imports programs from out of state (by satellite or over the airwaves).

nature, it clearly has strong interstate implications. The FCC's procompetitive views can therefore potentially be imposed on the state public utilities commissions either through legal or de facto preemption, as has happened for interconnection, or through other rearrangements of regulatory authority that would induce state public utilities commissions to open their markets or to cooperate regionally.

5

Retail Regulation of Local Exchange Carriers

ALTHOUGH ALMOST ALL the activities of the Bell operating companies concern the last ten miles to the subscriber, the regulation of those companies is the prototypical case of division of labor between two regulatory levels. The Federal Communications Commission is responsible for the conditions under which interexchange carriers and interstate (and mixed intrastate and interstate) enhanced services providers gain access to the local network, and for the rates they pay for that access. Meanwhile, state public utilities commissions, in principle, regulate local and intrastate services at both the wholesale level (provision of access to other service providers and large end users) and the retail level (sales of services to individual customers). We defer to chapter 6 an examination of access charge regulation and in this chapter concentrate instead on the retail level.

As described more fully in chapter 8, the Telecommunications Act of 1996[1] may have changed the division of labor between the FCC and the state public utility commissions from one between interstate and intrastate traffic to one between different levels of details for dealing with the same regulatory issues.

1. Telecommunications Act of 1996, Pub. L. 104-104, 110 Stat. 56 (Feb. 8, 1996).

PUBLIC SERVICE OBLIGATIONS AND STATE-REGULATED
PRICE STRUCTURES

Two types of regulation, public service obligations and state-regulated price structures, appear to have been the main regulatory impediments to opening LEC markets to competitors.

Public Service Obligations

States impose public service obligations on local exchange carriers as a condition of their franchises. The LECs are obliged to provide service of adequate quality, without undue discrimination and at reasonable prices, to all persons in the service area who request it. The standards for what is "undue" and what is "reasonable" are not fixed by law but evolve in court cases and may change over time.

The LECs are burdened by obligations that have not been imposed thus far on competing suppliers. The LECs must average their rates over geographic areas with unequal costs. They are required to file tariffs for nearly all services and to stand ready to provide service to any customer meeting the requirements of the tariff. Where ordered to do so, they must interconnect with all competitors.

The most important public service obligations relate to universal service. In its opening section the Communications Act of 1934[2] clearly states as the objective of communications policy to "make available, so far as possible, to all the people of the United States a rapid, efficient, Nation-wide, and world-wide wire and radio communication service with adequate facilities at reasonable charges." That statement was widely interpreted as establishing a goal of universal service. But the statement is not explicit enough to define universal service under competitive conditions. The Telecommunications Act of 1996 therefore includes a series of provisions that help define universal service and find explicit ways to finance and implement universal service obligations.

---

2. Communications Act of 1934, 76 Stat. 419, 15 U.S.C. 21, 47 U.S.C. 35, 151–609.

Universal service obligations are of two generic types. The first oblige carriers to provide service to low-income or otherwise deserving subscribers. Those are groups served by all LECs, and they are distributed over their entire service territories. The second require LECs to provide service to geographically remote and other high-cost subscribers. A disproportionate number of such subscribers are located in areas of low population density, and therefore that obligation affects some LECs much more than others. Thus, whereas universal service obligations of the first type could be provided and financed by each LEC in isolation, those of the second type may require financing across regions or even on a nationwide basis.

Regulation of Price Structures

Some public service obligations, such as the filing of tariffs, raise the costs incurred by the LECs compared with those of competitors exempt from such obligations. Other obligations lower some of the LECs' prices below compensatory levels. The traditional way of financing such obligations has been through cross-subsidies from one LEC service to another.

Cross-subsidies have evolved over time. Ever since the costs of the local network first began to increase markedly relative to the costs of providing long-distance service, "[s]tate regulators have generally chosen to increase rates for special business services, intrastate toll and enhanced services before increasing rates for basic residential local exchange services."[3] That practice of determining residential local rates after setting the other rates at what the market will bear has been called "residual pricing."[4]

As a result, traditional Bell System rate structures implied substantial revenue transfers from long-distance and local business charges to local residential rates, and from urban to rural

3. *See* NATIONAL ASSOCIATION OF REGULATORY UTILITY COMMISSIONERS, BULLETIN 15 (1986).

4. *See* Roger G. Noll, *State Regulatory Responses to Competition and Divestiture in the Telecommunications Industry,* in ANTITRUST AND REGULATION (Ronald E. Grayson ed., Lexington Books 1986).

customers. Before the Modification of Final Judgment,[5] almost all of those cross-subsidies were internal to the Bell System. The MFJ changed the character of most of those cross-subsidies from an intrafirm transfer to a transfer between firms. But the separations process (discussed in chapter 4) remained a key to the size of those transfers.

After the MFJ, state regulators encountered many new issues regarding rate structures and competitive entry.[6] The lack of clear rules has added to the difficulty. State regulatory options after the MFJ ranged from price restructuring, allowing competition and avoiding inefficient bypass, to maintaining existing cross-subsidies and blocking entry. In actuality, states continued to raise revenues from sources other than local residential rates. But there was a perceived need to increase local rates to keep the regional Bell operating companies healthy after divestiture. The high water mark of those local rate increases was 1984.[7] The impetus for the increases came from a combination of perceived and real effects of divestiture. The real effects included the line-of-business restrictions on the regional Bells. The perceived effects included the view that these companies had inherited the low-price and slow-growth part of the telecommunications market. The effects of local rate increases and of the subscriber line charge (discussed in chapter 6) on telephone penetration and on the welfare of the poorer parts of the population were compensated by the introduction of federal- and state-sponsored "lifeline" programs. Also, rate increases for rural areas were contained through the creation of a federal universal service fund that subsidizes high-cost rural areas.[8]

5. United States v. American Tel. & Tel. Co., 552 F. Supp. 131 (D.D.C. 1982) (test of the decree), aff'd sub nom. Maryland v. United States, 460 U.S. 1001 (1983); United States v. Western Electric Co., 569 F. Supp. 1057 (D.D.C. 1983) (approving the plan of reorganization).

6. See PAUL E. TESKE, AFTER DIVESTITURE—THE POLITICAL ECONOMY OF STATE TELECOMMUNICATIONS REGULATION 14 (State University of New York Press 1990).

7. Id. at 38–40.

8. For extensive discussions of all those programs and the accompanying federal-state interaction, see JOHN D. BORROWS, PHYLLIS A. BERNT & RAYMOND W. LAWTON, UNIVERSAL SERVICE IN THE UNITED STATES:

Rate restructuring has always been perceived as politically difficult, but some types of restructuring are likely to be easier than others. A particularly easy type of rate restructuring has been through optional pricing. The LECs have introduced a variety of local measured-service options, with various expansions of local calling areas. That has gradually moved the standard type of local pricing away from the traditional flat monthly charge with unlimited calling. In contrast, "elimination of the urban/rural price differential to reflect costs would affect consumer groups more than *any* other policy change, which is why only one state (Illinois) has tackled it directly by 1989."[9] According to Teske,[10] elimination of the urban-rural price differential could lead to an average net increase of $9 in the monthly rate for residential consumers, as opposed to only a $1 to $2 increase from rebalancing of local and long-distance rates. Teske considers those numbers on potential redistribution too small to provoke a grassroots consumer response. But the publicity of AT&T's breakup made people nervous and focused consumer attention to some degree. As a consequence, increases from price rebalancing of even that magnitude were viewed as politically infeasible at the same time that other price increases were being implemented.

Rate restructuring is therefore taking its time. As Palmer found, business service revenues clearly still subsidized the residential services of New England Telephone customers in 1986 and 1987.[11] The subsidy from long-distance to local telephone services apparently has been reduced in nearly all states.[12] Full rebalancing

DIMENSIONS OF THE DEBATE (Mar. 94) (WIK Diskussionsbeitrag No. 124), and for lifeline rate programs, *see* BRIDGER M. MITCHELL & INGO VOGELSANG, TELECOMMUNICATIONS PRICING: THEORY AND PRACTICE, ch. 11 (Cambridge University Press 1991).

9. TESKE, *supra* note 6, at 57.

10. *Id.* at 58–59.

11. Karen Palmer, *A Test for Cross Subsidies in Local Telephone Rates: Do Business Customers Subsidize Residential Customers?* 23 RAND J. ECON. 415–31 (1992).

12. William F. Fox & John W. Mayo, State-Level Telecommunications Policy in the Post-Divestiture Era: An Economic Perspective (March 1991) (unpublished manuscript, Center for Business and Economic Research, College

appears to have been achieved in Illinois, and the California Public Utilities Commission has made a large step in this direction.

New Approaches

Since public service obligations are needed only for certain subscribers (high-cost service areas or the poor) or for certain events (such as emergencies), cross-subsidization that affects all subscribers is a costly way to finance such obligations. That holds in particular if penetration rates are high, so that there are only a very few excluded or marginal consumers. In addition, financing public service obligations through cross-subsidies distorts the LECs' competitive positions. In those areas that are subsidized, the LECs become largely immune to entry even by more efficient rivals, whereas in those areas from which the subsidies come, the LECs face serious challenge even from the entry of less efficient rivals. In particular, large contributions to public service obligations contained in the interconnection charges paid by the IXCs lead to bypass of LEC networks.

Since regulators favor maintaining public service obligations, they must either regulate entry or change the way those obligations are financed. Some alternative financing vehicles to broad cross-subsidies are now available, and some new policy tools are under discussion. At the same time, attempts are being made to reduce the costs of public service obligations by targeting them more narrowly than in the past.

The new policies already in place include so-called lifeline rate programs for deserving parts of the population and a universal service fund for high-cost areas. Both those approaches are more directly linked to the burdens imposed by public service obligations than are cross-subsidies. The problems are how to define the obligations, how to minimize the costs of fulfilling them, and how to finance them without imposing high transaction costs and without distorting competition (for example, by inviting inefficient bypass).

New policy proposals for public service obligations include auctions for low-cost provision of service to remote areas (as is

of Business Administration, University of Tennessee at Knoxville).

already being done in Australia) or to low-income (and therefore probably low-use) customers. The proposals also include financing of obligations through levies on all telecommunications services offered by all carriers. The main common feature of all those proposals is an attempt to make the fulfillment of public service obligations compatible with competition. In the United States, at least two states have made practical moves in that direction. Vermont has a state tax to finance lifeline and emergency services.[13] The tax is used to fund the provision of such services by any local telecommunications carrier. Similarly, Connecticut has made it possible for consumers to use their lifeline contribution toward the services of any competing local telecommunications carrier, and the establishment of a universal service fund has been legally authorized.[14]

The Telecommunications Act of 1996 makes universal service a specific issue by requiring the creation of a new Federal-State Joint Board to make recommendations to the FCC and by requiring the FCC to act upon those recommendations within fifteen months after signing of the act. The rules resulting from that proceeding shall include the definition of services to be supported by federal universal service support mechanisms and a timetable for implementation. Predictable federal and state support mechanisms are required. In particular, all major interstate telecommunications carriers will be required to contribute to the advancement of universal service, either through facilities or through financial contributions. The universal service provisions of the act specifically prohibit cross-subsidies from a carrier's monopoly to its competitive services.

13. *See* 1994 Vermont Senate Bill 311 (act relating to an enhanced 911 emergency response system) (June 20, 1994).
14. *See* State of Connecticut Public Act No. 94-83 (act implementing recommendations of the telecommunications task force) (May 26, 1994).

ALTERNATIVE REGULATION

Incentive Regulation

The traditional method of public utility regulation in the United States is known as rate-of-return regulation, under which regulated firms may earn no more than a prespecified rate of return on their assets (the rate base). In the 1960s and 1970s the economics literature criticized rate-of-return regulation as an inefficient way of regulating monopoly because it provides insufficient incentives for cost reduction, leads to excessive use of capital equipment relative to other inputs, and distorts the regulated firm's pricing decisions in favor of those outputs whose production is capital intensive.[15] Because rate-of-return regulation puts its main emphasis on the firm's rate of return rather than on its output prices, it is usually combined with fully allocated cost methods of pricing individual services. That can lead to additional inefficiencies because fully allocated cost assignments are not causally justified.[16]

Rate-of-return regulation with fully distributed cost pricing is inefficient but at least workable under monopoly. It appears to be

---

15. There is a vast literature on this subject, starting with Harvey Averch & Leland L. Johnson, *Behavior of the Firm Under Regulatory Constraint,* 52 AM. ECON. REV. 1052 (1962). For insightful surveys, *see* SANDFORD V. BERG & JOHN TSCHIRHART, NATURAL MONOPOLY REGULATION (Cambridge University Press 1988), and ROGER SHERMAN, THE REGULATION OF MONOPOLY (Cambridge University Press 1989). For an accessible and insightful survey of the literature on incentive regulation and its application to telecommunications, *see* DAVID E. M. SAPPINGTON & DENNIS L. WEISMAN, DESIGNING INCENTIVE REGULATION FOR THE TELECOMMUNICATIONS INDUSTRY (MIT Press and AEI Press 1996).

16. A systematic analysis of pricing based on fully allocated costs was first provided by Ronald R. Braeutigam, *Analysis of Fully Distributed Cost Pricing in Regulated Industries,* 11 BELL J. ECON. 182 (1980). He finds that such pricing sacrifices efficiency and can lead to inefficient entry. *See also* William J. Baumol, Michael F. Koehn & Robert D. Willig, *How Arbitrary Is "Arbitrary?" or, Toward the Deserved Demise of Full Cost Allocation,* PUB. UTIL. FORT., Sept. 3, 1987, at 16, and Ronald R. Braeutigam & John C. Panzar, *Diversification Incentives Under "Price-Based" and "Cost-Based" Regulation,* 20 RAND J. ECON. 373 (1989).

quite inappropriate under competition, however. If the regulated firm faces unregulated competition, fully allocated cost prices are particularly damaging. The firm may then, for example, have to charge prices in some of its markets above those of competitors, even though it is more efficient. In other markets it may have to charge prices too low to break even overall.

Thus, the increase in competition and the pressure on firms to become more efficient after the AT&T divestiture triggered various alternative regulatory schemes. Today, close to three-quarters of state public utilities commissions have replaced traditional rate-of-return regulation with a variety of regulatory schemes, such as price caps, price moratoria, profit sharing, and partial deregulation.

The new schemes seek to fulfill two basic functions. First, they induce regulated operators to become more efficient by cutting costs, improving services, and modernizing their networks. That makes regulated operators better prepared to face competition. Second, the new schemes reduce or eliminate both the incentives and the ability of regulated firms to cross-subsidize their competitive activities from price increases on their remaining monopoly services. That makes the regulatory environment more readily compatible with competitive entry by unregulated firms.

Many states divide LEC services into three categories: basic, emerging competitive, and fully competitive. Fully competitive services tend to be free from rate regulation. Emerging competitive services are usually subject to streamlined regulation, with substantial pricing flexibility within a band. Basic services are usually tightly regulated, very often under a rate moratorium or under price caps with very narrow banding. More-limited incentives are often provided through profit sharing with consumers instead of price caps. The flexibility to fine-tune regulation according to the competitiveness of service categories has been facilitated by the new approaches, which are much less ostensibly cost-based than rate-of-return regulation and therefore do not require cost assignment to individual service categories.

In August 1987 the FCC followed the lead of several states and proposed price-cap regulation for dominant telecommunications carriers.[17] The proposal was strongly influenced by the British

17. Policy and Rules Concerning Rates for Dominant Carriers, CC Dkt.

experience with price-cap regulation, described in chapter 9. The FCC price-cap proceeding became highly controversial. It went through several iterations and faced the threat of congressional interference. Only in 1989 did the FCC decide to go ahead with price-cap regulation, and then for AT&T only.[18] Under the 1989 ruling, AT&T's outputs are grouped into baskets. Prices of service categories within each basket were permitted to rise or fall by up to 5 percent annually relative to the cap, which was adjusted for inflation, for a 3 percent productivity growth factor, and for factors outside AT&T's control. The baskets followed the same price-adjustment formula, but rebalancing was allowed only within baskets, not between them. Also, banding requirements (of plus or minus 5 percent) for individual service categories severely restricted rebalancing.[19] Price changes that fell outside the 5 percent band were permitted only on the basis of a special showing by AT&T. In October 1995 the FCC declared AT&T a nondominant carrier of domestic interexchange services and ended the price-cap regulation that had been retained on residential services. In doing so, the commission imposed a series of "safety net" transitional provisions for low-income and low-volume consumers that provide for discounted or frozen rates for three years.[20]

The FCC's price-cap order for the LECs came out in 1990. In the case of the regional Bell companies (and GTE), the FCC regulates interstate access charges, combining price caps of the type used for AT&T with profit sharing. Profit sharing takes effect whenever the achieved rate of return falls outside a prespecified band. When that type of regulation was initiated, the regional Bells

No. 87-313, Notice of Proposed Rulemaking, 2 F.C.C. Rcd. 5208 (1987) (Aug. 7, 1987).

18. Rep. & Order & Second Further Notice of Proposed Rulemaking, Dkt. No. 87-313, FCC 89-91 (Apr. 17, 1989).

19. Service categories themselves consist of sometimes many service elements that can be priced freely, as long as their average price change provides the permissible price change for its category (or subcategory). Price-cap regulation of AT&T's interexchange services is described in MITCHELL & VOGELSANG, *supra* note 8, at 167-73, 276-85.

20. *AT&T Makes Pledges About "Nondominance" Plea*, TELECOMM. REP., Nov. 27, 1995, at 10.

could select between two profit-sharing and price-adjustment combinations, one with a higher productivity adjustment factor and less profit sharing than the other. (Some of the details and further developments are covered in chapter 6.) Small LECs have been permitted to choose between a price-cap and a rate-of-return regulatory regime.

A 1994 analysis by the National Association of Regulatory Utility Commissioners showed the status of alternative regulatory plans in the fifty states in 1993.[21] In that year thirty-seven states had such plans (with some states having more than one plan), although twenty-four of those plans were on a trial basis. Given the experimental nature of that regulation, it may come as a surprise that nineteen plans were considered permanent. Since 1993 additional states have enacted alternative regulation plans, including Illinois, which approved a price-cap plan for Ameritech-Illinois with a number of innovative features.[22] Most states with alternative plans allow for some pricing flexibility and make the stringency of regulation depend on the level of competition experienced for a service. The most common incentive feature is revenue sharing; pure price caps are less widely used.

In 1987 Nebraska became the first state to deregulate all telephone services. The Nebraska Public Service Commission may only review rate increases for basic local exchange service, and then only upon petition of enough affected customers.[23] In return, the LECs have to maintain price caps for five years. Bolter, Connaughey, and Kelsey describe some problems that have emerged under that approach.[24] But there is no indication that rates in Nebraska have increased any faster than in the surrounding states served by Nebraska's main carrier, U S West.

21. NATIONAL ASSOCIATION OF REGULATORY UTILITY COMMISSIONERS, NARUC REPORT ON THE STATUS OF COMPETITION IN INTRASTATE TELECOMMUNICATIONS (Sept. 1994), at 214–15.

22. *Price Regulation Plan for Ameritech-Illinois Approved*, TELECOMM. REP., Oct. 17, 1994, at 16.

23. *See* WALTER G. BOLTER, J. W. CONNAUGHEY & F. J. KELSEY, TELECOMMUNICATIONS FOR THE 1990s AND BEYOND 139 (M. E. Sharpe, Inc. 1991).

24. *Id*. at 139–40.

Regulatory Infrastructure Initiatives

At the state level, it is common for public utilities commissions to invite the LECs to propose the form of incentive regulation they prefer, which is then either accepted or modified in the course of regulatory proceedings. Thus, states leave considerable discretion to the regulated firm.[25] A number of states have provided for regulation-induced infrastructure investment, often combined with rate freezes. A good example is the "Opportunity New Jersey" plan, originally suggested by New Jersey Bell and approved by the New Jersey Board of Regulatory Commissioners in 1992.

The current rate freeze in New Jersey remains in effect until 2000. In addition, New Jersey Bell has committed "to accelerate modernization of the network to provide advanced intelligent network features, narrow band services, wide band services, and broadband services over a period of years. The plan include[s] a freeze on monthly basic residential rates for the term of the plan and specifically addresse[s] distance learning, telemedicine and video dialtone services."[26] Thus, the New Jersey regulators received assurances for general infrastructure investments, for specific investments benefiting state services (schools and hospitals), and for frozen residential rates (although those might have gone down under cost-based regulation as well). Such plans have two main characteristics. First, the regulated LEC receives some regulatory flexibility or relief in exchange for a commitment to undertake substantial infrastructure investment (for example, Michigan Bell has been required to use a percentage of above-base earnings to fund extra construction).[27] Second, in the absence of a plan, the regulated LEC is perceived to have deficient incentives to invest, for example because it is under a rate moratorium. In some states (such as Utah), infrastructure commitments by the LECs have been part of regular rate proceedings, without being linked

---

25. *See* Dennis L. Weisman, *Why Less May Be More Under Price-Cap Regulation*, 6 J. REG. ECON. 339 (1994).

26. NATIONAL ASSOCIATION OF REGULATORY UTILITY COMMISSIONERS, BULLETIN 96 (1993).

27. *Id.* at 71.

specifically to incentive regulation. In others (such as Pennsylvania), infrastructure plans are required by the state legislature, independent of other regulatory action.[28]

Links between mandated infrastructure investment and regulatory relief are a two-edged sword. On the one hand, the investment is likely to provide the basis for improved services, making the state more competitive in attracting and maintaining certain industries and improving consumer welfare. On the other hand, the benefits may be small and the costs high. Problems include the fact that it is hard to measure the incremental investment generated by such plans. In addition, the LECs might have revised their original investments upward even without such plans. Moreover, consumers may have to pay higher rates now in return for some promised future benefit (that is, there is cross-subsidization of future by current services and consumers). Also, any additional LEC investments may simply preempt investments by potential LEC competitors. Finally, the investments may go beyond efficient levels.

Although no empirical studies have yet traced the effects of specific infrastructure investment requirements imposed by regulators, there is some empirical indication that alternative forms of regulation are associated with greater infrastructure investment than under rate-of-return regulation. In particular, Greenstein, McMaster, and Spiller have estimated the relationship between type of regulation and the amount of LEC investment in modern digital infrastructure.[29] They related four types of infrastructure

---

28. *Id.* at 122.

29. Shane Greenstein, Susan McMaster & Pablo T. Spiller, *The Effect of Incentive Regulation on Local Exchange Companies' Deployment of Digital Technology,* 4 J. ECON. & MGMT. STRATEGY 187 (1995). Their results broadly confirm those of an earlier study by William E. Taylor, Charles J. Zarkadas & J. Douglas Zona, Incentive Regulation and the Diffusion of New Technology in Telecommunications (1992) (unpublished research paper, National Economic Research Associates), partially updated in Timothy J. Tardiff & William E. Taylor, Telephone Company Performance Under Alternative Forms of Regulation in the U.S. (1993) (unpublished research paper, National Economic Research Associates, on file with authors). Conflicting evidence is presented by W. P. Montgomery, Promise Versus

investment (in fiber-optic cable, advanced signaling networks, ISDN, and digital stored program controlled switches) to four types of regulation (rate-of-return, price caps, price freezes, and earnings sharing). They found, for the years 1986 to 1991, that each of the alternative schemes induced greater investment in digital infrastructure than had occurred under traditional rate-of-return regulation. Price-cap regulation in particular is associated with increased investment. Earnings-sharing regulation is associated with less investment than price caps, and this effect comes out most strongly if price-cap regulation and earnings sharing are combined.

Those results still have to be seen as preliminary, because the new schemes had just been introduced at the time of the study, and some were viewed as temporary. Thus the regulated firms probably had not yet adjusted fully to the new schemes. It is therefore unlikely that the schemes caused the investment. More likely, the choice of alternative regulation and higher investment are determined jointly by the same exogenous factors.[30] For example, those firms opting for alternative regulation may be the more progressive ones and therefore more inclined to invest in modern technology. Also, the authors did not capture any specific investment commitments made by firms in return for getting alternative regulation, and they only partially controlled for competition faced by the LECs.

REGIONAL REGULATION

Regulation by the states is complicated by the fact that each of the regional Bell operating companies spans several states, so that costs and rates of return are not easily assigned to individual states. A

Reality: Telecommunications Infrastructure, LEC Investment and Regulatory Reforms (Aug. 1994) (unpublished research paper, on file with authors) in a number of case studies. But Montgomery does not control for factors other than the type of regulation that might have affected investment. *See also* SAPPINGTON & WEISMAN, *supra* note 15, at 318–19.

30. For the determinants of specific types of regulation, *see* Stephen G. Donald & David E. M. Sappington, *Explaining the Choice Among Regulatory Plans in the U.S. Telecommunications Industry*, 4 J. ECON. & MGMT. STRATEGY 237 (1995).

uniform approach for the intrastate regulation of the regional Bells could therefore be appropriate. Tendencies among the regional Bells to centralize their telecommunications businesses make regional regulation even more important. For example, all the regional Bells are trying to centralize common-channel signaling. Only three of the seven regional Bells (Ameritech, Bell Atlantic, and to some extent NYNEX) have organizationally separated their telecommunications operations by state. Thus, individual state public utilities commissions are mostly regulating entities for which no fully separate accounts exist.

One way of dealing with the problem of regulating multistate companies is for each state regulatory agency to have authority over its state and over the parent holding company. The obvious defect of that approach is that the parent holding company may be regulated several times over, and possibly in contradictory fashion. But one state may take the lead in regulating the regional parent, while the others simply follow. In New York, for example, the state public service law gives the public service commission "jurisdiction over affiliated interests having transactions . . . with utility corporations . . . to the extent of access to all accounts and records of such affiliated interests relating to such transactions."[31] New York was even able to implement a plan to restructure NYNEX and its affiliates by restricting and governing affiliate transactions and requiring major changes in corporate governance.[32] The plan established New York Telephone as a stand-alone company. The restrictions imposed include the requirement that senior management compensation be based only on the performance and financial results of New York Telephone and not on the results of the parent corporation. The question remains open whether such restructuring is necessarily compatible with the genuine interests of the other states served by NYNEX and its subsidiaries.

An alternative way of dealing with multistate utilities is through regionwide regulation, in which two or more state commissions

31. *Cited in* Gail Garfield Schwartz & Jeffrey H. Hoagg, *Virtual Divestiture: Structural Reform of an RHC*, 44 FED. COMM. L.J. 285, 300 (1992).

32. *Id.* at 285, 319.

carry out their regulatory responsibilities by acting together.[33] Arrangements for such regulation could span a range from irregular, informal meetings of regulators to an "interstate compact" approved by Congress.[34] Since state interests often diverge, regional regulation is not easily undertaken. The National Regulatory Research Institute cites six conditions that tend to favor regional regulation:[35] a threat of federal preemption that can be avoided through cooperation across states; a misfit between jurisdictional and operational boundaries for multistate utilities; a need for more rational comprehensive planning regarding capacity or configuration of a multistate utility (for example, planning of regional databases); inconsistency between regulatory rules and the practices of multistate utility systems; regulatory inefficiency through duplication or loss of scale and scope economies; and a need to strike a more even balance between the technical staff resources and political power of the regulatory authority and those of the regulated utility.

Regional Regulation of the Regional Operating Companies

Regional regulation is often accomplished through voluntary cooperation under the auspices of the National Association of Regulatory Utility Commissioners (NARUC). In 1987 the NARUC Executive Committee created regional oversight committees corresponding to the territories of each of the seven regional Bell companies. Voluntary regional cooperation among regulators usually includes exchange of information on the activities and costs of the regional Bells, consistent cost allocation for those activities that serve the needs of customers in several states, and joint advocacy,

---

33. National Regulatory Research Institute, *Regional Regulation of Public Utilities: Opportunities and Obstacles* (NRRI 92-19) (Dec. 1992), at iii.

34. Under the so-called compact clause of the U.S. Constitution (U.S. CONST. art. I, § 10, cl. 3) states need congressional approval to enter into formal agreements with each other. As far as we know, no interstate compact has ever been created for telecommunications regulation.

35. National Regulatory Research Institute, *supra* note 33, at ix.

whereby states in a given region support a common position before a federal court or regulatory body.

Regional regulation for three of the regional Bell companies (Ameritech, NYNEX, and U S West) is somewhat more formalized, through direct initiatives between regulators; it is virtually nonexistent for the remaining four. The number of states served by a regional Bell company is a weak indicator for the existence of such cooperation among regulators; however, BellSouth, which serves nine states, and Bell Atlantic, which serves six states and the District of Columbia, do not face regional regulation, whereas Ameritech, which serves only five states, does.

In 1989 the fourteen states served by U S West formed a regional oversight committee, which meets twice a year to discuss issues with the company and among the state regulators themselves.[36] The committee relies on the voluntary sharing of information and on states coordinating their approaches on issues of common concern.

The states served by Ameritech acted together as early as 1987 to oversee that company's activities, and even submitted to the FCC a joint open network architecture plan for the handling of rates associated with that issue in their region.[37] The oversight committee, now called the Ameritech Regional Regulatory Committee (ARRC), has some of the trappings of a more formal organization. It has a mission statement, a functional organization scheme, an issues framework, and even a committee logo.[38] The ARRC does not, as a rule, hold open meetings. ARRC positions are not binding on individual commissions. Indeed, commissions participate with less than a quorum of their members, because ARRC positions could otherwise be construed as official agency decisions, which would be a violation of the rule that state regulators must make their decisions independently. Even with those limitations, however, regionwide results can be achieved. For

36. *1991 State Regulators' Forum on Regional Regulation*, PUB. UTIL. FORT., Nov. 1, 1991, at 28.

37. For an extensive discussion of open network architecture, *see* chapter 6.

38. National Regulatory Research Institute, *supra* note 33, at 23.

example, Ameritech was able to get a clean sweep in similar (but not identical) price-regulation agreements across its five-state region.[39]

Regional telecommunications regulation in the six New England states (but not New York, the only other state in the NYNEX service territory) is informally located in the preexisting New England Conference of Public Utility Commissioners, which previously dealt mainly with regional electricity issues. At one of its first meetings the regional committee discussed, among other things, the restructuring of NYNEX with regard to LEC and affiliate transactions. Its reception of the corporate restructuring of NYNEX by the New York Public Service Commission, discussed above, was highly favorable.[40] State regulators generally advocate structural safeguards, such as separate subsidiaries, and have to defend their authority to impose them against the FCC, which prefers nonstructural safeguards, such as equal access rules. In that sense the New York regulators' plan for corporate restructuring of NYNEX was a preemptive move against federal preemption.

Assessment

The net benefits of cooperation are the difference between the gross benefits and the costs. Among the costs are those of an added layer of decision making. Cooperation may, for example, reduce the speed with which decisions are made. Among the gross benefits are better decisions and a stronger position against the regulated companies and against federal regulators.

The participants in *Public Utilities Fortnightly*'s 1991 State Regulators' Forum agreed that formal regional regulation that would in part replace state regulation was unlikely and undesirable. State regulation will stay with state commissions because "the public expects their government to be accountable to them for its actions," and because of "the desire for 'local' control."[41] Regional

---

39. *Ohio Action Gives Ameritech Regionwide Price Regulation*, TELECOMM. REP., Nov. 28, 1994, at 6.

40. National Regulatory Research Institute, *supra* note 33, at 22.

41. Lawrence B. Ingram, chairman of the New Mexico Public Service

regulation may, however, come about if the alternative is federal preemption.[42]

It would be interesting to identify divergent state interests with regard to the regional Bell operating companies and see to what extent those divergent interests affect coordination among state regulators. The most obvious divergence with respect to telecommunications seems to be between urban and rural states. Telecommunications networks in rural states tend to have much lower overall density and a lower concentration of very large users. NYNEX, for example, serves six states: New York and all the New England states except Connecticut. Those six states contain only two major metropolitan areas, New York City and Boston. Consequently, one would expect to observe tension between New York and Massachusetts and the other states (although Rhode Island may be viewed as dominated by Providence, and hence have common interests with the two other urban states). It comes as no surprise, then, that regional regulation of NYNEX is weak (though it does exist). In contrast, the fourteen states served by U S West are all predominantly rural. Given the large number of states and the commonality of their interest, stronger regional regulation could be expected. State telecommunications regulation differs markedly among those states, however. Thus, regional regulation can deal successfully only with those issues that are compatible with such different approaches to regulation, and the value of cooperation will depend on the amount of interdependency between state actions.

Regional regulation, moreover, faces two limitations that it cannot overcome. First, Congress and federal regulators will not allow a compact among state regulators to replace federal regulation. Second, state legislatures and governments will not give up their sovereignty in favor of regional regulatory bodies. Within these constraints, however, regional regulation will continue to have

Commission, *in State Regulators' Forum on Regional Regulation*, PUB. UTIL. FORT., Nov. 1, 1991, at 34.

42. Frank O. Heintz, chairman of the Maryland Public Service Commission, *in State Regulators' Forum on Regional Regulation*, PUB. UTIL. FORT., November 1, 1991, at 33.

a place at least as long as there are dominant regional
telecommunications carriers.

Whereas the 1980s were the decade of interexchange competition in
U.S. telecommunications, the 1990s have so far been, and promise
to remain, the decade of local competition. An important
prerequisite for the emergence of such competition is a functioning
market for interconnection, a topic we address in chapter 6, which
deals with open network architecture and expanded interconnection
as two ways to increase competition at the local level. Those two
developments primarily concern the input markets for enhanced
services and competition for IXC access. They also affect the input
markets for other local telecommunications services, such as
intraLATA (long-distance and local) competition in telephony.
These different markets and market segments are discussed in
chapter 7. This section provides only an introduction to the issues,
to round out this summary of state regulation.

Where competition was previously barred, state regulators have
been reluctant to open their intraLATA markets to competition,
largely because such a move is certain to interfere with traditional
patterns of cross-subsidy. As noted above, cross-subsidies invite
competition in those services that generate the subsidies. Facilities-
based switched local exchange competition, however, is still in its
infancy. A number of states now allow for such competition in
principle, and some, following the lead of New York and Illinois,
have actually licensed alternative LECs. The Telecommunications
Act of 1996 now requires states to permit competition in local
telecommunications markets.

State regulators' attitudes to local competition are likely to be
related to the amount of prior cross-subsidization and to the nature
of the state's telecommunications markets. Regulators in states
where network density is high and many businesses are
telecommunications-intensive—New York, Illinois, and California,
for example—are likely to take a different approach from that of
regulators in other states. Teske conducted empirical tests relating
several such variables against regulatory decisions on pricing and

competition.[43] He found that regulators in states served by U S West subsidiaries have been 96 percent more likely to allow competition than regulators in other states. He concludes, "U S West subsidiaries are significant factors in encouraging competition, because of their positive attitude towards open telecommunications markets."[44] U S West remains a puzzle, however, because of its largely rural service territory. It may be that serving a relatively sparse population is unattractive for competitors, so that competition is no threat to other regulatory policies. Other significant positive explanatory variables for competition are the presence of government-funded consumer advocates, a large number of service company headquarters, and a state government dominated by Democratic incumbents. Surprisingly, in Teske's analysis pricing and competition choices by regulators were not closely linked. Size of the regulatory budget is the most potent variable in explaining the allowing of price changes, but not in explaining the allowing of competition.[45]

Analysis of state regulation of LECs demonstrates substantial variation across states. Teske concentrated his analysis of that phenomenon on a few states, in particular New Jersey and New York.

New Jersey is served by New Jersey Bell, a Bell Atlantic subsidiary. New Jersey not only has a large population but also is the most densely populated of the fifty states. It has had a restrictive attitude toward competition and toward raising local rates. The New Jersey Board of Public Utilities has a history of reacting to requests from New Jersey Bell rather than initiating action. For example, "[i]n 1987, New Jersey Bell proposed . . . [a] three-year local rate increase moratorium, associated with the expected reduction in federal tax liability [from the 1986 federal tax reform], in exchange for reduced regulation on more competitive services. The board accepted this deal."[46] As mentioned above, a few years later the board made a further deal, giving concessions to New Jersey Bell in

---

43. TESKE, *supra* note 6, at 76.
44. *Id*. at 83.
45. *Id*.
46. *Id*. at 91.

terms of pricing flexibility in exchange for a commitment to substantial investment in infrastructure.

New York, in contrast, has been at the forefront of the movement to encourage LEC competition. In that effort, the New York Public Service Commission has relied heavily on "generic proceedings" in the postdivestiture period. Those proceedings are held separately from rate hearings and open the door for new initiatives by both the LECs and potential competitors.

Those differences in regulatory approach toward competition are explained by the fact that 15 percent of worldwide international telecommunications traffic either originates or terminates in Manhattan.[47] As a consequence, large business users are very active before the New York regulators. In contrast, New Jersey has had a totally reactive policy catering only to residential customers. Those observations are in line with Smart's empirical results that state regulatory restrictions on facilities-based LEC bypass are negatively correlated with the percentage of the state population employed in the financial sector.[48]

A commonality across jurisdictions in their approach to regulation and competition is the asymmetrical treatment of dominant incumbents, which continue to be regulated, and entrants, which face hardly any regulation. Thus, once regulators embrace competition, they resort to asymmetrical regulation. The asymmetry comes in many forms. Incumbent LECs, but not new entrants, are subject to price regulation, public service obligations, equal access rules, and the like. The main reason for asymmetrical regulation is probably consumer protection from monopoly power. The problem is that regulators cannot simply let go of that objective when entry occurs, because the market power of the dominant operator vis-à-vis consumers is still viewed as considerable. On the other hand, the entrants presumably have no market power and therefore need not be regulated. It is clear that, eventually, regulation should disappear when the incumbent is no longer dominant.

47. According to Mitchell Moss, *cited in* TESKE, *supra* note 6, at 97.

48. Susan R. Smart, The Impact of Divestiture on Telephone Pricing: State Regulatory Responses (1989) (unpublished manuscript, Stanford University).

Although local competition takes place within states, it is strongly affected by FCC decisions. That influence comes in several forms. First, through its jurisdiction over interstate services that use facilities in common with intrastate services, the FCC can bring about de facto deregulation of intrastate services. That has happened, for example, with private lines on which more than 10 percent of the traffic is interstate (see chapters 6 and 7). Second, the FCC can try to preempt state regulators from imposing local entry restrictions. Following the new federal legislation, such a preemption is expected soon. Third, the FCC can use its jurisdiction over alternative local access technologies to force local competition. Cellular and personal communications services, and telephony delivered by cable television companies, are of that kind.

CONCLUSIONS

After the breakup of AT&T, regulation of the U.S. telecommunications market changed in largely unforeseen ways. The widely expected total deregulation of what remained of AT&T did not happen. Rather, regulation of AT&T and its divested regional operating companies became much more compatible with and conducive to competition. The move from rate-of-return regulation toward alternative forms of incentive regulation prepared the LECs for competition and reduced their incentive and their ability to cross-subsidize their activities. And, as will be shown in chapter 6, the emphasis of state and federal regulators moved somewhat away from regulating retail markets toward regulating network interconnection and carrier access.

Characteristic of the current situation are the large differences in approach to telecommunications regulation among the states. Those differences relate to pricing, the type of regulation, and the status of competition. That considerable variation makes one wonder whether the different states have been adapting optimally to differences in their environments (including changes in interest groups), or instead dealing with the same new problems with different levels of efficiency.

After the MFJ, the most efficient approach for state regulators would have been to allow competition in intrastate long-distance services and other areas capable of supporting competition, to rebalance rate structures in favor of business and long-distance rates, and to impose incentive regulation that would be compatible with partial competition. State actions to regulate interconnection and access charges for intrastate services in concert with FCC requirements for interstate services would have enabled interconnecting carriers and service providers to use the same facilities and arrangements for both state and interstate services and avoid tariff arbitrage by customers between state and federal jurisdictions. From the perspective of political economy, the same actions (except, perhaps, that toward lower business rates) would have been advisable, but only after some states had moved first. That could have created some strategic maneuvering as to who should first test the new waters. Because different states would often differ in their interests, there would be natural forerunners.

Before the MFJ, there was somewhat more commonality in states' approach to rate structures (states had similar patterns of cross-subsidization, driven by residual regulation), to rate levels (driven by federal-state cost separations and the allowed rate of return), and to local competition (which was nonexistent). In the past decade some variation has set in on all three fronts. All states are moving away from traditional cross-subsidization. Some, such as California, have made major steps in that direction, while others, such as Illinois, have abandoned cross-subsidies altogether. Most states have moved away from rate-of-return regulation to other approaches to regulating rate levels. One, Nebraska, has deregulated rates altogether. Finally, all states have moved to accommodate some form of competition along at least certain stretches of the last ten miles, and many states have proceedings under way to decide on further liberalization. Full-fledged local exchange competition has begun in a number of states, following the lead of Illinois and New York. The Telecommunications Act of 1996 requires states to open local markets to resale competition and has provided strong incentives for facilities-based competition as well. But in all cases where regulators have allowed or facilitated competition, an asymmetry is in evidence: dominant incumbents continue to be regulated, while entrants face little or no regulation at all.

6

Interconnection and Wholesale Competition

INTERCONNECTION OF NETWORKS AND SERVICES is key to competition in the telecommunications sector. In particular, for those services that potentially anyone can use to communicate with potentially anyone else, interconnection is necessary to optimize on the network externality (see chapter 4). This holds true as long as there is any extra cost to a consumer from subscribing to more than one telecommunications operator. The most crucial interconnection is that with the local network, which is the link to the final consumer.

Chapters 2 and 4 discussed the bottleneck aspect of interconnection. The bottleneck phenomenon explains why interconnection may be a stumbling block on the path toward full competition in local telecommunications markets. This chapter analyzes the major dimensions of interconnection from the perspective of competition in wholesale and access markets.

THE HISTORICAL DEVELOPMENT OF INTERCONNECTION

Interconnection issues in U.S. telecommunications date to the period after 1894, when the original Bell patents expired. Almost immediately, independents entered the telephone market, and the Bell System quickly lost market share. By the turn of the century, nearly half of all cities with phone service had at least two different telephone companies. Those companies' networks usually were not interconnected, so that a subscriber could call only other subscribers of the same company. Wealthy people linked up to more than one network and, before calling, had to check directories to find out on which network the other party could be called. Although telephone companies were viewed as common carriers, obliged to provide service indiscriminately to all who sought it, in those early years a telephone company did not have to permit physical interconnection by another telephone company.[1] In particular, Bell's successor company, AT&T, made it a policy *not* to interconnect with independent companies in localities where AT&T had its own presence.

After AT&T acquired new cost-saving patents for long-distance services, that policy proved extremely successful in regaining lost market share and in establishing a nationwide grid. AT&T bought up many of its competitors until, in 1913, the federal government obtained from AT&T, in the so-called Kingsbury Commitment, its agreement not to acquire any other competitors and to interconnect with local independents (although not with other long-distance companies). At that time AT&T covered most of the United States and left for the most part only rural areas to the independents. Yet despite the Kingsbury Commitment, AT&T continued to acquire other telecommunications companies and refused to interconnect with competing local telephone companies well into the 1930s. That practice found support by the courts even over state regulatory statutes to the contrary.[2]

It was only in the 1970s that the Federal Communications Commission required the Bell System to provide interconnection to other long-distance companies. In granting MCI Communications Corp. the status of a specialized common carrier, the FCC simultaneously provided that "established carriers with exchange facilities should permit interconnection or leased channel arrangements on reasonable terms and conditions to be negotiated with the new carriers."[3] There followed a turbulent period in which MCI requested, and through a court injunction received,

1. *See* MICHAEL K. KELLOGG, JOHN THORNE & PETER W. HUBER, FEDERAL TELECOMMUNICATIONS LAW (Little, Brown & Co. 1992).

2. *Id.* at 157.

3. Establishment of Policies and Procedures for Consideration of Application to Provide Specialized Common Carrier Services, First Rep. & Order, FCC Dkt. No. 18920, 29 F.C.C.2d 870, 940 (1971).

interconnection for its specific services, which were a mixture of private line and switched services. AT&T was able to get that injunction lifted temporarily, however, and for a short time in April 1974 it disconnected some of MCI's customers. A week later, the FCC ordered the Bell System to reinstate or provide the disputed interconnections. In 1978 the U.S. Court of Appeals for the District of Columbia Circuit went even further. It required AT&T to provide MCI with interconnection for the full array of services it might choose to offer over its facilities.

In March 1974 MCI brought suit against AT&T for monopolizing intercity communications. A jury decided that case in MCI's favor in 1980, but AT&T filed an appeal. The appeals court, in 1983, backed the lower court's decision that AT&T's local switches were an essential facility, to which AT&T unreasonably denied access.[4] But the appeals court also held that AT&T's intercity network was not an essential facility, which implied that AT&T had no obligation to fill in gaps in MCI's network. Nevertheless, in 1980 the FCC had decided that AT&T must allow simple resale of its telephone services, so that MCI could fill its gaps by reselling services bought at the volume discounts that AT&T offered its business customers.[5] AT&T then immediately reduced its volume discounts to make such reselling less attractive.

When MCI had first entered the interexchange business, AT&T had offered to interconnect with it for ordinary private line services but not for the foreign exchange or common control switching arrangements (CCSAs) that MCI had demanded. Access to foreign exchange services would have allowed MCI to switch calls in its own offices and use AT&T to transmit them. Under the CCSAs, in addition, the switching would have been done by AT&T on switches that would handle calls for several customers in the same

4. MCI *v.* American Tel. & Tel. Co., 708 F.2d 1081, 1132–33 (7th Cir. 1983).

5. Regulatory Policies Concerning Resale and Shared Use of Common Carrier Domestic Public Switched Network Services, CC Dkt. No. 80–54, 83 F.C.C.2d 167, 175–76 (1980). In an earlier decision the commission had ordered the resale of private lines: Regulatory Policies Concerning Resale and Shared Use of Common Carrier Services and Facilities, FCC Dkt. No. 20097, 60 F.C.C.2d 261 (1976).

position as MCI. Since AT&T was already providing such services to independent (local) phone companies, feasibility was not an issue. In 1977, in the *Execunet I* decision,[6] the U.S. Court of Appeals for the Third Circuit decided in favor of MCI, and AT&T had to provide the requested types of interconnection. Because that interconnection was only for private line–type services, it took another appellate court decision in 1978 (*Execunet II*) to extend interconnection to all the switched services that MCI was offering.[7]

REGULATION OF ACCESS CHARGES

The market for interconnection is largely dominated by regulatory intervention. The Modification of Final Judgment,[8] the FCC, and the state public utilities commissions have established rules for interconnection through court cases and regulatory proceedings. In accordance with those rules, the LECs file tariffs for interconnection services under which they are willing and obliged to serve interexchange carriers, other service providers, or final customers. The tariffs usually contain definitions of services, prices, and conditions under which the services are offered; the conditions may include obligations on the buyers of the services. The interconnecting parties then enter into service agreements, which usually take the form of purchase orders and, to the best of our knowledge, are fairly simple documents. In contrast, the rules and tariffs are lengthy and sometimes complicated.

Regulation of access charges (called interconnection charges outside the United States) became a major issue only after the MFJ. Until then interconnection charges between the Bell System and independent local operators had been part of the separations and settlements process, whereas new IXCs, and MCI in particular, had

6. MCI *v.* F.C.C., 561 F.2d 365 (D.C. Cir. 1977).

7. Motion for an Order Directing Compliance with Mandate, MCI *v.* F.C.C., No. 75-1635, 580 F.2d 590 (D.C. Cir.), *cert. denied,* 439 U.S. 980 (Apr. 14, 1978).

8. United States *v.* American Tel. & Tel. Co., 552 F. Supp. 131 (D.D.C. 1982) (text of the decree), *aff'd sub nom.* Maryland *v.* United States, 460 U.S. 1001 (1983); United States *v.* Western Elec. Co., 569 F. Supp. 1057 (D.D.C. 1983) (approving the plan of reorganization).

major battles with AT&T over such charges. After the MFJ all access charges involving interLATA traffic became external charges, with potentially different charges for interstate and intrastate interLATA traffic.[9] Now the cross-subsidy from long-distance to local telephone service had to be externalized as well.

The FCC's original plan called for the IXCs to pay cost-based access charges and for residential subscribers to pay up to $6 per line per month, to cover the cross-subsidy contained in the disproportionate attribution of the LECs' non-traffic-sensitive costs to interstate traffic.[10] That monthly payment, known as the subscriber line charge, became a major source of contention. Pressure on Congress from state governments and regulators, from the MFJ court, and from consumer advocates ultimately led the FCC to introduce the subscriber line charge gradually and to cap it at about $3.50 per month for a residential line. Thus, to compensate for the lower per-line charge, access charges had to contain a contribution element.

The FCC still wanted to make access charges at least reflect differences in the cost of access resulting from such factors as location or traffic volume. Therefore, in 1983 the FCC adopted "Part 69" rules for switched access that would have imposed different price structures on tandem and dedicated access (those terms are defined below).[11] But the court enforcing the

---

9. Jurisdictional cost separation continued after the MFJ and its principles did not undergo radical change. What did change was that internal settlements were now externalized.

10. *Access Charge Order*, CC Dkt. No. 78-72, Third Rep. & Order, FCC 82-579 (Feb. 28, 1983). The formula used in allocating local-loop costs to long-distance service is called the subscriber plant factor (SPF). In contrast, subscriber line usage (SLU) is the use of the local loop by long-distance traffic relative to total local-loop traffic. The SPF was related to SLU by a formula adopted by the Federal-State Joint Board in 1971 as a result of the Ozark Plan. It achieved an average relationship of SPF = 3.33 SLU and resulted in a rapid increase in the costs allocated to long-distance services. The SPF is now frozen and therefore has become independent of the actual development of SLU. That kind of "cost allocation" has deliberately departed from the drivers of interconnection costs.

11. "Part 69" is a section of the FCC's accounting rules that governs the computation of access charges. MTS and WATS Market Structure, 93 F.C.C.

Modification of Final Judgment had decreed that, from 1984 to 1991, the largest part of access charges (common line charges and transport charges) would follow an equal-charge rule, with charges derived by dividing the interstate portion of total common line and transport costs of all major LECs by the total number of interstate minutes. The FCC took a major beating when it had to retreat from its elaborate access charge order,[12] waive most of the new Part 69 rules, and, until 1991, adopt the simple equal-charge rule imposed by the MFJ court. The expiration of the MFJ restriction again raised issues of switched access pricing, including the future role of the Part 69 rules.

There are two forms of access to the LEC network, distinguished from each other by differences in composition, pricing, and regulatory treatment. *Special access* (figure 6–1) is essentially a private line (nonswitched) arrangement in which circuits are dedicated to a particular user for the distance between the customer's premises and the LEC's end office. Between the LEC's end office and an IXC's point of presence, traffic from a special access customer may use a common line with traffic from other special access customers. Special access is sold on a per-circuit basis for unlimited usage up to the capacity of the circuit. Alternatively, the special access service may be provided by a competitive access provider and bypass all LEC facilities (bottom panel of figure 6–1). Under *switched access* (figure 6–2) a LEC switch transfers traffic between local loops and interoffice circuits to an IXC's point of presence. The switch determines the direction a call takes, for example over the local network or to the IXC's point

---

2d 241, 309–13. As the Department of Justice observes: "Under these Part 69 rules, traffic carried over dedicated trunks would have been assessed certain fixed charges and a distance-sensitive per-line charge for transmission. Traffic carried via tandem access would have been assessed two charges: a fixed charge for the dedicated trunk between the POP [point of presence] and tandem switch, and common transport rates on a cents per minute basis between the switch and the LEC central office." Reply Comments, Notice of Proposed Rulemaking & Notice of Inquiry, CC Dkt. No. 91-141 (June 6, 1991).

12. Mem. Op. & Order, CC Dkt. No. 78-72, FCC 83-356 (Aug. 22, 1983).

FIGURE 6–1
SPECIAL ACCESS

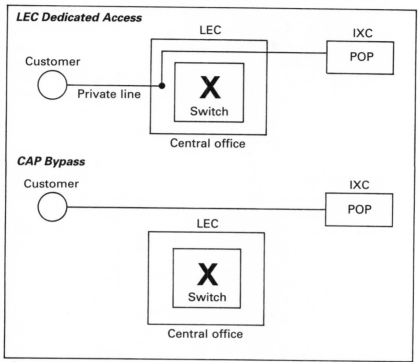

NOTE: POP, point of presence.

of presence. When there is a substantial volume of IXC traffic at a single LEC end office, the IXC will obtain dedicated access circuits between the end office and its point of presence (top panel of figure 6–2). Such an arrangement is known as dedicated switched access. Otherwise, the point of presence can be connected to the LEC network at the tandem switch where traffic from several offices is aggregated (bottom panel of figure 6–2). That is called tandem switched access. The transmission facilities used to provide the dedicated portion of switched access are physically indistinguishable from those used for special access.

FIGURE 6–2
SWITCHED ACCESS

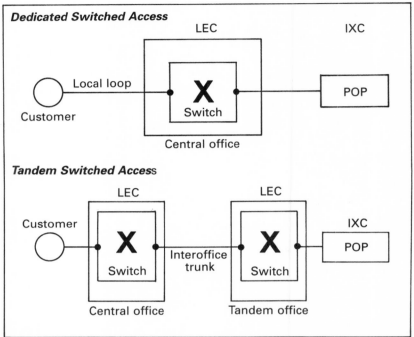

NOTE: POP, point of presence.

Special access is attractive when traffic volume from a customer's premises to the IXC point of presence is sufficient to fill out the capacity of a dedicated line and thereby justify payment of a flat per-circuit charge. Special access is used for a wide range of interexchange services, such as wide-area telephone service (WATS), telegraphy, audio and video, wideband data, and analog and high-capacity digital data services.[13] In contrast, switched

13. *See*, for example, U.S. Department of Justice, Reply Comments, Notice of Proposed Rulemaking & Notice of Inquiry, CC Dkt. No. 91-141 (Sept. 20, 1991), at 8 n.4.

access is most widely used for the ubiquitous public voice telephone service. Although the LECs' share of the market for switched access remains well above 90 percent, their share in the special access market has been substantially eroded and is less than 50 percent in some places, such as Manhattan.[14]

In the following discussion of access pricing we concentrate largely on its transport pricing aspect, although that component generates less revenue for the LECs than the carrier common line charges (CCLCs), which are only a contribution to the LEC's non-traffic-sensitive costs. The reason for our emphasis is that transport rates have strong competitive implications and are fairly complicated. Switching issues are treated later in this chapter under the heading "Expanded Interconnection."

Federal Regulation of Access Charges

As a large IXC, AT&T depends heavily on dedicated switched access. Smaller IXCs rely more on tandem switched access, because at their lower traffic volumes tandem switching is less costly. The tandem switch aggregates traffic coming from the IXCs to a particular LEC central office, or coming from multiple LEC central offices to a given point of presence. How dedicated access and tandem switched access are priced can therefore greatly affect the competitive positions of the IXCs relative to each other—a subject of central concern in the FCC's switched transport proceeding.

At its divestiture, AT&T was perceived to have a strong competitive advantage over its IXC rivals because it could obtain discounts on access prices for its large traffic volumes, and because many of its points of presence are physically collocated with LEC central offices, which reflects the predivestiture vertical integration of the Bell System.[15]

14. *See The Man Who Would Save NY for NYNEX,* N.Y. TIMES, Apr. 3, 1995, at D1.

15. MCI estimates that 43 percent of AT&T's points of presence are within or very close to LEC central offices. MCI, Comments, Notice of Proposed Rulemaking & Notice of Inquiry, CC Dkt. No. 91–141 (Aug. 5, 1991), at 16.

Two government-imposed requirements reduced, on an interim basis, that perceived competitive disadvantage of the smaller IXCs. First, until September 1, 1991, the MFJ imposed the "equal charge per unit rule," under which the Bell operating companies had to charge all IXCs an equal amount per unit of switched access traffic regardless of whether dedicated or tandem access was used. A second requirement imposed on the Bell companies by the MFJ until September 1, 1992, and still reflected in LEC tariffs, is the "five-mile rule," which mandates that all IXC facilities within five miles of a class 4 (tandem) AT&T switch be treated as though they were in the same exchange area or subzone as the AT&T switch.[16] That rule serves to offset the advantage that AT&T enjoys from having its points of presence close to LEC central offices. The sustainability of that rule in a competitive environment is in doubt, as are its effects on economic efficiency.

The Equal-Charge Rule

The problems with the equal-charge rule arose through the tension it produced between promotion of entry and the efficient allocation of resources. Initially, the rule was designed to subsidize access for AT&T's competitors, which were assumed to have lower volumes of traffic and have points of presence at greater distances from LEC offices that caused them to have a higher cost of transport for switched access than AT&T. That assistance to entry, however, came at a social cost, in that traffic was priced and routed inefficiently. Under that rule an IXC could order dedicated transport and then underutilize it, because it paid only the per-minute charge of its actual use.[17]

Although the equal-charge rule clearly helped small IXCs by reducing their average burden from access charges, the implementation of the rule had some contrary incentive effects at

16. U.S. Department of Justice, Reply Comments, Notice of Proposed Rulemaking & Notice of Inquiry, CC Dkt. No. 91–141 (Sept. 20, 1991), at 71.

17. Illinois Commerce Commission, *Local Competition and Interconnection*, Staff Report, July 1, 1992, at 64.

the margin.[18] A large portion of the per-minute charge (the carrier common line rate, or CCLR) was derived by dividing a predetermined portion of the previous year's total accounting costs of the LEC's network by the total number of switched long-distance minutes. Therefore, the incremental charges borne by an IXC from a long-run increase in its number of minutes declined as its market share increased. Thus, for example, if AT&T had a market share of 60 percent, a permanent increase in its minutes of access would lead to a steady-state increase in the CCLR portion of AT&T's access charges (after the first period) that was only 40 percent of the increase in the initial year. Conversely, if the market share of MCI was 15 percent, its corresponding steady-state increase of the CCLR portion of access charges would be 85 percent of the increase in the initial year. That gave AT&T more of an incentive than the smaller IXCs had to expand its customer base and its customer usage. At the same time, the combination of rate-of-return regulation with that pricing approach gave AT&T less of an incentive to bypass LEC access (even if bypass would have been efficient).[19] Thus, the need for a different pricing approach was evident.

The rate structure under the equal-charge rule and the five-mile rule presumably promoted significant inefficient use of LEC networks by IXCs and other access customers.[20] The FCC therefore set three goals for a new approach to transport pricing: to encourage efficient use of transport facilities by allowing pricing that reflected costs, to adopt a rate structure conducive to full and fair interexchange competition, and to avoid interference with the development of interstate access competition. In September 1992 the FCC adopted an interim rate structure, originally intended for use from November 1993 through October 1995 but then retained

---

18. BRIDGER M. MITCHELL & INGO VOGELSANG, TELECOMMUNICATIONS PRICING: THEORY & PRACTICE 218–21 (Cambridge University Press 1991).

19. DAVID E. M. SAPPINGTON & DENNIS L. WEISMAN, DESIGNING INCENTIVE REGULATION FOR THE TELECOMMUNICATIONS INDUSTRY (MIT Press and AEI Press 1996).

20. In the Matter of Transport Rate Structure and Pricing, Petition for Waiver of the Transport Rules filed by GTE Service Corp., Rep. & Order & Further Notice of Proposed Rulemaking, CC Dkt. No. 91-213, FCC 92-442 (Oct. 6, 1992) ¶ 1.

beyond that deadline. That interim rate structure is only partially cost-based, out of fear of major competitive shifts and of a reduction in cross-subsidization.

The interim rate structure has four rate elements: (1) a flat-rate entrance facilities charge to cover transport from the IXC point of presence to the serving wire center (the LEC central office designated to serve the IXC point of presence); (2) a flat-rate direct-trunked transport element for dedicated transport from the serving wire center to the LEC end office serving the long-distance customer; (3) a usage-based tandem switched transport element for any traffic between the serving wire center and the end office that requires switching at the LEC tandem office; and (4) a usage-based interconnection charge for all IXC traffic interconnected with the LEC switched access network.

For the first two rate elements cost-based pricing is used. Those elements are similar to special access pricing, which we treat below. The third rate element is treated differently. Although most of the costs accounted for in the revenue requirement vary directly with the amount of tandem switching, the FCC nevertheless prescribed that initially only 20 percent of the tandem revenue requirement be collected through the tandem rate element and the remaining 80 percent through the fourth rate element, the interconnection charge. That deliberate deviation from cost-based pricing has protected the small IXCs (which are the main users of tandem switched transport) from some of the rate shock from the new rate structure.

Having determined the entrance facilities charge, the direct-trunked charge, and the tandem switched transport charge as described, the FCC ordered that the initial interconnection charge be calculated as a residual charge on a per-minute basis. That residual interconnection charge (RIC), which makes up about 80 percent of transport rates, obviously contains any universal service or local access deficit contribution of transport rates to the LECs. Because that charge is determined as a residual, the introduction of the new rate structure in total has been revenue neutral for the LECs. Again, the FCC, fearing political consequences, avoided any explicit decision on the appropriate amount of compensation for local price constraints or for universal service obligations. The continuing proceedings to establish the long-run transport price structure is very likely to lead to a reduction in the RIC, something that has been partially achieved through tightened price caps, as we discuss in the next section.

The FCC also allowed additional transport pricing flexibility to LECs that are subject to expanded interconnection requirements, which we discuss at length below. That flexibility includes zone-density pricing for switched transport services.[21] Volume and term discounts may also be offered after enough DS1 connections have been signed up in a zone.

The interim rate structure went into effect in November 1993, and the long-term rate structure was not even in sight two years later. The FCC's decisions seem to confirm the conjecture of Owen and Braeutigam that regulatory action smooths the impact of change over time.[22] In that case small and medium-sized IXCs have been shielded from AT&T's superior efficiency by the shift to cost-based transport rates in small doses, generously spaced over time.

Rate Changes over Time

The FCC currently uses price caps to regulate the access charges of all large LECs.[23] The price-cap rules differentiate among service elements, service categories, and service baskets. *Service elements* represent the lowest level of aggregation in tariffing. They are the thousands of items that are individually priced. At the other extreme, *service baskets* represent the highest level of aggregation. For price-cap-regulated LECs there were initially four baskets: common line services, traffic-sensitive services, special access services, and interexchange services. Traffic-sensitive services were subdivided into three categories: local switching, local transport, and information services. Service baskets are subject to a price-cap index calculated as *GDPPI* − *X* + *Y*, where *GDPPI* is the gross domestic product price index, *X* is a productivity adjustment factor,

---

21. The LECs would have to use the same pricing zones as for special access services, which we discuss below.
22. BRUCE M. OWEN & RONALD BRAEUTIGAM, THE REGULATION GAME: STRATEGIC USE OF THE ADMINISTRATIVE PROCESS (Ballinger 1978).
23. Small LECs can opt for rate-of-return regulation. For rate-of-return-regulated carriers the same rules that govern initial rates are used to adjust access charges.

and *Y* a pass-through for regulatory and tax changes. This means that, on average, all services in the basket can increase in price at most by *GDPPI – X + Y.*

Within each basket are several *service categories* with banding requirements. Thus, relative to the basket as a whole, the average prices of service elements in each category can move only within a band of, say, plus or minus 5 percent. Prices for individual service elements within each category can move freely, as long as the average obeys the banding requirement.

The common line basket consists of only one category. It is treated differently from the other baskets in that it has its own price-cap formula, known as the balanced 50-50 formula. The reason for that formula is that the LECs can reduce (non-traffic-sensitive) per-minute costs of common line services either by reducing costs per line or by increasing traffic. The balanced 50-50 formula shares the benefits from increased traffic between the LECs and the IXCs and thus gives incentives to both parties to increase traffic. Apart from reducing access charges, however, it is unclear what the LECs could do to increase IXC traffic.

With regard to transport rates the question arose, Should there be as many as three separate rate categories for transport, with strict banding requirements, as the FCC had originally proposed in its August 1991 notice? For price-capped carriers, transport previously constituted a single service category within the basket of traffic-sensitive services. Transport as a whole was subject to a price band of plus or minus 5 percent relative to the price-cap index. Maintaining that rule would have allowed the carriers to restructure individual price relationships inside the service category. For example, a LEC could increase the tandem switched transport element relative to the price-cap index by 10 percent and simultaneously reduce the direct-trunked rate element by 10 percent to stay within the banding rule.[24]

Although the LECs would have liked that kind of flexibility, in its decision for an interim rate structure the FCC separated direct-trunked and tandem switched transport into two service categories.

---

24. That assumes that the weights of the two elements in the service category are not excessively far apart.

That, by itself, has limited the LECs' ability to restructure prices between those two types of transport. The FCC argued that combining the two types would have allowed the LECs to offset decreases in direct-trunked transport rates with increases in tandem switched transport rates, thereby creating an artificial price advantage for LEC transport over that furnished by competitive access providers under (the then anticipated) expanded interconnection. In addition, according to the FCC, the large IXCs, as heavy users of direct-trunked transport, would have gained an unfair, non-cost-based advantage over smaller competitors. The FCC has therefore further limited the pricing flexibility of the LECs.

As illustrated in figure 6–3 (in the box labeled "flat-rate transport"), the entrance facilities charge was lumped together in one category with direct-trunked transport. Whereas that category remained subject to the usual 5 percent banding rule, the tandem switched transport category became subject to a band of +2 to –5 percent. That reduced the LECs' "ability to offset decreases in direct-trunked transport rates with increases in tandem-switched transport rates."[25] For the RIC the FCC determined an upper band of 0 percent relative to the price-cap index and a lower band of –5 percent.

Special access services were subdivided into the following categories: high-capacity/digital data services; voice grade, WATS, metallic, and telegraph, wideband data and wideband analog; and audio and video.[26] As figure 6–4 shows, however, in January 1994 the FCC altered the price-cap rules governing switched and special access. It adopted a second report and order in the transport rate proceeding and moved transport services from the basket for traffic-sensitive rates into a new "trunking" basket along with special access rates.[27] All transport rates are now in the same basket. That eliminates the option for the LECs to lower transport prices, for

25. FCC, as quoted in TELECOMM. REP., Oct. 26, 1992, at 36.

26. The LEC price cap program is described and discussed in detail *in* In the Matter of Policy and Rules Concerning Rates for Dominant Carriers, Second Rep. & Order, CC Dkt. No. 87-313 (Oct. 4, 1990).

27. Transport Rate Structure and Pricing, Second Rep. & Order, CC Dkt. No. 91-213, 9 F.C.C. Rcd. 615 (1994).

FIGURE 6-3
PRICE-CAP BASKETS AND SERVICE CATEGORIES IN THE FCC'S FIRST TRANSPORT ORDER

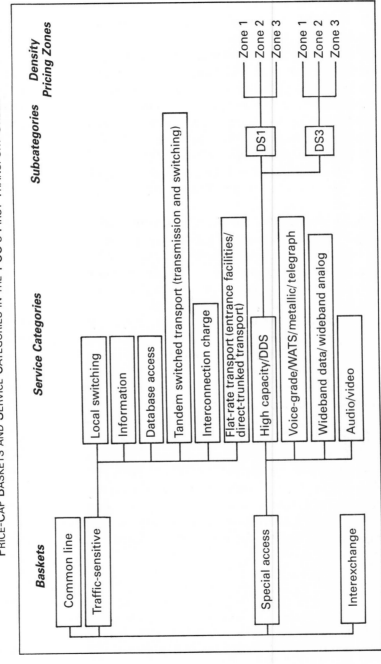

SOURCE: Third Memorandum Opinion and Order on Reconsideration and Supplemental Notice of Proposed Rulemaking, CC Dkt. No. 91-213, FCC 94-325 (released December 22, 1994).

FIGURE 6-4

PRICE CAP BASKETS AND SERVICE CATEGORIES IN THE FCC'S SECOND TRANSPORT ORDER

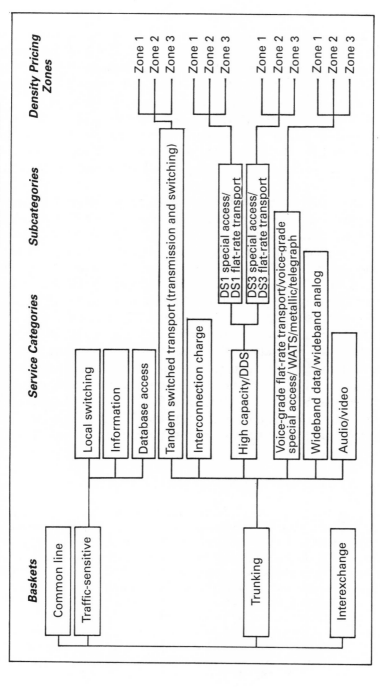

SOURCE: Third Memorandum Opinion and Order on Reconsideration and Supplemental Notice of Proposed Rulemaking, CC Dkt. No. 91-213, FCC 94-325 (released December 22, 1994).

example, to compete against competitive access providers, and offset those reductions with higher prices from local switching.[28] The new basket separates direct-trunked transport and entrance facilities into so-called DS3, DS1, and voice-grade service categories, along with the analogous special transport services. Those categories are subject to 5 percent bands, whereas the +2 to –5 percent bands were retained for tandem switched transport services and the 0 percent band for the RIC.[29] Thus, the RIC has so far been reduced only by the overall adjustment factor of the price caps.

Until early 1995 the LECs could choose between an overall adjustment factor of 3.3 percent with substantial profit sharing, and one of 4.3 percent with less profit sharing. In March 1995 the X factor was increased to a range of 4.0 percent to 5.3 percent (again at the choice of the LECs themselves, but now among three alternatives). The reason given for that increase is that a mistake in the FCC's original calculation of LEC total factor productivity during the 1980s had led, in the 1990 LEC price-cap order, to an underestimate and thus to inappropriately low adjustment factors. Therefore, the FCC also ordered an immediate one-time reduction in access charges by 2.8 percent.[30] To increase incentives for cost reduction, the FCC eliminated the earnings-sharing option for LECs that elect the 5.3 percent adjustment factor. To increase the ability of the LECs to respond competitively, the FCC increased the LECs' downward pricing flexibility in the traffic-sensitive and trunking

28. *FCC Puts Transport in New "Trunking" Price Cap Basket*, TELECOMM. REP., Jan. 24, 1994, at 6.

29. The FCC has also established rules on common-channel signaling (CCS) transport. That refers to transport between an IXC's CCS network and a LEC signaling transfer point (STP). The FCC created a dedicated signaling transport rate element consisting of a signaling link and an STP port termination. The signaling link charge is a flat rate set at the same level as equivalent special access facilities and may be distance-sensitive. The STP port termination charge is also a flat rate but is based on the price cap new services rule (meaning that it is specially scrutinized) or, in the case of rate-of-return-regulated LECs, on proper cost support. The dedicated signaling transport rate element is in the same price-cap service category as direct-trunked transport.

30. Price Cap Performance Review for Local Exchange Carriers, First Rep. & Order, CC Dkt. No. 94-1, FCC 95-132 (Apr. 7, 1995).

baskets to 10 percent and indicated that it would allow further flexibility on a case-by-case basis.

Overall, up to now a large subsidy element has been maintained in switched access charges. Competitive shifts between IXCs have thus been contained by constraints on rebalancing under price caps and on volume discounts. As a further result, inefficient substitution of dedicated access for switched access continues to occur, as do inefficient bypass and entry. In addition, incentives for AT&T to bypass the LECs had increased under AT&T's own price-cap rules, where LEC access charge changes were passed through with a virtually neutral effect on AT&T's profits, while cost savings from bypass could be passed on either in lower prices or in higher profit margins.[31]

State Regulation of Access Charges

The Problem of Imputation. State regulators can regulate access charges for intrastate (both intraLATA and interLATA) long-distance traffic. Access charges are prices for intermediate inputs that may be used in the production of services that compete with those of the LECs. Since the IXCs and the LECs compete to offer intraLATA long-distance services, intrastate LEC access charges raise delicate issues, in particular that of equal treatment with respect to access conditions and charges. The issue is known as "imputation."[32] Under imputation, a LEC has to impose the same access charge for providing service to itself as it charges to outsiders who interconnect to the LEC's network.

---

31. That asymmetrical treatment of access charges and bypass costs has been the subject of some controversy. *Id.* ¶¶ 274–320. *See also* SAPPINGTON & WEISMAN, *supra* note 19, at 48–50. AT&T has been restricted by banding requirements only in the way it passes on access charge decreases to consumers. Thus, AT&T seems to have targeted optional calling plans for such rate decreases. *See* Price Cap Performance Review for Local Exchange Carriers, CC Dkt. No. 94-1 ¶ 61.

32. For an extensive treatment, *see* Alexander C. Larson & Margaret Z. Starkey, Unbundling Issues and State Telecommunications Regulatory Policy (Feb. 16, 1994) (unpublished manuscript, on file with authors).

The issue of imputation is driven by the fact that access charges are above the average incremental cost of providing access. Thus, a LEC that competes with an interconnecting operator could undercut that competitor by providing access to itself at a lower price than it offers to outsiders, and yet not show cross-subsidies. Imputation provides for an internal price floor that would show whether a LEC is unduly cross-subsidizing its competitive services.[33] That price floor corresponds to a simple version of the efficient component-pricing rule (described in chapter 4) that would hold if the interconnector's retail service replaced the LEC's retail service one-for-one. Under that rule the LEC would price access at incremental cost plus the LEC's retail margin on the service for which interconnection is used. An effective imputation policy would therefore prevent a LEC from pricing access to other firms above the efficient component price. If it did, it would also have to price access to itself above the efficient component price and would therefore show the internal access service subsidizing the competitive service.

Because their line-of-business restrictions have prevented the regional Bell operating companies from offering interLATA services, imputation has not in the past been an issue for FCC regulation. Imputation will become important for the FCC once the regional Bell operating companies enter interstate retail markets in their own service territories. Imputation is called for in many state laws and public utilities commission orders. In particular, the California Public Utilities Commission required imputation and imposed nonstructural accounting separation on the LECs for that purpose. The commission also used unbundling and imputation as a quid pro quo for allowing the pricing flexibility the LECs desired. The California regulators recognized the problem of cost differences between providing to oneself and to outsiders, or between bundled services and the equivalent set of unbundled services:[34] "[B]ecause

33. *See* David L. Kaserman & John W. Mayo, Regulatory Policies Toward Local Exchange Companies Under Emerging Competition: Guardrails or Speedbumps on the Information Highway? (Mar. 1995) (unpublished manuscript, on file with authors).

34. *In re* Alternative Regulatory Frameworks for Local Exchange Carriers, 107 P.U.R. 4th 1 (Cal. P.U.C. 1989), Decision 89-10-031 (Oct. 12, 1989), at

of economic efficiency considerations, the local exchange carriers should be allowed to propose that tariffed rates reflect any cost differences between provision of monopoly function as part of a bundled utility service and provision of that function on an unbundled basis. " In practice, however, the LECs have so far been unable to convince the California commission that they achieved economies of scale or scope from bundling access services provided to themselves rather than selling them unbundled to others.

The California imputation policy reveals two major problems. The first is that imputation is not easily monitored. Charges internal to a company are usually wash transactions that only affect the company's behavior to the extent that internal incentive structures and further external constraints are linked to them. Absent such constraints, for example, a LEC could charge itself the same high access charge that it charges outsiders and still charge a low retail price to its customers. In that way, the access business makes a higher profit while the retail business sees its profit reduced. The California Public Utilities Commission tried to prevent such behavior through an accounting separation that would uncover the resulting cross-subsidies. Such regulation is costly and highly imprecise, however.

The second major problem with imputation is that it may lead to inefficient behavior. The socially optimal internal price may well deviate from the price charged to outsiders, for example if outside provision carries some extra costs not incurred internally.

Variation in State Access Charges. Most of the cross-subsidy flowing from long-distance to local services has been extracted by means of the CCLR. Under the equal-charge rule the interstate CCLR (for terminating minutes) fell from $0.0461 to $0.0123 per minute between 1985 and 1990, partly as a result of the introduction and gradual increase of the subscriber line charge. As can be seen from table 6–1, the intrastate CCLRs differed quite substantially from those numbers. In 1985 the interstate CCLR was about 10 percent below the median of the intrastate CCLRs. Among thirty-eight states with figures available for that year, ten mirrored the

141.

TABLE 6–1
CARRIER COMMON LINE RATES BY STATE

State	1990		1985	
	CCLR	Rank	CCLR	Rank
Texas	0.0611	1	0.0792	2
Wyoming	0.0524	2	NA	NA
Minnesota	0.0480	3	0.0524	15
North Carolina	0.0444	4	0.0519	20
South Carolina	0.0444	5	0.0524	17
Louisiana	0.0426	6	0.0831	1
Colorado	0.0378	7	0.0524	13
Massachusetts	0.0359	8	0.0443	33
Alabama	0.0352	9	0.0682	5
Kentucky	0.0347	10	0.0524	18
Florida	0.0343	11	0.0461	26
Tennessee	0.0335	12	0.0629	7
Nebraska	0.0320	13	0.0461	24
Iowa	0.0300	14	0.0300	35
North Dakota	0.0299	15	0.0461	25
Oregon	0.0297	16	0.0524	14
Kansas	0.0273	17	0.0461	27
Georgia	0.0267	18	0.0280	36
New Mexico	0.0257	19	0.0524	16
Utah	0.0255	20	NA	NA
Mississippi	0.0245	21	0.0672	6
New Jersey	0.0242	22	0.0242	38
Wisconsin	0.0239	23	0.0461	31
Montana	0.0231	24	0.0504	21
California	0.0215	25	0.0613	8
Maryland	0.0213	26	0.0461	23
Indiana	0.0207	27	0.0543	10
Arizona	0.0204	28	NA	NA
New York	0.0204	29	0.0427	34
Pennsylvania	0.0173	30	0.0461	28
Oklahoma	0.0171	31	0.0740	3
Washington	0.0162	32	0.0491	22
Missouri	0.0152	33	0.0521	19
Michigan	0.0147	34	0.0543	9
Ohio	0.0123	35	0.0543	11
South Dakota	0.0121	36	0.0461	29
Arkansas	0.0000	37	0.0686	4
Idaho	0.0000	38	NA	NA
Illinois	0.0000	39	0.0270	37
Nevada	0.0000	40	0.0524	12
Virginia	0.0000	41	0.0461	30
West Virginia	0.0000	42	0.0461	32
Interstate (FCC)	0.0123		0.0461	

NOTES: Rates are in dollars per minute. NA, not available.

SOURCE: Fox and Mayo (1991, 17), reporting AT&T responses to their data request.

FCC rate, twenty-two were above it, and the remaining six were below it. In contrast, in 1990 the FCC rate was about 50 percent below the median of the intrastate CCLRs. There was hardly any mirroring of the federal CCLR by state regulators, and thirty-four of forty-two were above, and seven below, the FCC rate. Both in relative and in absolute terms the intrastate CCLRs became more dispersed during those five years. In particular, six states did not assess any CCLR in 1990, whereas twenty states charged more than double the interstate figure. That means that six states decided not to use the CCLR as a source for cross-subsidization. Those six included Illinois, which had fully restructured its rates to be free of cross-subsidies, and Virginia, which had totally deregulated intrastate interLATA long-distance services. States with high CCLRs are predominantly rural, possibly indicating higher local-loop costs and a greater need to cross-subsidize local residential services through intrastate long-distance calls.

Federal versus State Issues

LEC interstate access charges are regulated by the FCC, and intrastate access charges by the state public utilities commissions. Functionally, both types of access are the same, and for incoming calls they cannot even be distinguished. That implies arbitrage possibilities for interconnectors, which will try to use the jurisdiction more favorable to them. That can lead to two possible reactions (other than letting it happen, which means that the higher priced jurisdiction will experience no traffic).

First, regulators may seek to monitor the jurisdictional distribution of traffic. For example, the FCC in its switched access interconnection proceedings requires customers or IXCs to report their percentage of interstate usage (PIU). That was done specifically because of differences in access charges for interstate and intrastate traffic.[35] Because the measurement of the PIU is

---

35. Expanded Interconnection with Local Telephone Company Facilities, Transport Phase I, Second Rep. & Order & Third Notice of Proposed Rulemaking, CC Dkt. 91-141, FCC 93-379 ¶ 135 [hereinafter *Expanded Interconnection*].

very inexact yet so much depends on it, it has become such a contentious issue that private intervenors have asked the FCC to preempt state determinations of the PIU.[36] Sievers estimates that the administrative costs of determining the PIU approach $30 million annually.[37] Also, there clearly is duplication of regulatory effort in establishing and regulating access rates.

Second, regulators may adapt state-regulated rates to federally regulated rates in such a way that rate arbitrage becomes unprofitable. The applicability of such "mirroring" should be particularly relevant for local access rates. But although the Illinois Commerce Commission staff report states that it has been customary for intrastate access charges to mirror interstate access charges to eliminate the possibility of arbitrage,[38] table 6–1 shows that intrastate access charges actually differ substantially among themselves and from interstate access charges. Mirroring requires coordination between jurisdictions, whereas the pressure from local exchange competition occurs at the state level. In the late 1980s innovative states, in particular, faced pressure to come up with a new access charge structure, but at the same time had to wait for the FCC to come up with its own methodology to mirror its rate structure.

Thus, the relationship between federal and state regulation of access charges is sometimes one of frustration and can be the source of inefficiencies. In the long run, however, traffic will migrate to where rates are lower. That is likely to lead to pressure for lower access charges overall.

OPEN NETWORK ARCHITECTURE

Information services providers, including firms in the highly competitive and fast-changing computer industry, have long sought access to individual elements of the telephone network to reach

---

36. NATIONAL ASSOCIATION OF REGULATORY UTILITY COMMISSIONERS, 1993 REPORT OF THE ADMINISTRATIVE DIRECTOR ON LITIGATION 87 (1993).

37. Mark Sievers, Percentage Interstate Usage: The Case for Occam's Razor and Access Parity (October 4, 1993) (paper presented at the 21st Annual Telecommunications Policy Research Conference, Solomons Island, Md.).

38. Illinois Commerce Commission, *supra* note 17.

customers, provide services over wide areas, and interconnect information processing centers. But the LECs, with voice telephone calls as their primary market, have been slow to satisfy those demands for access to unbundled network components and have instead sought to produce and market information services themselves.

Unsurprisingly, the terms of access to the network for information processing firms and, conversely, the activities of the LECs in information services markets have been the repeated focus of regulatory attention. The government has sought a more nearly level playing field for participants by applying two types of constraints on the LECs and other network operators: structural separations and line-of-business restrictions.

Structural separation requires a carrier to completely separate all the operations (including facilities, management, marketing, and financial accounting) of one type of service from those of another. Whenever a carrier's subsidiary uses the parent's transmission and switching services, it must pay common-carrier tariffs for them.

In its *Computer III* orders (1986–1988) the FCC reversed its earlier requirement that carriers provide enhanced services through a fully separate subsidiary.[39] In its 1986 Phase I Order of that proceeding, the commission concluded that requiring the Bell operating companies to structurally separate their provision of enhanced services imposed costs in the form of reduced efficiency and innovation that more than offset the benefits from limiting anticompetitive behavior. The commission retained the two regulatory categories initially established in the *Computer II* proceeding: basic services, which are subject to common-carrier regulation, and enhanced services, which are not regulated.

In place of structural separations, the FCC imposed a set of requirements that permitted the Bell operating companies to offer enhanced services on an unseparated basis. The carriers could offer services subject to two primary requirements: they had to provide

39. Amendment of § 64.702 of the Commission's Rules and Regulations, Third Computer Inquiry (*Computer III*), Rep. & Order, 104 F.C.C.2d 958 (1986). With minor exceptions, enhanced services (the term used by the FCC) and information services (the term used by the MFJ court) are the same.

comparably efficient interconnection (CEI) and draw up open network architecture (ONA) plans. In addition, they were required to file cost-allocation plans, follow network information disclosure requirements, file nondiscrimination reports, and follow procedures to protect customers' proprietary network information. Thus, the LECs were now offered structural relief. They would be free to offer enhanced services on an integrated basis, provided they made their network services publicly available to all other enhanced services providers on an unbundled and nondiscriminatory basis.

The FCC justified its *Computer III* order in terms of the economies of scope that a LEC could realize by providing enhanced services on an integrated basis. The expected gains to a LEC's enhanced services division included access to the parent firm's expertise, access to marketing information, and reduced costs of research, development, and marketing. In a series of subsequent proceedings the FCC added the requirements that Bell operating companies minimize the transport costs incurred by enhanced services providers connecting with basic access facilities, make deployment projections for CEI and ONA services, provide data on timing of installation and maintenance that demonstrate nondiscrimination, and inform enhanced services providers of new or modified network services.

The ONA Requirements

The Bell operating companies filed their initial ONA plans in February 1988, and the FCC adopted its ONA order the following November. The commission's order approved, in part, the Bell companies' ONA plans and set out a comprehensive discussion of the issues surrounding the initial implementation of an ONA and matters expected to require further attention. The major actions included approval of a common model of ONA services; direction to the operating companies to work toward greater uniformity of services; the determination that ONA services are subject to dual federal-state jurisdiction and that their tariffs must be set at both federal and state levels; and the requirement that the operating companies file three-year deployment schedules for initial ONA services. In April 1990 the FCC, in its ONA amendment order, approved the amended ONA plans submitted by the Bell operating companies and acted to remove the structural separations requirements for each company when it became technically prepared to offer ONA services and had put federal and state tariffs into effect.

AT&T, although included in the original *Computer III* order, was subsequently relieved of ONA requirements on the grounds that AT&T's services are offered in a competitive environment. AT&T was still required to file an ONA plan, however. Independent LECs, such as GTE, have been exempt from ONA requirements, but the FCC has subsequently imposed ONA rules on GTE's exchanges located in urban areas.[40]

Comparably Efficient Interconnection. A standard of comparably efficient interconnection applies to the basic services that a carrier uses in its production of enhanced services. The CEI standard requires that, whenever a carrier is engaged in offering enhanced services, it must offer potential competitors access to the same basic services that is effectively equal in quality to what the carrier itself enjoys. The standard does not, however, require that the access conditions be identical or even strictly equal.

The LEC must account for its basic exchange functions on an unbundled basis and make those functions available to enhanced services providers under comparable technical terms and prices. For example, an enhanced service such as voice mail would need both basic access to the subscriber's line and an alerting or signaling service to notify the subscriber of stored messages.

The FCC expected that new forms of interconnection for competitors, using multiplexing to reduce the number of access lines, would enable competitors to obtain effectively equal access to LEC facilities without requiring the LEC and interconnectors to use identical interconnection technologies to provide enhanced services.[41]

---

40. Application of Open Network Architecture and Nondiscrimination Safeguards to GTE Corporation, Mem. Op. & Order, CC Dkt. No. 92-256, 9 F.C.C. Rcd. 4992 (1994).

41. Amendment of § 64.704 of the Commission's Rules and Regulations, CC Dkt. No. 85–229 (1986).

The ONA Concept. Open network architecture, in contrast to the service-specific nature of CEI, was a more far-reaching concept, intended to apply to the overall design of a carrier's basic network facilities and services. An ONA should permit all users of the basic network to interconnect to basic network functions on an unbundled and equal access basis. Under an ONA, a carrier must unbundle each of its basic services, regardless of whether its own enhanced services offerings make use of those basic services. Thus, the principle of ONA goes beyond equal treatment for specific services; it seeks to make the constituent basic network components available to all users.

The FCC has left the actual unbundling of basic services largely to the LECs. The ONA plans, which were initially filed in 1988, classify network offerings into three categories:

- *Basic serving arrangements (BSAs).* These are access arrangements that combine dial tone, local-loop transport, basic local switching, telephone numbering, and directory assistance.
- *Basic serving elements (BSEs).* These are optional, local, switch-based features that can be selectively activated at the local switch and tend to be used by enhanced services providers. They enable service providers to purchase specific call-processing and call-information services, such as automatic number identification and multiline hunting, separately.
- *Complementary network services (CNSs).* These consist of other unbundled, switch-based services (such as call waiting and call forwarding) that tend to be offered to end users rather than enhanced services providers.

Under the Bell operating companies' ONA plans the access components remained largely bundled, combining in a single BSA the local-loop transport, connection to the local switch, and assignment of a telephone number. The three types of access arrangements are depicted in figure 6-5. The ONA plans preserved the three widely used types of access "feature groups" services that had been available from all LECs:

- feature group *A*, consisting of a lineside connection to a local switch and a local seven-digit access number;

FIGURE 6–5
LOCAL SWITCH ACCESS ARRANGEMENTS

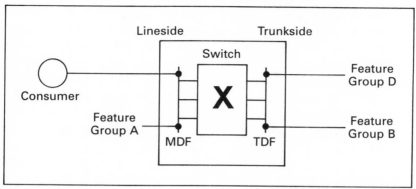

NOTE: MDF, main distribution frame; TDF, trunk distribution frame.

- feature group *B*, consisting of a trunkside connection and a 950–1XXX access number; and
- feature group *D*, consisting of a trunkside connection, 1+ and 10XXX access, and, optionally, automatic number identification, answer supervision, and tandem routing (feature group *C*, which provides trunkside access and 1+ dialing, was available only to AT&T).

In contrast, under an ONA the call-processing and call-information services were unbundled into separate BSEs or CNSs. But here there was considerable variation in the services available and in the terms of offerings among the seven regional Bells' ONA plans. Enhanced services providers decried the lack of national uniformity when they found that just 27 of the 102 requested services would be available under an ONA in all areas of the country.[42]

Descriptions of the ONA services available from the regional Bells are published periodically by Bellcore.[43] The BSAs are grouped into four categories: circuit-switched, packet-switched,

42. HATFIELD ASSOCIATES, ONA: A PROMISE NOT REALIZED, filed in CC Dkt. No. 85-229, Apr. 4, 1988, at annex 11.
43. BELLCORE, ONA SERVICES USER GUIDE (Jan. 31, 1992).

dedicated, and dedicated network access link. The BSE and CNS descriptions are grouped into the same four categories. As noted, a specific service is not necessarily available in all regions, or it may be supplied under different names. Some services require a digital local switch, and several require common-channel signaling.

Enhanced services cover a wide range, from voice mail to audiotex services (calls to 900 and 976 numbers charged on a per-call basis). For enhanced services providers supplying local rather than national services and operating in a single LEC's territory, the lack of uniformity in ONA services from state to state is not necessarily a major impediment. But to the extent that enhanced services providers can realize economies by replicating their services across territories, the checkerboard pattern of BSEs does represent a barrier.

Major Issues

Many enhanced services providers objected that the ONA plans retain a substantial degree of bundling. Under an ONA, an enhanced services provider must use a basic serving arrangement to purchase any basic serving element. And the serving arrangement itself must be purchased as a whole—an enhanced services provider cannot provide its own transport and order only a telephone number and local switching. Nevertheless, the FCC declined to reconsider its ONA decision. It maintained an evolutionary view of unbundling and sought to avoid imposing additional costs on the Bell operating companies.

The ONA order did not initially require the Bell companies to offer operations support systems (OSS) services. Subsequently, however, the commission required certain OSS services to be offered as ONA services: service order entry and status; trouble reporting and status; diagnostics, monitoring, testing, and network reconfiguration; and traffic data collection. It justified that regulation by classifying those OSS services as either basic services or services to be treated as basic.

Billing and collection services are not common-carrier services and are thus not regulated, except as incidental to communications. Some enhanced services providers argued that the Bell operating companies have an incentive to discriminate against them in providing those services. Customer proprietary network information (CPNI) includes all information about customers' network services, and specifically the billing information for each network service used by a customer and usage data and information on customer calling patterns. Without restrictions on their access to CPNI, the Bell operating companies would have access to data about the enhanced services providers' customers that they could then use in marketing their own services. The FCC required the Bell operating companies to establish password and other access controls on databases and to obtain prior authorization from customers with more than twenty lines before making use of such data.

The FCC's ONA order required the Bell operating companies to provide installation and maintenance to customers without discriminating between enhanced services providers and other customers. The Bell companies were required to report, by sampling the service reports of the enhanced services providers and their own enhanced services customers, statistics such as service intervals for installation and delays in maintenance of circuits. Some difficulties arose because the Bell companies' information systems did not track individual service items at the BSE and the CNS level; the commission therefore required modified aggregative reports on enhanced services operations compared with other Bell companies' operations.

The FCC asserted its jurisdiction over ONA services used in conjunction with interstate services and required federal tariffing of ONA services, providing for access by means of BSAs, and offering unbundled interstate BSEs with such access services. Full federal tariffing requires the application of federal ratemaking principles and regulatory review, not simply cross-referencing a state ONA tariff. Resale of federal ONA services may not be restricted with respect to intrastate ONA tariffs. The commission's jurisdiction is limited to preventing anticompetitive or discriminatory effects on enhanced services providers and ensuring that the tariffs are clear and complete.

The effectiveness of the ONA system has been limited, because for access charge purposes enhanced services providers are treated as end users. They are thus permitted to purchase intrastate access arrangements and avoid paying the interstate access charges that constitute the largest single cost of interstate IXC services. As a result of the price differential, most enhanced services providers "tariff shop" and do not purchase interstate ONA services.

The Bell operating companies' ONA plans did not offer collocation to enhanced services providers, and the FCC decided against requiring collocation. Thus, enhanced services providers have to purchase some transport service from the LEC to connect the location point of its equipment to the interconnection point at the LEC switch. The FCC established a "two-mile rule," which effectively eliminated any distance-sensitive charge for all providers, LEC and non-LEC, collocated or not, whose equipment was terminated within two miles of the switch. Beyond that distance the LEC may charge enhanced services providers distance-sensitive transport rates. In the subsequent expanded interconnection proceeding (see below) that elimination of distance charges became know as "virtual collocation."

Under comparably efficient interconnection, a Bell operating company may have a connection at the central office, while other enhanced services providers are located outside.[44] To recover the costs of common interconnection facilities used by those providers, each Bell company levies a basic interconnection charge on all such providers, including itself, regardless of the type of interconnection.

Establishment of tariffs for BSEs has been surrounded by debate over the data and methodology for determining the costs of service elements. Tariffs went into effect in early 1991.[45] At the same time the FCC began an investigation of the tariffs and cost models. Most of the Bell operating companies use a Bellcore computer model known as the Switching Cost Information System (SCIS) to develop cost elements. A limited version of the model and data were provided to parties, and many filed comments also contained proprietary data. Critics of the methodology argue that the operating companies have excessive leeway in choosing assumptions and values for the model inputs, and disapprove of the use of marginal rather than average cost by some Bell companies. Thus, the pricing

---

44. KELLOGG, THORNE & HUBER, *supra* note 1, at 567.

45. The FCC required the initial round of ONA services to be tariffed within one year of approval of the Bell operating companies' ONA plans.

of ONA has become entangled in the regulatory process of sorting through accounting and modeling procedures.

Development of Interconnection Standards

Voluntary organizations of interested industry participants have greatly facilitated the development of technical standards and commercial procedures for interconnection arrangements among U.S. carriers. The Exchange Carrier Standards Association was created in 1983 as part of the breakup of the Bell System. Now called the Alliance for Telecommunications Industry Solutions, it initially sponsored Committee T1-Telecommunications, which focused on developing technical network interconnection and interoperability standards for the United States within the American National Standards Institute. The alliance now includes eight committees, with participants from more than 300 telecommunications industry companies. Issues are generally resolved by consensus.

The Information Industry Liaison Committee (IILC) was established in 1987 to facilitate exchange of information on network capabilities and the development of ONA services. Its domain includes technical, operational, and administrative issues associated with the provision of an ONA. Participants include the LECs, enhanced services providers, IXCs, end users, equipment manufacturers, trade associations, government agencies, and others. The FCC has directed the LECs to work through the IILC to resolve industry problems. As one example, in 1993 the FCC directed the Bell operating companies, working through the IILC, to develop methods to enable enhanced services providers to use LEC operations support systems for support of complementary network services. A major issue, recently resolved after three years of continuing discussion and analysis, is that of long-term unbundling and network evolution.

Assessment

Despite the FCC's initial statements, which envisioned a thorough opening up of the local network, the effect of ONA has largely been the unbundling of prices of separate calling features. ONA can now be seen as a limited step toward unbundling existing LEC services. In return for taking that step, the Bell operating companies obtained relief from structural separations requirements. In practice, apart from the BSAs for trunkside and lineside access to the network, the demand for ONA service elements has been rather limited. In their annual ONA reports to the FCC, the Bell operating companies report receiving few requests for new ONA offerings and only modest progress in making available services previously deemed technically infeasible or requiring further evaluation.[46]

Faced with high cost estimates for comprehensive unbundling, the FCC declined to push for more thoroughgoing opening of the network in the ONA proceedings. Instead, regulators, carriers, and enhanced services providers have turned to voluntary industry standards organizations to advance the technical and practical aspects of making local networks more open to other suppliers. But the objective of unbundling has been pursued in consideration of the design of intelligent networks (examined below) and in proceedings devoted to expanded interconnection (discussed later in this chapter). Hence, although it may not have been a great success in its own right, ONA has become a prerequisite for those two other important developments.

INTELLIGENT NETWORKS

The LECs have a dominant if not a monopoly position in the provision of local switching. For most calls the LEC end office is the first point of switching. Although wireless access is growing rapidly, other competitors in the supply of access—competitive access providers and cable television operators—may find the entry costs of supplying local area switching prohibitive in many markets. Furthermore, most information services providers need access to the LEC's network intelligence and call control services. In some instances those information services compete directly with offerings by the LEC; in others they represent new demands.

46. *BOCs Sketch Plans in ONA Annual Reports for Services Based on Advanced Technologies*, TELECOMM. REP., Apr. 25, 1994, at 33.

Advances in switching technology are on a path to a new architecture for the local network in which network control and information functions are no longer built into a single machine but are distributed over several specialized devices controlled by computer tones and linked by a data network. That "intelligent" network can be used by the LEC to provide enhanced services to its subscribers. It also has the potential to be used selectively by other carriers and service providers to design, control, or operate services they would supply to the market, provided they can obtain access to what may prove bottleneck resources.

The central question for competition policy with respect to the intelligent network is whether the LEC, other carriers, and services providers will access the network intelligence in the same way. The conditions of access to the LEC's network intelligence will increasingly affect the competitive position of other carriers and service providers.

In late 1991 the FCC began an inquiry into the relationship of ONA to the emerging design of intelligent networks, with the goal of encouraging "development of future local networks that are as open, responsive and procompetitive as possible" while "ensuring network reliability and integrity and avoiding the imposition of uneconomic costs."[47] The inquiry is a sequel to the FCC's initial ONA proceeding,[48] which was limited to opening the local network to access by enhanced services providers.

The fundamentally broader inquiry into intelligent networks is directed to all types of providers and end users, including competitive access providers, IXCs, and wireless access providers, as well as enhanced services providers. A central issue is whether the intelligent network can be designed along principles of openness that would permit other carriers and service providers to access network signaling, databases, and intelligence at a highly unbundled level. Many players now seeking access to the network endorse the goal of openness as a principle of design for the intelligent network.

---

47. Notice of Inquiry in the Matter of Intelligent Networks, CC Dkt. No. 91–346, 6 F.C.C. Rcd. 25 (1991) [hereinafter *Intelligent Network Inquiry*].

48. Filing and Review of Open Network Architecture Plans, CC Dkt. No. 88–2, Phase I, Mem. Op. & Order, 4 F.C.C. Rcd. 1, at 42–43 (1988).

The LECs, for their part, generally argue that the design should develop in response to market demand. The continuing debate is about both the technical characteristics of the network architecture and the regulatory provisions that should govern the terms on which the intelligent network is made available.

Opening intelligent network services to competitive supply would put downward pressure on rates for those services and be likely to shift some demand to other providers. To the extent that those services provide net contributions, the unbundling and repricing of intelligent network services will again confront regulators with difficult choices between maintaining subsidies for basic service and encouraging greater efficiency. As described in chapter 8, the FCC has started to address those issues.

Overview of the Architecture

Existing LEC networks are built around stored-program-control switches, both analog and digital, purchased from large manufacturers. The switches comprise the hardware that switches calls, the associated equipment that terminates lines and trunks, and "generic" software for both the operating systems and call-processing features of the switching equipment. A primary factor driving the LECs to develop an intelligent network has been their dependence upon switch vendors for the critical components of virtually all customer services. To introduce a new service, a LEC must otherwise persuade the vendors to develop new generic software, test it, and ultimately install the software on all the switches in its network. With the former architecture, major expenditures and some two to four years were required to deploy a new service once its technical requirements had been fully specified.

An intelligent network provides LECs with far greater flexibility to design and modify services and to inject information processing and control into the flow of network traffic. Through Bellcore, the Bell operating companies have developed one particular implementation of an intelligent network, which they call the Advanced Intelligent Network (AIN).[49] The AIN places the

49. Bellcore, Advanced Intelligent Network (AIN) Release 1 Switch-Service

features and functions needed for new services in adjunct computers, databases, and intelligent peripherals. Those components are separate from the local switch and connected to it over dedicated data links or common-channel signaling. The AIN enables the LECs to create and customize services by specifying and testing packages of applications parameters without changes to the switch software. And it offers other service providers the same opportunities and the chance to use their own databases and computer processing.

The AIN is initially being implemented using digital common-channel signaling (SS7) networks to control the existing digital and electronic analog local switches. That network infrastructure can also support the signaling needed for integrated services digital networks, although to date very little in the way of digital local loops and customer premises equipment has been deployed in the United States.

Features

The Bell operating companies have used the first versions of the AIN to support 800-number service, virtual networks, and line information databases needed for credit-card and third-party billing services. An example illustrates how one service makes use of the basic features of the intelligent network. Business customers purchase toll-free 800-number service to answer calls from customers with a recorded message. The message provides a series of menus that ask the caller to press a sequence of keys to direct his or her inquiry to a particular message or department. That 800-number service with interactive dialing requires four features: number translation (to look up the dialed 800-number in the database), announcement (to ask the caller to press the appropriate keys), collection of the digits pressed by the caller, and finally routing of the call (to the actual telephone number at which the requested service or time of day is provided).

Control Point/Adjunct Application Protocol Interface Generic Requirements (TA-NET-001126) (May 1991).

Evolution of the Architecture

In the early 1980s AT&T introduced the first network services built upon network intelligence. Using its common-channel signaling network, the carrier accessed centralized databases at network control points to support 800-number and calling-card services.

Following AT&T's divestiture in 1984, the Bell operating companies began to extend SS7 network capability throughout their local networks and to establish centralized databases at service control points to support their own 800-number, credit-card, and other billing services. That functionality became known as Intelligent Network 1.

A succession of Bellcore efforts to expand the capabilities of the intelligent network encountered opposition from equipment manufacturers. Thereafter, a wider design effort, including most vendors, led to development of the AIN, which foresees an evolution of the network in a series of specifications.

Figure 6–6 shows the AIN Release 1 architecture in schematic form. The major physical components are the following:

- *Service switching points (SSPs)*. These are switches, either end-office or tandem, that also interface with the SS7 data signaling network. Most stored-program-control switches in the United States can be upgraded to add this capability.
- *Signal transfer points (STPs)*. These are high-capacity packet switches that terminate signaling links and route messages between nodes in the signaling network.
- *Service control point (SCP)*. This is a real-time, rapid-response data processing system with associated databases that represents the main engine of the intelligent network. The SCP connects to the network over SS7 links (dotted lines in the figure) and to operations support systems over lower speed links (dashed lines) that use the X.25 data messaging protocol.
- *Adjunct*. This is an especially rapid-response database processor, with functionality similar to an SCP, that is collocated with a switching system and interfaces directly with it over high-speed SS7 or other data links.
- *Intelligent peripherals (IPs)*. These convert user input from the voice channel into signaling-level information (for example,

FIGURE 6-6

ARCHITECTURE OF THE ADVANCED INTELLIGENT NETWORK

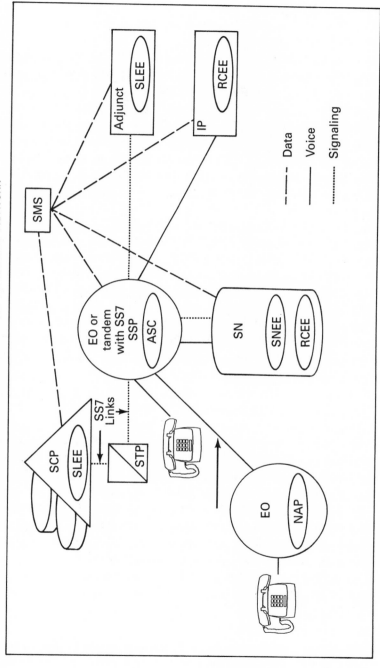

NOTE: ASC, analog signal converters; EO, end office; IP, intelligent peripheral; NAP, network access point; RCEE, resource control execution environment; SCP, service control point; SLEE, service logic execution environment; SMS, service management system; SN, service node; SNEE, service node execution environment; SSP, service switching point; STP, service transfer point.
SOURCE: Southwestern Bell.

speech recognition or keypress tones to digits), using ISDN access for both transport and signaling.

• *Service node (SN)*. This element contains service logic, much like an adjunct, and also has switching capability. It uses ISDN access for both transport and signaling.

• *Service management system (SMS)*. This system interacts with a user to update customer service parameters and install them in the intelligent network. For example, when a user changes the routing for his or her 800 number, the system accepts the information and updates the number translation tables in the SCPs throughout the intelligent network.

Two "execution environments" provide the software that controls that complex system: the network service logic execution environment (SLEE) delivers a service when a call is in process, and the resource control execution environment (RCEE) makes voice transport resources available as a call progresses. In addition, the OSS provides for testing, traffic management, and data collection and for creating and maintaining intelligent network services, and the database administration system (DBAS) processes changes to line-information, billing validation, and automatic intercept databases.

Competitive Implications

As information processing and network control advance, the design and provision of telecommunications services will become a major area of competition among service providers. Who will provide the service logic that defines intelligent network services? In the AIN architecture the LEC controls the service logic. Other service providers are limited to setting parameters made available by the LEC's implementation of the architecture, using the LEC-controlled operations support systems to create the desired service.

An alternative architecture would allow a more open set of interfaces.[50] In that model both the LEC and other service

---

50. MCI, Comments, Notice of Proposed Rulemaking & Notice of Inquiry, CC Dkt. No. 91-191 (Aug. 5, 1991).

providers would establish all of the elements of their service logic and access the basic call-processing operations in a symmetrical manner. The intelligent network would then include mediation at the basic call-processing level to resolve conflicts or ambiguities between different service providers' access to the basic operations.

Protecting an intelligent network from inadvertent or deliberate damage and maintaining a high level of reliability pose a major challenge to the concept of openness. Widespread disruptions in AT&T's and Sprint's SS7 networks in the early 1990s emphasize the risks that threaten even single-provider systems. As a consequence, implementation of early versions of the intelligent network was delayed by the need to ensure reliable operation.

The FCC is considering whether some form of "mediated access" could resolve concerns about security and reliability and establish more nearly symmetrical access to network intelligence for a LEC and its competitors.[51] The commission has proposed requiring the larger LECs to provide third parties with mediated access to their service management systems, and several LECs are proceeding to provide some degree of access to service management functions to create services, customize services, modify service data, store data, and manage the network.

Extending mediated access more deeply into the intelligent network, to the SCP and ultimately to the switch, raises difficult issues of technology and implementation. Third-party access at the SCP level could result in signaling messages' being sent between the LEC switch and non-LEC SCP databases for a large number of calls, which could cause perceptible delay in completing a connection. That delay could be avoided if other carriers directly interconnected to the switch. But modification of switch software to provide mediation and third-party access would involve a far greater number of installations than would access at the LEC's SCP sites, with potentially high implementation costs and adverse effects on quality of service and congestion in the LEC network.

51. *Intelligent Network Inquiry, supra* note 47, ¶ 21.

Assessment

Intelligent network technology is in its infancy, and in this fluid developmental period there do not appear to be technical barriers to creating an architecture in which LECs and other providers would obtain basic network services in essentially identical ways. The issue becomes, rather, What extra costs would such an architecture incur, and what benefits would it yield?

In confronting that issue the FCC again faces the question with which it has struggled since it first addressed the convergence of information processing and telephony, namely, whether the economies of scope a LEC enjoys by integrating services outweigh the forgone benefits of potentially more effective competition from other providers that depend on the LEC for some of those services. In its *Computer III* ruling the FCC decided that the additional costs of separate LEC subsidiaries for enhanced services exceeded the procompetitive benefits. It then went on to provide for requirements of an open network that was intended ultimately to compel the LECs and other enhanced services providers to obtain basic services under standardized tariffs. What makes intelligent networks special is that they require innovation and, as described in chapter 2, are likely to become a bottleneck facility. Companies that innovate in that area may deserve to be rewarded with extra profits, but such profits are hard to accommodate in an open access policy.

EXPANDED INTERCONNECTION

Among the most significant regulatory developments since the AT&T divestiture are the decisions, at both the federal and the state level, to require expanded interconnection under reasonable terms and conditions between the LECs and their competitors. Those decisions, reminiscent of the requirements for interconnection between AT&T and other IXCs that evolved during the 1970s, have the goal of promoting competition at the local exchange level. The regulatory proceedings on expanded interconnection serve as an example of successful interaction between federal and state regulation. A few innovative states pioneered the way. The FCC then built on those experiences and forced the laggards among the states to move into line with the more progressive ones. Expanded interconnection has also paved the way for the local competition provisions of the Telecommunications Act of 1996.[52]

FCC Proceedings on Special Access and Expanded Interconnection

This section describes the environment within which competition for interconnection to interstate service has grown at the local level and the eventual consequences of mandating expanded interconnection; the key issues that arose in that highly contentious arena and the conflicting arguments advanced by interested parties; and the decisions made by the FCC to resolve these issues. Actions by state regulatory commissions are addressed to the extent that they directly relate to the discussion at the federal level. A more detailed treatment of state activities is presented below (see also the section on "State Regulation of Access Charges" above).

This section discusses in some detail the issues and regulatory treatment of special access services, because it is here that the FCC moved most rapidly in adopting new rules designed to encourage competition. That contrasts with the situation in the United Kingdom, where interconnection of switched access has been the more pronounced vehicle of competition. We then turn to a discussion of switched access, where we consider the key problems and opportunities for regulatory action in that market and the nature of the FCC's actions to date.

Two main factors have triggered regulatory action in special access. First, bundling by the LECs of special access services initially limited the development of competition. For example, to reach the point of presence of an IXC, a customer was left with the choice of either purchasing LEC facilities for the entire special access connection or bypassing the LEC entirely, through its own or third-party facilities. Second, aside from the problem posed by bundling, interconnection between alternative providers and LEC networks was not at parity with the interconnection a LEC enjoyed between its own central offices. Alternative providers were, of

---

52. Telecommunications Act of 1996, Pub. L. 104-104, 110 Stat. S6 (Feb. 8, 1996).

course, free to extend LEC circuits into their own offices and connect them with non-LEC facilities. But those arrangements, many argued, inhibited full and fair competition. Only by collocating LEC and alternative providers' interconnection equipment within the LEC central office, or perhaps nearby in a form of "virtual" collocation, discussed below, would alternative providers achieve economic, technical, and administrative parity with the LEC's own central office interconnections.

As described in chapter 2, within an environment of bundled LEC access pricing and limitations on interconnection, a rapidly growing (but still small) market has emerged for competitive access providers to provide bypass services in competition with the LECs. Typically using a fiber-optic ring architecture within a metropolitan area, those providers connect customers with each other and with the points of presence of the IXCs. The ring architecture provides two separate paths from the customer to a node of the fiber network that increase reliability against outages. Because substantial volumes of traffic are required to justify bypass of LEC facilities for special access, competitive access providers depend primarily on large businesses, as well as the IXCs, for their customer base.

Responding to the limitations noted above, Metropolitan Fiber Systems (MFS), the largest competitive access provider, petitioned the FCC in 1989 to establish rules governing the interconnection of facilities for competitive carriers that offer local access services in the interstate market.[53] MFS argued that each separable component of the exchange access network should be priced on an unbundled, cost-supported basis and that competing access services providers should be able to connect to LEC networks at reasonable access points.

The FCC subsequently initiated a formal rulemaking process and, in October 1992, adopted specific rules that require LECs above a certain size (so-called tier 1 LECs) to offer expanded interconnection to all interested parties that need special local access

---

53. *See* Expanded Interconnection with Local Telephone Company Facilities, Rep. & Order & Notice of Proposed Rulemaking, CC Dkt. No. 91-141, FCC 92-440, at 5. In 1987, two years before the MFS petition, Teleport Communications Group (Teleport) filed a similar petition with the FCC for a declaratory ruling.

to interconnect with interstate services (for example, competitive access providers, IXCs, and end users). Following a court decision in June 1994, the FCC had to revise part of that ruling but left its spirit and direction intact. The FCC's implementation of expanded interconnection for special access is one of the most significant actions taken so far to encourage local exchange competition.

In the remainder of this section we discuss: the scope and timing of decisions regarding special access relative to switched access, taking into consideration that the two markets are interrelated; the nature of interconnection that should be required, in particular the range of physical and virtual collocation arrangements for competitors' and LEC facilities in LEC central offices or in other locations; and issues of pricing and rate structure.

The Scope and Timing of Regulatory Action. The FCC has been criticized for separating the regulatory treatment of special access from that of switched access. Without an integrated investigation taking into account the relationships between the two markets, as well as between federal and state jurisdictions, serious economic distortions could emerge. In commenting on the FCC's proposed rules, Ameritech argued: "Special access and switched access services are obviously cross-elastic. The Commission unrealistically and inappropriately partitions the two services by attempting to promulgate rules for special access interconnection without simultaneously doing so for switched access interconnection."[54]

The potential for significant cross-elasticity is apparent. With sufficient volumes and attractive special access tariffs, the customer can route its switched traffic over a high-capacity special access facility, such as DS1, directly to the point of presence of an IXC for switching. Empirical estimations of factor demand equations indicate that switched and special access are in fact substitutable by IXCs.[55] Migration from one jurisdiction to another is also encouraged, because no hard operating line exists between interstate

54. Ameritech Operating Companies, Comments, Notice of Proposed Rulemaking & Notice of Inquiry, CC Dkt. No. 91-141 (Aug. 5, 1991), at 2.
55. Steve G. Parsons & Michael R. Ward, Vertical Disintegration of the Bell System: The Effects on Access Markets (Oct. 22, 1993) (unpublished manuscript, on file with authors).

and intrastate special access service, and the LEC is unable to monitor usage over a circuit to determine the jurisdiction of the traffic.

Furthermore, under the "10 percent mixed access, special access line" rule, the states have the right to regulate all charges for a private line system that carries less than 10 percent interstate traffic, whereas the FCC has authority to regulate all charges for special access where interstate traffic exceeds 10 percent.[56] Thus, application of that rule to interconnection permits a user to connect at the LEC central office under the FCC's rules, even if nearly 90 percent of its traffic is intrastate.[57]

Despite those arguments for simultaneous treatment of special and switched access, competitive access providers wanted to expedite action on special access to reap the competitive benefits as soon as possible. Long delays would accompany the integrated, comprehensive approach of the LECs and state regulatory commissions.

Recognizing the potential benefits, the FCC adopted rules for special access in September 1992 without further delay. While acknowledging that there is substitutability between special and switched access, the commission noted that significant price disparities had developed between the two markets and had already caused significant migration by large users to special access. The commission concluded, "There is no credible showing in this record that significant additional migration will occur with the implementation of expanded interconnection for special access."[58] The FCC, however, took notice of the criticisms and followed up with a compatible decision on switched access expanded interconnection (though not on pricing) in August 1993.

Collocation. A key question in the debate about reasonable access to the LEC network is whether the LECs should be required to

56. The 10 percent rule shows that alternatives to jurisdictional cost separation exist.

57. National Association of Regulatory Utility Commissioners, Comments, Notice of Proposed Rulemaking & Notice of Inquiry, CC Dkt. No. 91-141 (Aug. 5, 1991), at 6.

58. Rep. & Order, CC Dkt. No. 92-440 ¶ 26.

provide physical collocation or be free to specify virtual collocation for interconnection with their central offices. The fundamental distinction between those two approaches involves the division of responsibility between the LEC and the interconnector in selecting and controlling the use of terminating equipment.

With physical collocation, the interconnector extends its existing network into the LEC's central office and establishes a "node"—a location at which its network circuits terminate. As a rule, the node is partitioned from the rest of the central office, and the interconnector is granted easy access to the node for installation, operation, and maintenance of its terminating equipment (for example, multiplexers and digital cross-connect systems). At the node, circuits from the interconnector and circuits from the LEC are cross-connected, with the LEC and the interconnector each responsible for its own equipment. Thus, the interconnector, as well as the LEC, can replace or upgrade its equipment at any time, to introduce new services or to improve the efficiency of its network.

Under virtual collocation, the interconnection point lies outside the central office, often in a nearby manhole to which the LEC extends its network. The interconnection equipment, which remains in the central office, is owned by the interconnector or leased to it by the LEC. Although the interconnector does not necessarily have the right of routine physical access to the equipment, the interconnector typically is able to monitor and control the equipment to specify performance standards, detect service problems, and reconfigure circuits to avoid service degradation or outages.

The LECs, supported by a number of state regulatory commissions, argued that they should be permitted to decide whether to provide physical or virtual collocation. They claimed that the choice should reflect the circumstances in individual central offices, "including space availability, office design, security, equipment type, power requirements, and staffing."[59] Most competitive access providers, however, as well as large users, argued that the FCC should require physical collocation, unless the LEC demonstrates that insufficient space exists in a given central office. That would place the burden of proof for the standard of

59. *Id.* ¶¶ 29, 31.

interconnection arrangements on the LECs. In either case, the competitive access providers argued, interconnection arrangements should be technically and economically comparable to the interconnections LECs provide to themselves.[60]

Those parties also pointed to the successful use in New York State of physical collocation for intrastate access. In 1986, in direct negotiations, Teleport Communications had sought but failed to obtain virtual collocation with New York Telephone's facilities. It had then brought the case before the New York Public Service Commission, which had ruled in 1989 that New York Telephone (a NYNEX operating company) must provide "comparably efficient interconnection" to private line competitors but had permitted New York Telephone to choose virtual rather than physical collocation. In the words of the Department of Justice:

> After first attempting to establish a virtual collocation tariff which led to considerable dispute with competitors about technical and economic comparability to physical collocation, NYNEX ultimately agreed in December 1990 to implement a tariffed physical location arrangement, having recognized that the effort to mimic physical collocation in a virtual collocation environment would involve significant operation inefficiencies.[61]

Taking such considerations into account, the FCC in October 1992 ordered the LECs to offer physical collocation to all interconnectors requesting it. Interconnectors and the LECs would

---

60. The International Communications Association, for example, pointed out that space limitations at central offices may not be a pervasive problem because "most of these facilities were built to accommodate equipment requiring four to 12 times the physical space required by modern digital and fiber optics facilities." International Communications Association, Comments, Notice of Proposed Rulemaking & Notice of Inquiry, CC Dkt. No. 91-141 (Aug. 5, 1991), at 6.

61. U.S. Department of Justice, Reply Comments, Notice of Proposed Rulemaking & Notice of Inquiry, CC Dkt. No. 91-141 (September 21, 1991), at 36–37.

be free to negotiate virtual collocation arrangements if both parties preferred such arrangements over physical collocation.

The FCC's efforts were set back in June 1994, however, when the U.S. Court of Appeals for the District of Columbia Circuit overturned the physical collocation requirement. The FCC reacted quickly and in July 1994 issued a requirement of virtual collocation instead. Since some LECs had already begun offering physical collocation and implementing the initial rule, existing physical collocation arrangements were allowed to remain in effect if the LEC so desired; the LECs could also generally choose to continue to offer physical collocation. The Telecommunications Act of 1996 again makes physical collocation the rule and virtual collocation the exception. But to the extent that a regulator succeeds in making virtual collocation arrangements as tight as those imposed by the New York Public Service Commission (see below), the actual outcome may be the same as under the FCC's physical collocation rule. Under the strict rule in New York, NYNEX opted to continue with physical collocation.

Clearly, physical or strict virtual collocation rules facilitate more sophisticated types of interconnection and thereby increase competitive pressure on the LECs. Besides the issues of market power and externality, however, there appears to be at stake a genuine issue of economies from vertical integration and the boundaries of firms. Interconnectors want collocation because they want to make use of their specific investments in equipment, internal standardization, and procedures. Therefore, they want to extend their reach vertically, further into the LEC switch. At the same time, the LEC wants to protect *its* specific investment and maintain control over its facilities. In the United Kingdom, British Telecom has in the past decade sharply reduced the number of its switching offices. One may wonder how that would have been possible under collocation arrangements. Of course, if interconnectors are viewed as customers who bring in substantial business, the LECs may not want to change their switching offices. For restricting the flexibility of the LECs, however, the interconnectors may have to pay a price. For interconnectors that are liquidity-constrained, the initial outlay for physical interconnection may also be so high that they would prefer virtual interconnection.

Pricing and Rate Structure. Special access pricing in the context of expanded interconnection involved three key issues: how to reprice the bundled channel termination portion of special access services, whether LEC charges to interconnecting parties should include a contribution to further universal service and other regulatory goals, and whether additional pricing flexibility should be accorded to the LECs in response to increased competition.

Channel termination charges. The FCC discussed two alternative ways of restructuring channel termination charges, which we shall illustrate in terms of virtual collocation. Under the first alternative, the LEC would impose a connection charge on interconnectors that substitute their own facilities for a portion of LEC special access facilities, instead of the then existing channel termination charge (which also includes a transmission component).[62] Rate changes would not be required for other LEC special access customers. The rationale for that approach is that only interconnectors are put at a disadvantage by bundled rates. Under the second alternative, the channel termination charge would be unbundled for all customers into two separate charges: a connection charge paid both by LEC special access customers and by interconnectors, and a transmission charge paid only by the former.

The interested parties were split between those alternatives, with some LECs, competitive access providers, IXCs, and other groups supporting each. The LECs largely supported the first alternative on administrative grounds: it would better suit the many customers who are not interested in expanded interconnection and would avoid the huge administrative expenses for the LECs to convert the computerized systems used to assign, inventory, and bill for special access services.[63] Other parties (including some LECs) supported

---

62. Of course, interconnectors would also pay separate charges for any special central-office features, such as specially designated electronics. A connection charge would also be established for physical collocation, but it would be lower than for virtual collocation, since all connections would be within the central office. With physical collocation the LEC would also impose charges for space rental and associated services for use of the central office.

63. Ameritech, Reply Comments, Notice of Proposed Rulemaking & Notice

the second alternative, largely on grounds of greater economic efficiency. The Department of Justice pointed out that the LEC has averaged channel termination charges across all such terminations. Thus, all customers with comparable usage volumes pay the same amount per circuit, regardless of their distance from the LEC's central offices. With such pricing, IXCs have weak incentives to locate their points of presence close to the LEC central office, because they do not capture the cost savings achieved by such proximity. Conversely, customers close to LEC central offices have incentives to engage in uneconomic bypass of LEC facilities, because the cost of purchasing bypass service may be less than the averaged LEC channel termination charges, while the incremental costs incurred by the LEC to serve the customer may be less than the bypass costs incurred by the customer.

That objection could be met, even with unbundled rates, by making the rates for transmission (bundled with connection) distance sensitive. The Justice Department noted that (bundled) channel termination charges already are subject to volume discounts through established tariffs, and observed that:

> A particularly large IXC such as AT&T that is able to purchase multiple high capacity DS3 lines will pay considerably less [per circuit] for special access than a smaller IXC or alternative access provider that uses only a few lower-capacity lines. These discounts apparently resulted from LEC concern that AT&T might be able to engage in end-to-end bypass of the LEC's special access services in high traffic areas.[64]

If there is no barrier to making channel termination rates a function of volume, no barrier is likely to exist for making them a function of distance as well.

of Inquiry, CC Dkt. No. 91-141 (Sept. 21, 1991), at 45.

64. U.S. Department of Justice, Reply Comments, Notice of Proposed Rulemaking & Notice of Inquiry, CC Dkt. No. 91-141 (September 21, 1991), at 12.

Thus, the issue is not one of bundling or unbundling (for noninterconnectors) but one of average cost pricing versus deaveraged rates. That issue relates to the appropriate degree of price flexibility that should be accorded to the LEC in responding to growing competitive pressures—a matter discussed below. In light of the conflicting arguments, the FCC has adopted the first alternative, that of requiring unbundling only for service to interconnectors.

Contribution. The LECs have generally argued that they should be permitted to charge interconnectors a contribution element, in addition to connection charges, to help recover costs associated with geographic cost averaging, various cross-subsidies designed to promote universal service, and the cost of plant needed to meet "carrier of last resort" obligations. Those arguments are quite similar to the ones raised for the contribution element contained in the RIC for switched access. Under special access, however, the ability to bypass the LEC networks is greater, and the relationship of services provided by special access to those for which LECs carry burdens of public service obligations is much weaker than under switched access.

Many observers agreed nonetheless that a contribution element would in principle be justified. As the FCC observed:

> The LECs' rates for various access services may reflect certain regulatory mandated support mechanisms designed to achieve social policy objectives. In a competitive environment, we believe that all market participants must be required to share the cost of such support mechanisms.[65]

The key challenge was to estimate the appropriate contribution. One approach involved taking the contribution simply as the difference between the then-current LEC special access revenue and the incremental cost of providing these services, reduced to a per-unit basis.[66] But basing the contribution on such a calculation would

65. *Expanded Interconnection*, Rep. & Order, *supra* note 35, ¶ 145.
66. Alfred Kahn, affidavit, CC Dkt. No. 91-141.

have required LEC competitors simply to reimburse the LECs for whatever disparities exist between the cost and the revenues of providing service. As the Justice Department observed:

> For any firm in a competitive environment, particular services do not provide a static contribution to recovery of overall costs of the enterprise. Rather, such contribution will vary in response to changes in competitive conditions.[67]

The FCC rejected that approach and concluded from the record that the only significant support flow imposed on special access by FCC regulations is the overallocation of general support facilities (GSF) costs to "special access" as a consequence of the commission's Part 69 requirements.[68] Consequently, the commission decided that, "instead of allowing a contribution charge, it would be far more desirable to revise the Part 69 rules to allocate GSF costs proportionately to all service categories."[69]

Price flexibility. The degree of pricing freedom that the LECs should have in facing competitors is one of the most pervasive public policy issues associated with the evolution of U.S. telecommunications markets. Events here in many ways are replaying those during the past twenty-five years in the interexchange market. Throughout the 1970s and 1980s AT&T chafed under the restrictions imposed by regulators, who feared the company would engage in predatory pricing, while AT&T faced increasing competition in the interexchange market.

---

67. U.S. Department of Justice, Reply Comments, Notice of Proposed Rulemaking & Notice of Inquiry, CC Dkt. No. 91-141 (Sept. 21, 1991), at 58.

68. *Expanded Interconnection*, Rep. & Order, *supra* note 35, ¶ 147. That outcome results from the Part 69 requirement that the LECs exclude local-loop investment when allocating GSF overhead costs among access categories. That exclusion, which reflects the regulatory goal of preserving universal service by reducing cost pressures on local telephone rates, imposes a larger GSF overhead allocation on special access than would otherwise exist.

69. *Id.* ¶ 148.

In the local exchange market, the LECs similarly place high priority on obtaining greater pricing flexibility, as well as freedoms in other directions, so that they can engage competitors on a level playing field. GTE well categorized the kinds of freedoms desired by the LECs:

> geographic deaveraging of access services pricing; increased flexibility in the timing of price adjustments keyed to action in the marketplace; assembly of service packages as end-to-end offers to customers, including the resale of competitive access providers' facilities, with the ability to go "off-tariff" to satisfy unique customer demands and service arrangements through contracts; and increased flexibility in the range of allowable prices under the price-cap program.[70]

The FCC itself has expressed well the dangers of maintaining average cost price constraints on the LECs while leaving their rivals essentially unregulated:

> Retention of . . . rate averaging could create a pricing umbrella for the CAPs [competitive access providers] and deprive customers of the benefits of more vigorous competition. It would also undermine efficiency by preventing the LECs from competing effectively even when they are the low cost service provider. Handicapping the LECs in this fashion could also increase their competitive losses under expanded interconnection, bringing upward pressure to bear on LEC rates for less competitive services, including those used by residential customers.[71]

Competitive access providers and the IXCs have generally argued that the LECs already have substantial flexibility under price caps, and that additional flexibility would permit the LECs to exploit their

---

70. GTE Corp., Comments, Notice of Proposed Rulemaking & Notice of Inquiry, CC Dkt. No. 91-141 (Aug. 5, 1991), at 22.

71. *Access Charge Order,* Rep. & Order, *supra* note 10, ¶ 178.

monopoly positions. For example, MFS recited several cases in which the LECs have demonstrated "striking" price flexibility and argued that "the Commission has already provided LECs subject to price cap regulation with an unprecedented level of pricing flexibility, which previously had been designed exclusively for carriers facing effective competition."[72]

The FCC concluded its pricing regulation for special access by granting the LECs somewhat more flexibility than before to adjust prices of individual services. The Commission adopted a zonal approach similar to one developed earlier in Illinois for intrastate expanded interconnection. The Illinois Commerce Commission permits Illinois Bell to set rates for residential and business local exchange service, as well as for Centrex and private line service, that are based on three "density pricing zones": downtown Chicago, the remainder of Chicago and some suburbs, and the rest of the state. Rates are averaged within each zone but are lower in the two more urban zones.[73]

Similarly, the FCC decided to allow the LECs to establish a number of density pricing zones within each "study area" (consisting generally of a LEC's service territory within a single state). The commission did not explicitly limit the number of zones but specified that LECs seeking to establish more than three zones "shall be subject to increased scrutiny and must carefully justify the number of zones proposed in their density pricing plan."[74]

For a LEC regulated on the basis of rate of return, rates for the same service in different zones were permitted to diverge by a maximum of 15 percent in the first year that the tariff was in effect, by 30 percent in the second year, and by 45 percent in the third.[75] For LECs under price caps, there is now for each zone a subindex for DS1 service and a subindex for DS3 service.[76] Those subindexes have 5 percent upper bands and −10 percent lower

---

72. MFS, Comments, Notice of Proposed Rulemaking & Notice of Inquiry, CC Dkt. No. 91-141 (Aug. 5, 1991), at 88.

73. *Access Charge Order*, Rep. & Order, *supra* note 10, ¶ 176.

74. *Id.* at n.413.

75. *Id.* at n.421.

76. The special access basket is one of four baskets in the FCC's price-cap regime for LEC interstate services.

bands. Thus, for example, the LEC could lower the price for its DS1 service by a maximum of 10 percent per year in one density zone (adjusted for the price-cap index) and raise the price in another by as much as 5 percent. But the weighted average for rates in all the zones must continue to fall within the existing 5 percent overall pricing bands applicable to the existing DS1 and DS3 subindexes within the special access basket subject to the price-cap program.

The FCC Proceeding on Switched Access

In phase I of its proceeding on expanded interconnection for switched services, the FCC proposed to adopt essentially the same interconnection requirements for switched transport that it had adopted in September 1992 for special access. It argued:

> As with special access expanded interconnection, CAPs and other interconnectors would be able to physically (or virtually) collocate transmission equipment in LEC central offices to enable them to interconnect their circuits to the part of the LEC network needed to complete the service. Under this proposal, CAPs and others could interconnect for the first time to LEC switches, subscriber lines, and portions of LEC switched transport.[77]

In phase II of the same proceeding, the commission envisioned broader competition, including the provision by LEC competitors of switching facilities that would perform functions similar to those of LEC tandem switches. According to the commission, "This broader form of switched access competition could open the door to a robust 'network of networks,' in which the switched networks of CAPs and others interconnect with, but also compete with, each others' as well as the LECs' switched access networks."[78]

Reform of switched access regulation had proceeded on a slower regulatory track than special access, because changes here

---

77. *Expanded Interconnection*, Second Notice of Proposed Rulemaking (Oct. 16, 1992) ¶ 2.
  78. *Id.* ¶ 4.

would potentially have a greater impact on other services, on the LECs, and on IXCs, than is true of special access. Among the complications, switched access services have been far more laden with cost-price disparities arising from, for example, the use of a "frozen" subscriber plant factor rather than actual subscriber line usage to allocate non-traffic-sensitive loop plant costs;[79] the allocation of tandem switching costs; the non-distance-sensitive allocation of interexchange trunk circuit equipment; and contributions to carrier common line support pools.[80] After acting on expanded interconnection for special access, however, the FCC took less than a year to pass an expanded interconnection ruling on switched access that completely paralleled the ruling on special access.

The FCC's "transport phase 1" order[81] of August 3, 1993, permits third parties to interconnect their own transmission facilities to LEC switched transport services. Interconnections are allowed to LEC central offices, serving wire centers, tandem switches, and certain remote nodes—the same standards as for special access expanded interconnection. Those rules also include the same pricing, tariffing, and rate structure requirements as for special access. Rate structures must also reflect cost-causation principles and must be unbundled so that interconnectors can buy only those services they need.[82] The FCC did not, however, provide for a contribution element, because one is already contained in the per-minute access charge elements that, under switched access, had to be paid anyway (the residual interconnection charge; see above). To the extent that special and switched access transport are substitutes, that decision to exclude a contribution element may partially alleviate the incentive for uneconomic bypass of the LEC network.

---

79. As explained above, subscriber plant factor is the ,formula used in allocating local-loop cost to long-distance service, and subscriber line usage is the use of the local loop by long-distance traffic relative to total local-loop traffic.

80. *Expanded Interconnection*, Rep. & Order, *supra* note 35, at n.336.

81. *Expanded Interconnection*, Second Rep. & Order & Third Notice of Proposed Rulemaking, *supra* note 35.

82. *See* TELECOMM. REP., Aug. 9, 1993, at 6.

The implication for competition of the proceedings on switched access expanded interconnection was that a competitive access provider could compete for the transport portion of the interexchange business in switched access just as it could in special access arrangements.

State Policies on Expanded Interconnection

The interests of the states in expanded interconnection for switched access have been mixed. The New York Public Service Commission has encouraged FCC policy for expanded interconnection for switched access, though it also argued for a contribution element.[83] Other states, such as Alabama and Missouri, have opposed the FCC's policy. Alabama officials argued that such a move by the FCC would place rural and poor communities at a disadvantage and would unlawfully preempt state interests in intrastate switched transport policy.[84] Competitive access providers, particularly Teleport and MFS, had succeeded in negotiating collocation arrangements with state regulators and LECs in several metropolitan areas before the FCC reached its decision on expanded interconnection for special access.

Illinois and New York provided the first testbed of actual competition by competitive access providers interconnected to LECs. As seen above, state regulatory provisions for collocation and pricing have influenced the debate over those issues when subsequently taken up by the FCC for application to interstate services.

Collocation in Illinois. In 1991 the Illinois Commerce Commission approved a negotiated virtual collocation arrangement between Illinois Bell Telephone and Teleport. Teleport was allowed to specify the multiplexing equipment that it would place in the Illinois Bell central offices. Teleport also had the ability to monitor and control the multiplexing equipment that it leased to Illinois Bell and

---

83. *Expanded Interconnection*, CC Dkt. 91-141, FCC 93-379 ¶ 9.
84. *Id.* ¶ 12.

that would be located in the operating company's central offices. Illinois Bell personnel would perform repairs on that equipment, but Teleport would specify and supply inventories and spare parts. Teleport actually chose the type of equipment used elsewhere by the operating company itself and thus minimized adaptation problems for Illinois Bell personnel.

In 1991 Illinois Bell and certified local carriers negotiated a collocation tariff, called Optical Interconnection Service, to establish virtual collocation at three Chicago central offices. The arrangements applied to nonswitched private lines and special access only. Rates included an element for contribution to common costs.

Collocation in New York. The New York Public Service Commission required New York Telephone to establish comparably efficient interconnection (see the discussion of CEI earlier in this chapter) for intrastate private line traffic in the metropolitan New York LATA, using tariffs for nonswitched collocation that is technically and economically comparable to actual location if the physical point of interconnection is outside a LEC building.[85] New York Telephone received rate flexibility: for its own competitive responses it was authorized to increase rates on high-capacity and interoffice private lines by 25 percent annually and to reduce them to incremental costs.

New York Telephone proposed a virtual collocation option for interconnection in which competitive access providers' fiber-optic cable would be interconnected at a LEC-designated manhole located outside a LEC central office. A quarter-mile local distribution channel rate would apply. Teleport and MFS successfully argued, however, that physical collocation was required.[86] The Radio Common Carriers Association, representing paging and ancillary services, also pressed for physical collocation, on the grounds that it

---

85. The interconnecting competitive access provider was required to offer similar reciprocal access to the LEC and to other carriers.

86. Competitive access providers such as Teleport offer their retail customers interconnection services at 135, 405, and 565 megabits per second over fiber cables. They have significantly greater capacity than the LEC "platform" (DS1 and DS3) services developed to provide a connection between interconnectors.

needed interconnection of lower capacity than the LEC was proposing.

In 1991 MFS interconnected with New York Telephone and began providing service through a working virtual collocation arrangement that had gone through contentious negotiations that involved a task force established by the New York Public Service Commission. New York Telephone and MFS had not been able to agree on whether competitive access providers could include digital cross-connect systems and multiplexers in their virtual collocation arrangements, or on whether they retained primary responsibility to monitor or control their traffic.[87]

In the other New York proceeding, that with Teleport, New York Telephone had withdrawn its option for virtual collocation and instead filed a proposal it called Optical Transmission Interconnection Service (OTIS). Under OTIS the competitive access provider would install fiber to the LEC's wire center, where the LEC would provide the optical terminating equipment. The LEC would specify technical standards for the interconnection, where repair time is especially important. The rate structure for the terminating equipment would be designed to duplicate the results of actual ownership of the device by the interconnector.

Following negotiations among the interested parties, the Public Service Commission approved, with some modifications, tariffs for optical interconnection. The agreement, which became effective March 29, 1991, was termed OTIS II. It has four major provisions.[88] First, the interconnector was permitted physical collocation at any wire center or central office using a multiplexing node. Second, the node would contain optical line terminating multiplexers, DS0/DS1/DS3 multiplexers, and digital cross-connect systems, provided they met industry standards. Third, encaged floor space, power, and environmental support were to be supplied by the LEC. Rental terms were governed by tariffs and individual lease arrangements. Finally, the interconnector was responsible for

87. MFS, Comments, Notice of Proposed Rulemaking & Notice of Inquiry, CC Dkt. No. 91-141 (Aug. 5, 1991).

88. New York Public Service Commission, Order Regarding OTIS II Compliance Filing (May 8, 1991).

maintenance. The LEC was allowed to recover actual costs, based on the type of connection, and to include a rate element for a universal service charge to generate a contribution to basic services. The regulatory agreement with the state commission granted the LEC statewide pricing flexibility for its competitive services, where it previously had been required to offer them under tariff.

The New York Public Service Commission has found that, in principle, collocation for switched access and for unswitched access need not be distinguished. The commission has taken the approach of requiring CEI, framing the requirement in terms of concept and substance, and leaving the technological mode of compliance unspecified. The LEC must respond to a request for collocation by offering a specific technical arrangement, but it is not required to do so in advance for every end office.

The LECs (New York Telephone and Rochester Telephone) raised the issue of synchronizing the effective date with that of the FCC proceeding, to avoid extra costs, but in the end decided to acquiesce in what their state commissions had decided.

Tariffing of Expanded Interconnection. Pursuant to the 1993 FCC order on switched access expanded interconnection, the regional Bell operating companies had to file tariffs for such services by November 18, 1993, to become effective February 15, 1994. NYNEX, for example, filed for expanded interconnection that would provide customers with (1) space within a NYNEX serving wire center (SWC), access tandems, and certain remote nodes to locate certain fiber-optic or microwave facilities and transmission equipment; and (2) connection(s) to NYNEX-provided DS1 and DS3 level switched services. NYNEX proposed to offer expanded interconnection for switched services by physical collocation.

A large part of the tariff was concerned with the space made available by NYNEX for collocation. There were four types of space provided: multiplexing node space, roof space, transmitter and receiver space, and cable space. The largest items were the roof spaces for antennas and the spaces within each central office to be used by the collocated customer as a multiplexing node. The standard size for the latter was 100 square feet, with a minimum of 80 and a maximum of 300 square feet. Customers could locate either central office multiplexers or optical line terminating multiplexers. In addition, they could locate transmitter and receiver equipment.

NYNEX designated points of termination within each office as the physical demarcation point between customers' facilities and equipment and its own. NYNEX provided a cross-connection (office channel termination) between the customer's point-of-termination and the switched access entrance facility channel terminations or multiplexers provided by NYNEX.

Costs could be either recurring or nonrecurring. The recurring costs were monthly rentals, based on a composite carrying charge factor from the Automatic Reporting Management Information System (ARMIS, a new cost information system used for the FCC) for switched and special access interconnection. A cost composite had to be used because the ARMIS produced different costs for switched and special access expanded interconnection, even though investments and services are identical, and NYNEX decided to charge the same in both cases.[89] Rates were based on costs and usually differed by location. The nonrecurrent costs were one-time expenses for NYNEX's multiplexing nodes ($54,878 for a 100-square-foot node). The multitude of recurrent and nonrecurrent rate elements contained in that tariff gives a clear picture of the many items to be provided under collocation. Although not particularly complex, they become quite cumbersome once regulatory costing and pricing procedures need to be applied.

Because NYNEX also had to provide switched access expanded interconnection under state tariffs (in New York), which differed from federal tariffs, and because the expanded interconnection space was used jointly for interstate and intrastate services, the recurrent and nonrecurrent rates were proportionally based and applied according to the percentage of interstate use.

The New York example shows how complicated a product expanded interconnection is. Although the tariffed items differ somewhat under virtual collocation, they are nevertheless many, and pricing them continues to be a contentious issue. One way in which the LECs will make virtual collocation arrangements mimic physical

---

89. The filing therefore also include revisions for the special access expanded interconnection tariffs.

collocation is through "operational leaseback" programs, under which interconnectors may purchase their own equipment, sell it to the LECs, and lease it back from them.[90]

ASSESSMENT OF INTERCONNECTION POLICIES

The analysis in this chapter has been limited largely to competition in the market for interconnection of IXCs and service providers to LECs. But interconnection of LEC networks with other carriers and service providers raises all of the principal issues of competition in local telephone markets—hence the continual involvement of regulatory authorities in those matters (and the length of this chapter). The technical conditions of access in that area are most prominent in decisions regarding collocation and access to LEC network intelligence functions. Regulatory decisions on pricing of interconnection determine the relative cost advantages among the LEC's competitors and the flexibility left to the LEC to respond to competitive entry. Unbundling requirements determine the extent to which competitive entry is possible without duplication of local network facilities. Mixed into those decisions are other objectives of supporting universal service and mitigating the dislocations due to rapid rebalancing of rate structures that are not cost-based.

Access charges in the United States have so far not been very sophisticated. In the switched access area, pricing has been by minutes of use (instead of call attempts or contribution to peak capacity utilization); there has been hardly any peak-load or two-part pricing. In special access pricing, geographic deaveraging has barely begun. Here the FCC has followed the innovative lead of Illinois.

Carrier common line charges and transport services provided to the IXCs are huge sources of revenue to the LECs. The potential loss of contribution, were the IXCs to shift to competitive providers or to supply transport on their own, would have a major impact on other services, including residential and business local exchange services. The importance of the FCC's transport pricing policy lies

---

90. *LECs File New Tariffs for "Virtual Collocation"; NYNEX, Pacific Telesis Continue Physical Collocation*, TELECOMM. REP., Sept. 5, 1994, at 1.

in the potential effects on the LECs and IXCs. As the Department of Justice observes, "The LECs potentially face huge losses of revenues if AT&T, by purchasing its transport from competitive providers or supplying transport on its own, is able to avoid paying the LECs much of what it now does for switched access."[91] Implementation of expanded interconnection for switched services, leading to direct competition in the switched transport market, has started to further erode LEC revenues and contributions generated by switched access services.

The regulation of access charges reveals a major conflict between federal and state regulation when it comes to contributions to social policy (universal service) objectives. Many states have tried to preserve higher intrastate access charges than those prescribed by the FCC for interstate services. But because of the resulting opportunities for arbitrage and bypass, those states either do not see the desired contributions materialize or have to resort to costly monitoring or to restrictions on local competition.

The contribution element also creates potential conflicts among states. Companies face different opportunities in different states because of the large variation across states in intrastate access charges. Although variations in opportunities due to differences in state policies are common in other markets, in the telecommunications area firms gain increasing opportunities to engage in arbitrage between states (for example, by rerouting calls through other states). This frustrates differentiation in state policies.

The MFJ court and the FCC had, through the equal-charge rule, provided entry help to small IXCs. The equal-charge rule, urged upon the FCC by the MFJ court in lieu of cost-based access charges, represented a case of the FCC's bowing to pressure at a

---

91. U.S. Department of Justice, Reply Comments, Notice of Proposed Rulemaking & Notice of Inquiry, CC Dkt. No. 91-141 (Sept. 21, 1991), at 79. As reported by the Justice Department, AT&T estimated that it was paying some $400 million more annually to the LECs than it would have under Part 69 rules. Bell Atlantic estimated that within its region a shift of $130 million in charges between dedicated and common switch transport would occur as a result of abandoning the equal charge per unit rule. Bell Atlantic, Comments, Notice of Proposed Rulemaking & Notice of Inquiry, CC Dkt. 91-141 (Aug. 5, 1991), at 15.

time when it was vulnerable, because the MFJ had occurred without its involvement and because of the controversy surrounding the subscriber line charge. That has probably resulted in costs to society from inefficient call routing and partial duplication of networks. It is uncertain whether those costs have been outweighed by the benefits from market share increases for AT&T's rivals.

The interim rate structure for transport has been a move in the direction of cost-based transport pricing, but it stopped short of being fully cost-based. The reasons given by the FCC for that interim approach were twofold. First, the FCC wanted to avoid an abrupt change in rates that would severely affect competitive positions among the IXCs. In particular, it wanted as much as possible to avoid hurting smaller IXCs. Second, the costs of tandem switched transport were not fully agreed upon between the FCC and the interested parties.

Can fully cost-based transport prices be expected in the near future? Through banding requirements, the FCC restricted the ability of price-cap-regulated LECs to restructure the transport rate elements on their own, thus reserving to itself any further move in the direction of more cost-based pricing. The continuing proceedings on the transport rate structure were initiated to focus on the need for cost-based transport rates in an emerging, increasingly competitive environment.[92] They will merge into new proceedings on access charge reform to be completed in 1997.

Despite the FCC's initial statements, which envisioned a thorough opening up of the local network, the effect of the open network architecture initiative has largely been to unbundle the pricing of calling features without fundamentally unbundling the physical components of the local loop. In return for taking that limited step, the Bell operating companies obtained relief from structural separations requirements. In fact, apart from the basic serving arrangements for trunkside and lineside access to the network, the demand for ONA service elements has been rather limited. To advance the technical and practical aspects of opening

92. *Transport Rate Structure and Pricing*, Third Mem. Op. & Order on Recons. & Supplemental Notice of Proposed Rulemaking, CC Dkt. No. 91-213.

LEC network features to other suppliers, regulators, carriers, and enhanced services providers have turned to voluntary industry standards organizations.

The high estimated cost of a comprehensive unbundling deterred the FCC from ordering more thoroughgoing unbundling in the ONA proceedings. But that objective has been pursued in considering the design of intelligent networks, in proceedings devoted to interconnection for special access and switched access, and, ultimately, in the Telecommunications Act of 1996.

Much more than the ONA, expanded interconnection has aimed to provide for potentially all interested parties direct, nondiscriminatory access to the LEC networks. Expanded interconnection was first promoted by progressive states such as New York (for physical and virtual collocation) and Illinois (for virtual only) before the FCC entered the fray. As a result of the experience with dual regulation of collocation, those innovative states influenced the FCC, which in turn homogenized state approaches. The Illinois Commerce Commission commented, "Several state commissions, including Illinois, are providing experimental cases for the FCC to learn from in order to substantiate tangible benefits of competition that are frequently claimed by proponents of competition and to develop a plan at the federal level."[93] The Illinois regulator judged the state experience as showing that competitive benefits did result from mandatory interconnection and unbundled access. Prices for digital access services have fallen, service has improved, and the diffusion of fiber-optic technology has accelerated.[94]

Why have some states innovated while others have lagged behind? Two states that have promoted expanded interconnection, New York and Illinois, are dominated by major metropolitan areas in which communications-intensive industries are concentrated.[95] The strong interests of their service industries should be reflected in

93. Illinois Commerce Commission, Comments, Notice of Proposed Rule-Making & Notice of Inquiry, CC Dkt. 91-141 (Aug. 5, 1991), at 2.

94. *Id.* at 5.

95. Massachusetts, which is dominated by the Boston metropolitan area, had also introduced expanded interconnection with physical collocation, but more quietly than New York and Illinois.

those moves. In contrast, some of the more rural states not only retarded but actually opposed expanded interconnection. Thus, the need for innovative (often high-capacity) services is first perceived in states with large telecommunications demand. Later, as learning curves are run down, the other states follow suit. It is not clear that the initial innovations could have been pursued so quickly under federal regulation only.

With respect to collocation, the New York Public Service Commission has done much of the legwork necessary for the FCC proceedings. The New York experience demonstrated that physical collocation is workable and that the associated problems of security, space, and organization can be overcome. It strongly suggests that virtual collocation should be considered a second-best alternative. On the other hand, the Illinois experience with virtual collocation appears to have been more favorable. The distinctive feature seems to be that the New York regulators defined virtual collocation very specifically in terms of technical and economic equivalence with physical collocation.[96] Such an equivalence is hard to achieve under virtual collocation. It is administratively onerous and requires many concessions from the LEC.

States have perceived at least two disadvantages of federal-state regulation of expanded interconnection. Although dual regulation has probably achieved innovative outcomes, the duplication of efforts is frustrating. Consequently, *ex post* harmonization was a problem when the FCC formulated its policy of expanded interconnection. Also, states fear that increased competition will reduce the LECs' total revenues, which could force states to lower the LECs' intrastate rates.

The FCC's expanded interconnection orders and those of some states carried the objective of equal access to LEC facilities substantially further than did the MFJ, which was principally concerned with equal access for the IXCs. The orders gave interconnectors access that promised to be equivalent to that which the LECs provided to themselves. The orders extended such access further, to competitive access providers, cable television companies,

---

96. Economic equivalence includes such issues as the ability to make use of tax advantages granted for the ownership of assets.

and large users for their private networks. In so doing they have provided the basic prerequisites for entry into local markets and set the stage for retail competition, which we examine in the following chapter. They have also provided the basis for the interconnection requirements of the Telecommunications Act of 1996.

7

Competition in Local Exchange Retail Markets

IN THIS CHAPTER we consider entry and competition in the LEC retail markets in more detail. This new competition is driven by regulatory, technological, and demand-side conditions and developments. The conditions conducive to the arrival of competition in telecommunications services include: an unbalanced (cross-subsidized) rate structure; new technologies that lead to lower costs and new service opportunities; new demands not being met by incumbents; regulatory help for entrants (for example, through low access charges); and regulatory incentives for incumbent LECs to promote entry by others (by making entry of regional Bell operating companies into interLATA markets dependent on the presence of sufficient local competition in their service territories).[1] Those conditions influence competition in each of the various LEC retail markets to different degrees. In the area of intraLATA long-distance services, competition is mostly driven by an unbalanced rate structure. In nonswitched and switched local services an unbalanced rate structure also plays a major role, but so do new technologies, new demands, and the provisions of the Telecommunications Act of 1996.[2] Competition in wireless services is driven by both new demands and new technologies. This chapter considers each of those markets and tries to identify the sources of competition in each

1. Curtis A. Cramer, *Local Competition for Telephone Services,* 9 REV. INDUS. ORG. 273 (1994).
2. Telecommunications Act of 1996, Pub. L. 104–104, 110 Stat. 50 (Feb. 8, 1996).

(including regulatory entry help, although this is hard to identify). We also examine video services and interLATA long-distance, two markets that the LECs want to enter and that have feedbacks on competition in the traditional LEC markets. Chapter 8 complements the current chapter by describing the FCC's order to implement the local competition provisions of the Telecommunications Act of 1996.

INTRALATA LONG-DISTANCE SERVICES

We first consider intraLATA long-distance service for switched telephony.[3] With about $13 billion in total revenues, that is an important part of the U.S. telecommunications market.[4] In many respects the LECs here face the most traditional type of entry competition. IntraLATA long-distance is like short interLATA long-distance service, and therefore competition in that domain has strong similarities with competition among the IXCs. Thus, the

3. The regional Bell operating companies have been barred by the federal MFJ from offering intrastate *inter*LATA services. Despite that federal antitrust jurisdiction, however, those services are regulated by state regulators because they are entirely intrastate. In the literature, intrastate *inter*LATA long-distance charges have been considered as an example of successful innovative regulation and deregulation. After the AT&T breakup many states deregulated those rates and allowed free entry. Some states introduced price-cap regulation in that area. David L. Kaserman & John W. Mayo, *Deregulation and Market Power Criteria: An Evaluation of State Level Telecommunications Policy*, in TELECOMMUNICATIONS DEREGULATION—MARKET POWER AND COST ALLOCATION ISSUES, 65–96 (J. R. Allison & D. L. Thomas eds., Quorum Books 1990), argue that most states used sound economic judgment on market competition when determining whether to deregulate AT&T's intrastate services or regulate them lightly. Alan D. Mathios & Robert P. Rogers, *The Impact of Alternative Forms of State Regulation of AT&T on Direct-Dial Long-Distance Telephone Rates,* 20 RAND J. ECON. 437–53 (1989), showed that states with little or no regulation of AT&T experienced lower intrastate interLATA long-distance rates than those that continued rate-of-return regulation. That had some influence on the introduction of federal price-cap regulation. At that time, however, it did not induce the FCC to deregulate AT&T. On LEC entry into interLATA services, see below.
4. *See* FCC, STATISTICS OF COMMUNICATIONS COMMON CARRIERS (1992), at table 3–4.

IXCs are the natural entrants in that market. Because they specialize in interLATA services, however, the IXCs currently do not have the optimal network architecture for the intraLATA market.

Local access and transport areas are an artificial result of the MFJ's separation of the Bell operating companies' spheres of influence from that of the IXCs. Thus, the Bell operating companies could offer (monopoly) services within LATAs but were not allowed, except under special circumstances, to offer interLATA services. Although the IXCs were not barred by the MFJ from offering intraLATA services, state regulators only gradually allowed them to do so. State regulators also determine what are local and what are long-distance calls within a LATA.

IntraLATA competition in long-distance services has been increasing in recent years and is today at about the level where interexchange competition was at the time of the AT&T divestiture, in terms both of the market shares achieved by non-Bell rivals and of the level of access granted to customers of such rivals. Current market shares by non-Bell rivals rarely exceed 5 percent. Those low market shares may be partly explained by the lack of equal access or "dialing parity." To access non-Bell rivals, customers usually must dial a five-digit prefix (10XXX), whereas LEC intraLATA toll services are reached by simply dialing the number. The MFJ court established that differentiation, arguing that intraLATA equal access would be too expensive to achieve and that automatic presubscription in their favor would keep the Bell operating companies viable.

Today's intraLATA long-distance markets differ substantially in several respects from long-distance markets before divestiture, however. First, regulation of intraLATA long-distance competition has rested with the states. As a result, policies with respect to intraLATA competition vary throughout the country. Until very recently, a handful of states did not allow any intraLATA toll competition. All states now allow at least facilities-based competition using LEC access and 10XXX dialing. In addition, in about fifteen states equal access proceedings have been under way that would move to one-plus presubscription, which, in the remaining states, is going to be implemented through FCC rulings in accordance with the Telecommunications Act of 1996. Among the early states is Minnesota, which has certainly been helped by the experience with one-plus intraLATA equal access in some rural areas of the state since 1992 through the Minnesota Equal Access Corp. The Minnesota Public Utilities Commission expected the conversion to equal access to cost about $29 million to $33 million.[5] Actual average costs per customer would be lower if those one-time costs were spread over many states. That hints at a possible advantage of federal regulation in that area. It is interesting that in that case rural telephony has been providing progressive solutions that are now paving the way for competition in urban areas.

Other states where experience with equal access has been gained through independent LEC ventures in rural areas include Iowa and South Dakota. That is therefore an area where the previous existence of small telephone companies provides yardsticks of interconnection that can be used for entry into the markets of the large LECs.

Subsequently, the FCC has ordered all LECs to provide dialing parity for all of their originating calls that require dialing. For all toll services, dialing parity will be implemented through presubscription that automatically routes dialed calls to the customer's preselected carriers, which may be different for intraLATA and interLATA calls. The schedule for implementation of dialing parity requires the LECs to begin dialing parity service not later than February 1999, with earlier requirements for LECs that provide intraLATA toll service before that date.[6]

Beside the technical costs of conversion, equal access carries with it organizational costs of presubscription. In the case of Minnesota the LECs (U S West and others) are allowed to recover the costs of conversion to equal access through intraLATA tolls based on minutes of use by their own customers and through access charges paid by their intraLATA toll competitors. Clearly, the costs of conversion have to be compared with the benefits, which may be harder to measure than the costs. That those benefits are real can be

5. *IntraLATA Equal Access Expected Early 1996 in Minnesota; PUC Affirms "Bona Fide" Request Rule,* TELECOMM. REP., Oct. 31, 1994, at 13.

6. Second Rep. & Order & Mem. Op. & Order, CC Dkt. 96-98, FCC 96-333 (Aug. 8, 1996).

seen from ads run by Ameritech against 10 percent price discounts offered by AT&T under "10XXX" intraLATA access, "arguing that AT&T's savings were largely illusory and that customers would have to dial an extra five digits to complete calls through AT&T."[7] Some extra costs from choosing entrants may, however, remain as a result of intraLATA equal access, because telephone customers may end up subscribing to three carriers simultaneously: the LEC, one IXC for interLATA, and a second IXC for intraLATA services.

The second difference between current intraLATA toll markets and predivestiture long-distance markets is that the intraLATA toll competitors of the LECs now include the large, well-established IXCs. Those companies have financial resources, know-how, and brand names that make them formidable competitors. Because the IXCs often have only one point of presence in a LATA, their network configuration is not ideally suited to intraLATA competition. The fact that there is large excess transport capacity between LEC access points and IXC points of presence, together with the lack of distance sensitivity of LEC access charges, makes that less of a problem for the IXCs.

The third difference is that a system of access charges is in place for intraLATA services that usually contains a (more or less explicit) contribution element. Unlike before divestiture, the LECs' rivals receive (to the best of our knowledge) no discount for lack of equal access to intraLATA long-distance services.

IntraLATA long-distance services have in the past provided sizable cross-subsidies for local residential access. States could nevertheless move to intraLATA competition because they retained most of the subsidy basis for the LECs through high intrastate access charges to be paid by competitors (and, through imputation, to the LEC itself). Indicating that cross-subsidies and competition may be compatible, Kaestner and Kahn claim that states allowing intraLATA long-distance competition have higher intrastate access charges.[8] That would imply that such competition can even help

7. Edmund L. Andrews, *Ameritech Forcefully Stays Home,* N.Y. TIMES, Nov. 22, 1994, at D1.

8. Robert Kaestner & Brenda Kahn, *The Impact of IntraLATA Competition on Local Exchange Company Prices, in* ECONOMIC INNOVATIONS IN PUBLIC

increase cross-subsidization. In line with that argument, Kaserman, Mayo, and Pacey show that intraLATA competition has failed to increase rates for basic local residential services.[9]

Some states, however, have used the opportunity of introducing intraLATA toll competition to restructure local rates and access charges. For example, at the beginning of 1995, California officially introduced 10XXX competition and allowed basic monthly rates to increase dramatically, by 30 percent to 75 percent, depending on the type of service. At the same time, rates for intraLATA toll calls charged by the large LECs (Pacific Bell and GTE) were reduced on average by about 40 percent. IXCs and other providers, which already had substantial sales in that market without official permission to offer service, have started out below those new rates, some by 40 percent (in the case of Cable & Wireless) or more.[10]

Despite the high access charges and unequal access, intraLATA competition was effective in reducing intraLATA long-distance prices. Blank, Kaserman, and Mayo show that competition on average reduces intraLATA toll rates by 20 percent.[11] To their surprise, they also find that the presence of alternative or price-cap regulation has a price-increasing effect. Their explanation is that such regulatory plans were chosen in high-cost states. In our view, however, the explanation may also lie in the specific design of many such plans, which emphasize reductions of or moratoria on basic local residential rates. Thus, higher intraLATA toll rates may have been allowed in compensation.[12] That conjecture may also explain

UTILITY REGULATION 37–55 (M. A. Crew ed., Kluwer Academic Publishers 1992).

9. David L. Kaserman, John W. Mayo & Patricia L. Pacey, *The Political Economy of Deregulation: The Case of Intrastate Long Distance,* 5 J. REG. ECON. 49 (1993).

10. *Telephone Companies Hear Call of New Round of Competition,* L.A. TIMES, Dec. 30, 1994, at D1; *California Says IntraLATA Competition Will Begin Jan. 1,* TELECOMM. REP., Sept. 19, 1994, at 18.

11. Larry R. Blank, David L. Kaserman & John W. Mayo, Dominant Firm Pricing with Competitive Entry and Regulation (May 1994) (unpublished manuscript, on file with authors).

12. Blank, Kaserman, and Mayo did not test for an interaction between

the finding of Kaserman, Mayo, and Pacey that the introduction of intraLATA toll competition did not increase local rates in those cases where regulators used alternative regulation.[13]

NONSWITCHED LOCAL SERVICES

Nonswitched local services consist of high-volume voice and data transport services. Most of the issues that arise in that area have already been treated in the context of wholesale transport and interconnection in chapter 6. Competition for nonswitched local services takes the form of private networks, private line services, and metropolitan-area network services. Because those services come under the "10 percent rule," according to which they fall under FCC jurisdiction if more than 10 percent of their traffic is interstate, and because the FCC chooses not to regulate them, they are regulated only if they are used almost entirely for intrastate purposes and if the state in which they are located imposes regulation.

Metropolitan-area networks have been built by competitive access providers in the form of high-capacity fiber rings, which can serve telecommunications traffic between large office buildings as well as collect traffic for transport to IXC points of presence. Consequently, nonswitched local services probably share the same market with special access transport services for IXCs. The Bell operating companies currently command a 10 percent to 20 percent price premium over competitive access providers for special access transport services.[14] Since the IXCs can build their own transport access, they are also potential competitors in offering transport services to others. The fourth set of players in that market consists of cable television companies with high-capacity networks outside the areas served by competitive access providers.

competition and alternative regulation.

13. See, however, the recent experience in California, where an increase in local rates was explicitly programmed into the introduction of intraLATA toll competition.

14. Cramer, *supra* note 1, at 273, 282.

SWITCHED LOCAL TELEPHONE SERVICES

One would expect pressure for market entry to be greatest for those services in which the LECs reap the highest profits or generate the largest subsidies per customer or per unit sold. Given the claim that local telephone services are subsidized, one is not surprised to find that they are the last LEC markets to experience entry, but one is surprised to find that pressure for entry is actually substantial. A principal reason for such pressure is that demands for local telephone services are not homogeneous, and their price-cost margins differ substantially. Within a LEC's territory the costs of customer lines can easily vary by a factor of five, while prices usually are the same throughout. Thus, within switched local services some segments are subsidized while others are a source of subsidies. Because switched local services are the LECs' core business, and because growth in demand for local telephone services has been slow, the LECs are vigorously defending their turf.

Competition for switched local services takes three forms. First, switched access services to IXCs can be converted to special access by means of access lines provided to large customers for their long-distance business with the IXCs. We have described the competitive role of special access in chapter 6. Second, resale of local services and so-called shared tenant services have made use of volume discounts available under LEC price structures and start to make use of wholesale discounts available under special plans or imposed by the Telecommunications Act of 1996. Third, facilities-based entry occurs in local market segments that are the source of cross-subsidies as well as in market segments serving new demands.

Resale of LEC Services

Resale of local services can be either a source of price reduction, due to aggregation of consumer demands, or a source of price increase, due to site-specific advantages in hotels, airports, and the like. Local resale at a profit had been allowed in 40 percent of the states, but will spread quickly as the Telecommunications Act of 1996 is implemented.[15] Resellers can have procompetitive effects

15. NATIONAL ASSOCIATION OF REGULATORY UTILITY COMMISSIONERS,

because they can reduce the exploitation of small customers and because they facilitate broad-based entry even with small initial network investments. Reselling is therefore a precursor for facilities-based competition. Shared tenant services, in addition to providing low rates, permit sophisticated services to be provided on a shared basis. They are often organized as nonprofit cooperatives.[16] Linked up with competitive access providers, shared tenant services can exert competitive pressure on the LECs.

Although regulators have been fairly permissive in allowing resale of local telephone services on a shared tenant basis or by hotels, the LECs have been fighting resale that might open the door to local facilities-based competition. For example, Ameritech in Indiana opposed MCI's attempt to sell Centrex or Centrex-like services under an agreement with Hancock Rural Telephone Corporation. That agreement would have involved resale of the use of Ameritech's switches for some calls outside Hancock's approved service area. Besides arguing that Hancock was subsidized by the Rural Electrification Administration (implying that MCI would benefit from rural subsidies for its local services), Ameritech concentrated on such issues as "unlawful use of its facilities" and "public convenience and necessity," meaning that this would represent undesirable competition.[17] Thus, although commercial interLATA resale services are now commonplace, competitors until recently encountered obstacles to entering broader local services markets.

The Ameritech and Rochester Plans for Local Competition

In 1993 Ameritech, one of the seven regional Bell operating companies, and Rochester Telephone in New York independently submitted plans with potentially broad competitive implications for the interaction of federal and state regulation. Rochester Telephone

NARUC REPORT ON THE STATUS OF COMPETITION IN INTRASTATE TELECOMMUNICATIONS (originally published Aug. 26, 1992; updated and republished Nov. 9, 1993).

16. *Id.*

17. *Ameritech Attacks MCI Plan to Resell Local Service,* TELECOMM. REP., Nov. 28, 1994, at 9.

proposed to split itself into wholesale and retail parts. The
wholesale part would offer nondiscriminatory and unbundled access
to other telecommunications providers (including their own retail
operations). In that way, the wholesale company would own and
operate the local network but would not deal with retail customers.
Instead, customers would be served by the retail company, which
would compete with potentially many other network and service
providers. Ameritech proposed to open access to its wholesale
network services on an unbundled basis. The access and unbundling
provided by both plans would go beyond what was then called for
in the FCC's open network architecture and special access
requirements. Because the Ameritech and Rochester plans raised
fundamental issues of federal and state regulation, the National
Association of Regulatory Utility Commissioners passed a resolution
suggesting that the FCC and state regulators treat such plans
cooperatively.[18]

Ameritech's Local Interconnection Proposal. Ameritech took the
lead in proposing a far-reaching plan for unbundling local network
elements and providing interconnection to other carriers and service
providers. In broad outline, Ameritech's strategy has been to make
unbundled local network components and services available to
competitors in exchange for freedom from the MFJ line-of-business
restrictions, permission to supply interLATA services, and pricing
flexibility.

Ameritech filed tariffs for a proposed trial of unbundled service
elements in Illinois in February 1994.[19] In response, AT&T
petitioned the Illinois Commerce Commission to open a
comprehensive investigation of the regulatory conditions that would
allow entry of competitors.[20] The Ameritech plan would require

18. NATIONAL ASSOCIATION OF REGULATORY UTILITY COMMISSIONERS,
1993 REPORT OF THE ADMINISTRATIVE DIRECTOR ON LITIGATION 107 (1993).

19. *See* J. KERN (director, Regulatory Affairs, Ameritech), ILLINOIS
COMMERCE COMMISSION ADVICE NO. 4975 (February 1994).

20. *Petition of AT&T to Establish Conditions Necessary to Permit Effective
Exchange Competition to the Extent Feasible,* at 94-0146 (filed before the
Illinois Commerce Commission, Apr. 2, 1994).

approval by both state and federal regulators and by the MFJ court. Action on the full plan was therefore slow and has led to many changes in the original plan.

Technical preconditions. According to Ameritech,[21] its proposal addressed the technical preconditions that potential competitors have identified as necessary for local exchange competition. Those include transparent interconnection, unbundling of the local loop or local switching, access to the LEC signaling network for call setup, and assignment of telephone numbers and local number portability.

Under the first precondition, other carriers would interconnect with the LEC to provide transparent calling among customers of different providers. Four interconnection options were proposed, covering LEC-provided DS1 or DS3 facilities; LEC-provided optical interface; physical collocation of competitor's equipment, cross-connected at the DS1 electrical level to the LEC switch; and virtual collocation, cross-connected at the DS1 level. Compensation for interconnected traffic would be reciprocal and based on the LEC's access tariff rates for transport to the end office and unbundled local switching for call termination.

Unbundling, the second precondition, would disaggregate exchange services into two components—the local loop and switching. The local loop is the physical facility from the network interface at the customer's premises to a point of interconnection on the main distribution frame in the LEC's end office. Further unbundling of the loop at intermediate points of the distribution network was not proposed at that stage. Switching includes the cross-connection to the switch, the switch port, dial tone, telephone numbers, exchange support functions (for example, operator services and usage, directory listings), and access to optional vertical central-office services.

---

21. In the Matter of a Petition for a Declaratory Ruling and Related Waivers to Establish a New Regulatory Model for the Ameritech Region, *Supplemental Materials to Ameritech's Petition of Declaratory Ruling and Related Waivers to Establish a New Regulatory Model for the Ameritech Region* (filed before the FCC).

Different technologies, selected by the provider, could be used to supply the loops, provided they met the service parameters and specifications. Loop prices were to be independent of technology and based on the grade of loop ordered: voice-grade analog; digital transmission up to 160,000 bits per second, suitable for basic rate ISDN; and primary-rate ISDN and DS1. Technical standards were specified by reference to Bellcore documents and industry and local practice.

Ameritech stated that it intended to set prices for unbundled loops above incremental cost. Rates would include a contribution to overhead but would not, on average, exceed fully distributed (state plus interstate) costs. Rates would be geographically deaveraged and could contain term and volume discounts.

Ports, in Ameritech's trial proposal in Illinois, would initially be offered for basic exchange and PBX services, two types of coin (public telephone) service, and WATS. Additional functions, for direct inward dialing and ISDN, could be added from existing tariff offerings.

Switching would be priced at a monthly access rate, based on area of service and type of port. Subscribers would presubscribe to one or more carriers for intraLATA and interLATA usage.

The third precondition was access to the LEC signaling network for call setup. Other carriers would, through expanded switched interconnection (described in chapter 6), be able to use Ameritech's advanced signaling (SS7) network to set up calls that they carry on their own networks. A competing carrier would interconnect its signal transfer points to the LEC's SS7 network at a local LEC signal transfer point.[22]

The interconnection facility could be provided by the competitor or ordered from the LEC. The interface point could be at either the LEC's or the competitor's signal transfer point, with a standard data interface that follows published Bellcore and Ameritech specifications.

---

22. The competitor's initial address message would be transported, without screening or modification.

The call setup service would be tariffed on an interim basis; eventually, when the LEC's local signal transfer points have recording capability, a per-message rate will be charged.

The final technical precondition was assignment of telephone numbers and local number portability. Ameritech, which has acted as the number plan administrator for states in its service area, stated that it will turn over that function to an independent administrator. A similar transfer of administrative functions for the North American Numbering Plan has been under way at the national and continental level.

Achieving ubiquitous number portability will require further development of database technology and establishment of a shared database and will impose significant additional costs. In the interim, more limited degrees of portability can be implemented that would allow a consumer to change carriers while maintaining the same telephone number. The means for doing so include:

- *Foreign exchange.* A leased line connects the local central office to a foreign (distant) central office.
- *Call forwarding.* Calls to a subscriber's original number are intercepted in the original central office, reoriginated, and directed to the forwarded number.
- *Separate NXX.* An entire block of 10,000 numbers is reserved for a single subscriber; when the subscriber changes carrier, the NXX code is reassigned to the new carrier. That option is applicable only to the largest subscribers.
- *DID (direct inward dialing) trunking.* Incoming calls are routed through the exchange, over dedicated DID trunks, directly to a customer or the customer's service provider. The final four or five digits of the called number are delivered to the customer for further processing (for example, routing to a specific telephone).
- *Intelligent network local database.* Unassigned NXX prefixes are designated as "portable codes." All carriers look up the number translation in a shared database and complete the routing accordingly. Implementing that solution requires further technical development.
- *Regional shared database.* Here the NXX would not be a geographic indicator, and number translation would function like a local intelligent network database.

Recent trials by equipment vendors and IXCs report progress in developing local number portability for service providers,[23] and Ameritech has issued a request for proposals for suitable technology. The proposed MFJ waiver would require Ameritech to implement "true" number portability when it becomes available, and to rely on call-forwarding technology in the interim.[24]

With regard to engineering, operation, maintenance, and administration practices and procedures, Ameritech proposed to integrate installation orders from competing carriers with orders from other customers and treat them similarly. Repair and monitoring procedures would also apply on a similar basis. With the unbundling of local exchange switching, access to white pages listings, 911 emergency services, and deaf-relay services would be available as optional services under contract. Ameritech committed itself to cooperate with competitors to connect switches with community emergency services. Subject to space limitations, Ameritech offered conduit and pole attachment space on a nondiscriminatory basis to competitors.

Controversial issues. Although the Ameritech plan has been praised as a major step toward local competition, it has a number of controversial elements. One is that Ameritech wants to recover "social pricing subsidies and other costs" that have been traditionally part of access charges.[25] That controversy has been resolved for Illinois, where the retail rate structure is deemed subsidy-free, but it lurks in the four other states of Ameritech's region.

Also controversial is Ameritech's linkage of its innovative interconnection proposal with relief from the interLATA line-of-business restriction. Ameritech argued that it had to be able to

23. *MCI, Manufacturers Unveil Number Portability Solution*, TELECOMM. REP., May 15, 1995, at 11–12.

24. *Justice Says Ameritech's InterLATA Service Waiver Request Is "More Limited, More Profound,"* TELECOMM. REP., May 8, 1995, at 28–30 [hereinafter *Ameritech's InterLATA Waiver*].

25. *Ameritech Modifies Universal Access Plan, Pursues Interim Number Portability in Effort to Quell Objections*, TELECOMM. REP., Feb. 21, 1994, at 25.

compensate losses from local competition with gains from long-distance traffic. We treat that issue below.

Recent developments and assessment. The Ameritech plan would have required a waiver of the AT&T MFJ and ratification by the FCC and the five states in Ameritech's region. Here the role of the Ameritech Regional Regulatory Committee (ARRC; see chapter 5) was crucial. In the spring of 1994 the ARRC staff gave its conditional backing to the plan and suggested some improvements.[26]

A large part of the interconnection proposals contained in the plan have actually been implemented. After several months of negotiations, the Department of Justice supported granting a waiver that would permit Ameritech to implement a version of the plan on a trial basis in Chicago and in Grand Rapids, Michigan.[27] The agreement between the Department of Justice and Ameritech had the support of several IXCs and competitive access providers. It provides for network unbundling, local number portability, reciprocal compensation for terminating interconnecting carriers' traffic, and resale of local services.[28] The Ameritech plan had substantial influence on the Telecommunications Act of 1996. In particular, the quid pro quo between opening the regional Bell operating companies' networks to completion and the RBOCs' entry into interLATA toll services in their region has influenced sections of the statute, and Ameritech's willingness to offer unbundled network elements to its competitors has left footprints in the act.

The Rochester Plan. Rochester Telephone Corporation's "Open Market Plan," with subsequent modifications, gained approval from the New York Public Service Commission and from the FCC.[29] It

26. *ARRC Staff Says Ameritech's "Universal Access Plan" Is "Viable" Basis for Local Competition but Lists Concerns,* TELECOMM. REP., Apr. 11, 1994, at 17–19.

27. *Ameritech's InterLata Waiver, supra* note 24.

28. AT&T has applied for authority to resell local exchange services in the two trial markets and stated that it plans to offer facilities-based services in the future. *See AT&T Applies for Local Service Authority in Two States,* TELECOMM. REP., May 8, 1995, at 35.

29. *See Rochester Tel's "Open Market Plan" Approved in New York;*

creates a holding company (Frontier Corporation) and two subsidiaries. The first, Rochester Telephone, is now the network operator, which offers predominantly wholesale services to other carriers on an unbundled basis subject to price-cap regulation. The second, Frontier Communications of Rochester, is a lightly regulated subsidiary providing retail services in competition with other companies and buying wholesale services from Rochester Telephone at regulated prices. Local competitors are thus able to select services from Rochester Telephone and combine them with their own service elements and equipment. The first major local competitor to have signed up with Rochester was Time Warner.[30] Frontier Communications of Rochester is envisaged as a marketing rather than as an asset-based company. Thus, reselling may, under that plan, become the norm rather than the exception. Local number portability has initially been achieved through direct inward dialing and remote call forwarding, while the company works on more advanced techniques. Competing network providers have gained parity in interconnection provisions that call for reciprocal compensation of access charges between Rochester Telephone and other carriers that complete calls. Only if the imbalance of calling in one direction exceeds 10 percent will access charges have to be paid per minute of use, on the basis of Rochester's current access charges. But Rochester Telephone has sought to change carrier common line charges from a per-minute basis to flat-rate charges.[31]

In an interim period Rochester Telephone continues to sell its services to end users and will transfer to Frontier Communications of Rochester only those services that have become competitive. In that way monopoly services will remain under price-cap regulation. To make the plan attractive to end users, Rochester Telephone has

Telco's Rates Will Drop by $21 Million over Seven Years, TELECOMM. REP., Oct. 17, 1994, at 1, and *F.C.C. Approves Waivers for Rochester Unbundling Plan, Supports Local Competition "Experiment,"* TELECOMM. REP., Mar. 13, 1995, at 8.

30. *Proponents of Rochester Tel Pact Make Case to PSC, Say "Open Market Plan" Balances Competition, Safeguards,* TELECOMM. REP., July 4, 1994, at 26.

31. *See F.C.C. Approves Waivers, supra* note 29, at 8.

agreed to an upfront reduction of retail rates and a further reduction (in nominal terms) over time. Conflicts of interest arising from the affiliation of Rochester Telephone with Frontier Communications of Rochester are reduced through very strict rules governing interaffiliate transactions.

Competitive Implications. An interesting feature of the Ameritech and Rochester plans is their implication that economies of scope from integrating wholesale and retail business are not overwhelming. The plans therefore suggest that it makes sense to look at the wholesale market for interconnection services and the retail market for telecommunications services as related but separate markets. The main relationship between them, from a competition perspective, is that integrated companies have a decisive advantage in the retail market if the wholesale market is dominated by them and is not efficiently regulated. The Rochester and Ameritech plans suggest that market dominance in the wholesale markets and the regulation of integrated firms may continue to be a problem.

That concern is borne out by early experience with the plans. In the first few months of its implementation the Rochester plan got off to a slow start.[32] Facilities-based competition was virtually nonexistent, and wholesale competition was hampered by the small rebate (5 percent) on Rochester Telephone's retail rates that Frontier offered its wholesale customers. In particular, AT&T's scaling back of its local service operations after an initial jump-start was attributed to those high wholesale rates. Frontier defended the rates on the grounds that the retail rates were noncompensatory to begin with and that cost savings from providing wholesale were small. Wholesale rates and unbundled rates for facilities-based carriers are being renegotiated as of this writing in the context of the FCC's local competition order discussed in chapter 8.[33] That episode and the similar one at Ameritech show two things. First, competition

---

32. *See Doubt Surfaces About Rochester "Open Market Plan"; Critics Say Competition Experiment Is Sputtering*, TELECOMM. REP., Aug. 14, 1995, at 7.

33. Implementation of the Local Competition Provisions in the Telecommunications Act of 1996, First Rep. & Order, CC Dkt. 96-98 (Aug. 8, 1996) (hereinafter *Implementation FRAO*).

takes its time to develop. Second, in the end, prices decide competitiveness, and therefore regulatory intervention may continue to be required.

Facilities-Based Local Competition

With the exception of wireless services, discussed below, non-LEC carriers have so far captured only a tiny fraction of the facilities-based local exchange market for telephone services. There appear to be three major hindrances to the development of facilities-based local competition:

• In many states, such competition was, until very recently, prohibited either by legislation or by regulatory rulings.
• The pattern of cross-subsidization has made local exchange competition unattractive, at least for the market of residential subscribers.
• Entry into the local exchange market is difficult because of the high costs that customers face in switching suppliers and because of lack of local number portability. At least until recently, local telephony was viewed by many as a natural monopoly. Even if that no longer holds for new business and housing developments, the sunk investments in copper in the local loop create a major entry barrier.

The first of those problems is diminishing quickly, as state regulatory commissions and state legislators recognize that such a prohibition makes little sense. If local exchange markets are subsidized and exhibit other high entry barriers, further legal prohibition is unnecessary to prevent entry. If there are no such barriers, competition will benefit consumers. The only remaining rationale for a prohibition of local competition is that some local consumer groups subsidize others. That subsidy can take two major forms: subsidy of residential by business customers, and of rural by urban customers. The first subsidy is in effect a tax on small business, because large enterprises can bypass the LECs through private networks, private line access, and other means. If cross-subsidized rates persist, that bypass will continue to increase over time and will ultimately undermine the subsidies. The second form of subsidy introduces discrepancies between states with small and those with large rural populations. The latter are likely to benefit more from a nationwide universal service policy than from an absence of competition in switched local services. A nationwide universal service policy would subsidize states with large rural populations. Prohibiting local competition may benefit rural populations at the expense of urban populations in the same state and may impose net costs in the form of inefficiency. With passage of the Telecommunications Act of 1996, states are being forced to open their local exchange markets.

The second factor hindering facilities-based local competition, cross-subsidization, is also likely to vanish over time. The sources of local subsidies are drying out as a result of competition in the subsidizing markets and federal and state moves to reduce charges in those markets.

The third factor, customer switching costs, has already lost much of its importance, and technical and market developments are continuing that trend. Already, most homes are supplied by two or more lines that serve as telephone lines or could be converted to do so. One can argue that such duplication of networks may increase total costs to the economy, but the duplication already exists. Hence, the question is only one of their expansion and conversion. Thus, entrants are likely to expand into switched local telephone and data services incrementally. The main candidates for providing local exchange competition are the competitive access providers, cable television companies, IXCs, mobile and personal communications services operators, and electric utilities. Most of those providers already have another service base apart from local switched telephone services, whether it be nonswitched services, cable television services, interexchange services, or electric power distribution. Their incremental cost of providing switched local telecommunications services is substantially lower than the stand-alone cost of building those services from the ground up.

Those different entrants will attack different parts of the LEC market. Competitive access providers and the IXCs will first go after high-volume business users and large downtown apartment buildings. Cable television companies will start with urban residential subscribers and new housing developments. New wireless technologies may have an edge in remote rural settings, but in time wireless services are likely to compete with LEC local services much more broadly. All those potential entrants face a common problem, namely, the need to build a diverse customer base to attain a good load profile that will fill their capacities. That may give rise to alliances between those different types of firms.

Competitive Access Providers. Competitive access providers started out primarily as suppliers of point-to-point dedicated circuits. They are authorized to offer switched access and transport services in a number of metropolitan areas, including Boston, Chicago, Los Angeles, New York, and San Francisco. They therefore compete with the LECs' Centrex offerings.[34] To provide its own telephone services, a competitive access provider has to install switches or use switches of other companies with which it interconnects.[35] Also, because of their traditional clientele and location, those providers are best suited to serve businesses and large downtown apartment buildings, rather than residences. MFS, through its Datanet subsidiary, is already offering switched services targeted at small business customers and local area network interconnection services supported by ATM (asynchronous transport mode) switching.[36]

Competitive access providers generally, and MFS and Teleport in particular, have been very active in pulling down legal and market power–related barriers to facilities-based entry into markets for local switched services. Their goal is to transform themselves into full-service companies that compete in all areas with the LECs.

---

34. Glenn A. Woroch, affidavit, U.S. *v.* Western Electric Co., Inc. and American Telephone and Telegraph Company, Motion of Bell Atlantic Corporation, BellSouth Corporation, NYNEX Corporation, and Southwestern Bell Corporation to Vacate the Decree, Civil Action No. 82-0192 (July 6, 1994), at 25.

35. Economics and Technology, Inc./Hatfield Associates, The Enduring Local Bottleneck 85 (Feb. 1994) (unpublished manuscript, on file with authors).

36. *See* W. H. Davidson, affidavit, U.S. *v.* Western Electric Co., Inc. and American Telephone and Telegraph Company, Motion of Bell Atlantic Corporation, BellSouth Corporation, NYNEX Corporation, and Southwestern Bell Corporation to Vacate the Decree, Civil Action No. 82-0192 (July 6, 1994), at 6.

MFS, through its MFS Intelenet subsidiary, has already obtained permission to provide switched services in several cities, including Seattle.[37] When applying for "co-carrier status," it has specifically asked for access to blocks of telephone numbers that it can assign its customers directly and use in routing calls, for reciprocal termination and access charge arrangements, and for local number portability for customers switching to its services.[38] MFS has achieved cocarrier status, for example, in New York and Maryland.[39]

Teleport, meanwhile, is already supplying local switched services in New York and Massachusetts. Teleport is also legally authorized to offer switched local services in Illinois but at the time of this writing has not yet been able to reach satisfactory interconnection agreements with Ameritech. Similar problems in Illinois have been resolved between MFS and Ameritech.[40]

Some competitive access providers were already applying for cocarrier status in states where the public utilities commission had not even the legal authority to grant entry for local switched services. For example, in 1994 FiberSouth, Inc., asked the North Carolina Utilities Commission for permission to offer basic local exchange services in the Raleigh area, presumably in an attempt to induce the commission to pressure the state legislature into changing the statute.[41] Similar initiatives were started by the National Cable Television Association (NCTA), which targeted entry barriers in six states.[42]

37. *MFS Plans to Build Networks in Seattle, Oregon,* TELECOMM. REP., July 11, 1994, at 33.

38. *MFS Requests "Co-Carrier" Status in Texas,* TELECOMM. REP., Aug. 8, 1994, at 11.

39. *IXCs, CAPs Like Maryland's Local Competition Efforts; Bell Atlantic Suggests Easing Regulatory "Restraints,"* TELECOMM. REP., Aug. 8, 1994, at 12.

40. Interconnection Agreement Under Sections 251 and 252 of the Telecommunications Act Dated as of May 17, 1996, by and Between Ameritech Information Industry Services, a division of Ameritech Services, Inc., on Behalf of Ameritech Illinois and MFS Intelenet of Illinois, Inc. (on file with authors).

41. *CAP Seeks Local Services Authority in North Carolina,* TELECOMM. REP., Oct. 24, 1994, at 15.

42. *NCTA Plans Local Competition Initiative with IXCs, CAPs; Entry*

Cable Television Companies. Like competitive access providers, cable television companies try to enter local switched telephone markets from a facilities base consisting of networks they have already built for a different purpose. Although cable companies have lines running into most U.S. homes, those lines are not well suited for telephony. Thus, cable companies either would have to run additional lines from the curb or would have to use newly developed equipment to convert existing lines for dual television and telephone usage. Further obstacles are that cable television companies do not ordinarily own switches, and their networks have a hierarchical architecture that is not well adapted to telephony. Cable companies are also geographically fragmented, so that their basis for forming contiguous networks is weak. They therefore must either consolidate service areas within one company or link up with partners (other cable companies or other types of providers) to create larger service territories.

Despite those drawbacks, cable television companies have vast advantages over *de novo* entrants into the telephone business. Unlike competitive access providers, cable companies already have access to a large number of residential customers, and their brand names are recognized locally and sometimes at the national level.

Like other entrants, cable television companies faced regulatory difficulties from state bans on local telephone competition. Most aggressive in overcoming those bans has been Time Warner, which in 1995 was offering telephone services to business customers in Ohio and several other states and was targeting residential subscribers in Rochester. When the company applied for permission to do the same in Ohio,[43] those plans drew strong criticism from Cincinnati Bell, which claimed to have an exclusive right to provide local telephone services. In contrast, Time Warner generated strong support from AT&T and the online services provider CompuServe, both of which would like to have alternative local access to their residential and small-business customers and therefore view cable television entry into telephony as complementary to their services.

Barriers in Six States to Be Targeted, TELECOMM. REP., Nov. 14, 1994, at 1.

43. *Cincinnati Bell Inc. Unit Files Protest Against Time Warner's Ohio Phone Plan,* WALL ST. J., Feb. 2, 1995, at D6.

Interexchange Carriers. Large IXCs are entering local markets through at least two avenues. The first is in combination with mobile operators, as exemplified by the successful acquisition of McCaw Cellular Communications by AT&T and MCI's abandoned attempt to acquire Nextel Communications. The second avenue starts and expands from the existing IXC access network. Thus, first in Atlanta and since then in other major metropolitan areas, MCI has begun building a local telephone network to expand local services under MCI Metro.[44]

MCI has meanwhile filed requests with regulators in many states. By early 1996, its subsidiary for local exchange services, MCI Metro, had built fiber-optic rings in twenty-five local markets.[45] MCI tries to achieve two goals with its entry into local switched services. One is local telephone service in its own right. The other is access service for its own IXC services, thus bypassing the LECs.[46] In contrast to MCI, AT&T has aggressively started to pursue a strategy of offering local telephone services as a reseller.

Interconnection Arrangements. Besides basic authorization, the main prerequisite for new entry into the basic local exchange market is an interconnection agreement with the incumbent LEC. The main purpose of interconnection here is to ensure the completion of calls in either direction, so that the entrant's subscribers can reach and be reached by all subscribers on the LEC's network (and on any other networks that can be reached via the LEC).

There have been several types of interconnection arrangements in that context. First is the use of interconnection arrangements that already exist for other services. For example, the Wisconsin Public Service Commission has directed Teleport to interconnect with Ameritech-Wisconsin through Ameritech's shared tenant services tariff for its local calls.[47] Those rates are charged for calls

44. W. H. Davidson, *supra* note 36, at 8.

45. *Legislation Earns Widespread Praise from Industry; Companies Announce Plans to Enter New Markets,* TELECOMM. REP., Feb. 5, 1996, at 35.

46. Edmund L. Andrews, *MCI Seeks to Be "Local" in 5 States,* N.Y. TIMES, Oct. 4, 1994, at D3.; *Washington Commission Grants MCI Local Service Request,* TELECOMM. REP., Nov. 14, 1994, at 10.

47. *Wisconsin Grants Teleport Authority to Offer Local Services,*

originating from Teleport subscribers, whereas calls originating from Ameritech subscribers required no payments to Teleport by Ameritech for their completion.

Second, interconnection agreements can build on existing rules and tariffs, for example, by adding or subtracting elements. The New York Public Service Commission has ruled that MFS Intelenet does not have to pay the intrastate carrier common line charge for local service interconnection arrangements with NYNEX.[48] More sophisticated interconnection agreements between the LECs could build on open network architecture and expanded interconnection tariffs.

Third, there can be reciprocity agreements, according to which rates in both directions are symmetrical. Such agreements may consist of complicated specifications about relative peak usage, as in the 1994 agreement between NYNEX and Teleport in New York,[49] or may be quite simple, with payments due only if traffic in one direction exceeds traffic in the other by a certain percentage. Although reciprocity of charges leads to substantial reductions in interconnection payments by entrants, such payments can still be substantial and can continue to be based on the size of the unidirectional charges. Most entrants expect that outgoing traffic from their networks will exceed incoming traffic. That assessment is certainly realistic if there is no local number portability, which would lead many subscribers to continue to use the incumbent carrier for incoming calls. That assessment also characterizes mobile services that often charge subscribers for incoming as well as outgoing calls.

Fourth, carriers could use a "bill-and-keep" approach, under which no interconnection payments are exchanged at all. Entrants tend to like that approach because they would not incur any costs from using the incumbent's system. The main argument in favor of bill-and-keep is that it can save on transaction costs for interconnection. That may be the wrong approach, however, if

TELECOMM. REP., Aug. 29, 1994, at 3.

48. *MFS Doesn't Have to Pay Carrier Common Line Fee,* TELECOMM. REP., Apr. 3, 1995, at 12.

49. *Teleport Reaches Compensation Agreement with NYNEX,* TELECOMM. REP., June 27, 1994, at 30.

traffic turns out to be highly asymmetrical and substantial resource costs are incurred for handling the interconnected traffic. But the argument advanced by the regional Bell operating companies,[50] namely, that they complete calls from small entrants over a larger system and therefore need greater compensation than does traffic in the opposite direction, is valid only to the extent that the regional Bells complete calls over a longer distance or serve low-density regions that require higher network costs. It is invalid to the extent that a peak-load call from the small rival adds at most the same absolute amount to peak capacity use of the incumbent's network as a peak-load call from the incumbent adds to the peak capacity use of the entrant's network.

Although prices are paramount, interconnection agreements contain many other items important for competition. We discussed most of those above in the context of the Ameritech and Rochester plans. They include, in particular, local number portability, unbundling of services and network elements, and access to crucial resources such as poles, ducts, rights-of-way, emergency numbers, directory assistance, and network intelligence (the signaling system). Because those items are numerous and some of them quite technical, they could, in principle, be best determined by negotiation between experts in the employ of the companies themselves. Such negotiations, however, tend to be marred by the asymmetrical market positions held by the negotiating parties (as documented in chapter 9 for the United Kingdom). Regulators therefore tend to get heavily involved and tend to rule on the outcomes. Again, the Ameritech and Rochester plans provide examples not dissimilar to what is happening elsewhere. Because the same entrants are seeking interconnection agreements throughout the country, and because large LECs are present in many states, a convergence of interconnection rules across the United States can be expected.

That convergence may also be promoted by the Telecommunications Act of 1996, which provides a checklist for

---

50. *See, for example, Ameritech Agrees to Offer Reciprocal Compensation,* TELECOMM. REP., Jan. 16, 1995, at 28, or *LECs, Competitors Debate Unbundling, Interconnection Details, Divide over Proposed Compensation, Universal Service Models,* TELECOMM. REP., Dec. 5, 1994, at 5.

determining the presence of competition. The checklist refers to access or interconnection offered by a Bell operating company. It includes:

- interconnection for transmission and routing of telephone exchange service and exchange access that is at least equal in quality to that provided to the company itself, at just, reasonable, and nondiscriminatory rates and conditions;
- nondiscriminatory access to unbundled network elements;
- nondiscriminatory access to poles, ducts, conduits, and rights-of-way at just and reasonable rates;
- unbundled local-loop transmission from the central office to customer premises;
- unbundled local transport from the trunk side of a LEC switch;
- unbundled local switching;
- nondiscriminatory access to emergency calling services, directory assistance, and operator call completion services;
- white pages directory listings;
- access to telephone numbers and databases for routing and signaling;
- some acceptable form of number portability;
- local dialing parity;
- reciprocal compensation arrangements for call completion; and
- telecommunications services for resale.[51]

In addition, sections 251(c) and 252 of the act de facto impose similar requirements on all LECs, as we explain in chapter 8. The FCC, after consultation with the Department of Justice and the relevant state commission, will determine whether a Bell operating company has fulfilled the items on the checklist. When those conditions are satisfied, the company may offer interLATA

---

51. For a more detailed discussion of the provisions of this checklist, *see* PAUL W. MACAVOY, THE FAILURE OF ANTITRUST AND REGULATION TO ESTABLISH COMPETITION IN LONG-DISTANCE TELEPHONE SERVICES 200–12 (MIT Press and AEI Press 1996).

telephone services in its region. As more and more regions comply with the checklist, their conditions of interconnection will become increasingly similar.

The Franchise at Risk

The LECs are obviously scared by the prospect of facilities-based entry into their basic local exchange business—otherwise, they would not fight it so extensively in the regulatory arena.[52] Three reasons may be most prominent in explaining that fear. First, the local exchange market, which is the core of the LECs' business, is growing only slowly, so that entry by others may result in shrinking output and stranded investment for the LECs. Second, the entrants are likely to take away the most lucrative subscribers and leave the LECs with the money losers. Third, the entrants will exert downward pressure on local rates, at least to the extent that those rates are themselves not subsidized (but possibly even there, if the entrants' incremental costs are sufficiently low). Hence, entry into basic local exchange services will counter the LECs' tendency to rebalance rates by increasing local residential rates and reducing rates on other services and access charges. On the other hand, compared with potential entrants, the LECs do have sunk cost advantages in their local networks and better balanced load patterns, thanks to their broad subscriber base.

Facilities-based local exchange competition for fixed (as opposed to wireless) services is still in its infancy. It is, however, an area of enormous activity that involves diverse and powerful new players. Given the diversity of approaches and the uncertainty in technological developments, it is hard to predict the scope and degree of market penetration that new entrants will achieve. But the experience with such competition in the United Kingdom, described in chapter 9, could be indicative. Also, the United States does have experience with new local competition in wireless services, which are substituting more and more for landline services. We turn to those next.

---

52. Another reason for fighting such entry is that accommodation can be used as a bargaining chip for getting regulatory relief, as we discuss below.

WIRELESS SERVICES

Wireless access to the telephone network has consistently been the fastest-growing segment of the telecommunications market. The mobility and portability that wireless telephones offer make many cellular telephones complementary to fixed LEC service. But, at the same time, other dimensions of service quality, including sound quality and geographic coverage, have been inferior to fixed telephone service. As a technology, radio is fundamentally competitive with fixed wires, and as increased spectrum allocations and technological advances expand the effective capacity of wireless systems, they will eventually substitute for some, and possibly a considerable fraction of, fixed local loops. The development of cellular markets is characterized by tight regulatory control over market structure and the promise of personal communications systems technologies to substantially broaden competition both within the wireless markets and also with landline carriers.

Cellular Telephony

Spectrum Licenses and Market Structure. Through its spectrum licensing policy, the FCC has determined the basic structure of the cellular industry. The FCC had initially intended to authorize a single monopoly cellular operator in each market because it reasoned that supply by a single firm would reap the greatest economies of scale and make the most efficient use of the spectrum. But that argument neglected the gains from price and service competition that additional firms would stimulate.

With the benefit of hindsight, many have criticized the FCC for dragging out the original introduction of cellular services by about ten years. The welfare loss of that delay, due largely to the struggle over how many firms should serve that market, has been put as high as $86 billion.[53] In 1981 the FCC finally decided to establish

---

53. Jeffrey H. Rohlfs, Charles L. Jackson & Tracey E. Kelly, Estimate of the Loss to the United States Caused by the FCC's Delay in Licensing Cellular Telecommunications, *cited in* William B. Shew, Regulation, Competition, and Prices in Cellular Telephony 15 (June 2, 1994) (working paper, on file with

a duopoly market.[54] In each metropolitan area the commission allocated 20 MHz of spectrum to one wireline LEC and the same amount to one nonwireline operator. The LEC had to provide its cellular service through a fully separated subsidiary. Five years later, in 1986, the FCC released an additional 10 MHz of spectrum, which it had reserved in anticipation of allowing a third competitor, so that each operator could expand its band to 25 MHz.[55] The commission followed the same duopoly allocation in rural areas.

Market Structure. Spectacular growth and market consolidation have characterized the cellular industry since the first U.S. systems began operating in 1984 (table 7–1). By 1995 the industry had grown to more than thirty-three million subscribers, and the market continues to expand at a rate of 40 percent or more annually. Initial cellular demand was largely for mobile (vehicular) units, but today the majority of new sales are for portable handsets.

Carriers have purchased and exchanged properties so as to cluster operating territories into wider area markets and thus achieved broader geographic integration over adjacent concentrations of population and high-density highways. That process has led to a mixed pattern of ownership and operation. The LECs have acquired interests in nonwireline cellular systems outside their wireline franchise areas.

The FCC managed the early competition by requiring the wireline cellular company to offer unrestricted resale of its service. That allowed the nonwireline carriers to market services to customers as they built their facilities. Once a competitor is fully operational in a market, resale is no longer required. The policy has proved effective: nonwireline cellular providers have large market shares in all urban markets and are the larger cellular carrier in several.

Nationally, the two largest cellular firms are McCaw Communications Corp., a nonwireline carrier now wholly owned by AT&T, and GTE Corporation, the largest non-Bell telephone

the American Enterprise Institute for Public Policy Research).

54. Rep. & Order, CC Dkt. No. 79-318, 86 F.C.C.2d 649 (1981).
55. Rep. & Order, CC Dkt. No. 86-333 (Sept. 26, 1986).

TABLE 7-1
GROWTH OF THE CELLULAR TELEPHONE INDUSTRY IN THE UNITED STATES

Year	Subscribers (thousands)	No. of Systems	No. of Cell Sites	Twelve-Month Revenues (millions of dollars)
1984	92	32	346	178[a]
1985	340	102	913	482
1986	682	166	1,531	823
1987	1,231	312	2,305	1,152
1988	2,069	517	3,209	1,960
1989	3,509	584	4,169	3,341
1990	5,283	751	5,616	4,549
1991	7,557	1,252	7,847	5,709
1992	11,033	1,506	10,307	7,832
1993	16,009	1,529	12,805	10,892
1994	24,134	1,581	17,920	14,230
1995	33,786	1,627	22,663	19,081

a. Figure is for July through December 1984.

SOURCE: Cellular Telecommunications Industry Association, wireless industry survey results (March 25, 1996).

company (table 7–2). Most regional Bell operating companies operate franchises both within and beyond their LEC regions; they have also entered into a variety of joint ownership arrangements with some nonwireline operators. For example, in the Los Angeles market the wireline operator, Pacific Telesis, held 69 percent of the

THE TOP THIRTY CELLULAR OPERATORS IN THE UNITED STATES, 1994
(percentages)

Rank	Company	Share of Total Market	Share of Total Subscribers	Share of Total Revenues
1	McCaw Cellular Communications, Inc.	13.59	13.60	16.24
2	GTE Corp./Contel Cellular Inc.	10.62	11.04	11.04
3	BellSouth Corporation[a]	8.37	10.81	10.87
4	Southwestern Bell Corporation[b]	8.15	14.17	12.41
5	AirTouch Communications	7.45	7.27	8.49
6	Bell Atlantic Corporation[a]	7.43	7.38	7.68
7	LIN Broadcasting Corporation	2.85	6.15	7.32
8	United States Cellular Corporation	5.07	1.89	2.09
9	Ameritech Corporation	4.70	6.10	NA
10	Sprint Cellular[a]	4.44	4.67	4.72
11	NYNEX Corporation[a]	4.32	4.14	4.67
12	U S West, Inc.	3.95	4.27	4.36
13	ALLTEL Corporation	1.69	2.07	2.21
14	Cellular Communications, Inc.	1.48	1.71	1.70
15	Century Telephone Enterprises[c]	1.47	1.03	0.89
16	Vanguard Cellular Systems, Inc.	1.38	0.96	0.94
17	Centennial Cellular Corp.	1.32	0.37	0.41
18	Comcast Corporation[b]	1.06	1.54	2.00
19	Western Wireless Corporation	1.04	NA	NA
20	Independent Cellular Network, Inc.	0.77	NA	NA
21	Puerto Rico Telephone Company	0.75	NA	NA
22	Southern New England Telecom[a]	0.70	NA	0.70
23	CommNet Cellular Inc.	0.68	0.40	0.38

(Table continues)

TABLE 7-2 (continued)

Rank	Company	Share of Total Market	Share of Total Subscribers	Share of Total Revenues
24	Cellular Comm. of Puerto Rico, Inc.	0.63	0.26	0.38
25	Horizon Cellular Telephone Co.	0.57	0.19	0.20
26	Palmer Communications Incorporated	0.50	NA	NA
27	Cincinnati Bell Inc.	0.48	NA	NA
28	Radiofone	0.46	NA	NA
29	Rochester Telephone Corporation[a]	0.44	NA	0.30
30	Crowley Cellular Telecom, Inc.	0.28	NA	NA
	Total	96.65	100	100

NOTE: NA, not available.

a. Cellular revenues include equipment revenues. NYNEX's cellular revenues also include intersegment sales. Rochester Telephone's revenues also include paging.

b. Revenues at Southwestern Bell and subscribers at Comcast are estimates.

c. Operating cash flow includes income from paging operations.

SOURCE: Donaldson, Lufkin, and Jenrette (1994, 11, 67–103).

market in 1987, the year McCaw and BellSouth jointly acquired LA Cellular, the nonwireline operator.[56] By 1990 LA Cellular's market share had reached nearly 44 percent.[57]

Direct entry into the cellular market has been blocked by the policy of allocating just two 25 MHz cellular licenses in each area. But the FCC has taken limited action to increase cellular competition by broadening the services that special mobile radio (SMR) licensees can offer in some cases. Heretofore, SMR operators were restricted to sharing frequencies with other licensees or providing dispatching services—such as for taxi and delivery service—without interconnection to the telephone network. The FCC has now authorized a radio dispatch carrier, Nextel (formerly FleetCall), to provide switched service in six major urban markets. Other SMR firms have announced plans to develop similar service in other markets. The FCC has also broadened the scope for competition in the SMR market by allowing the regional Bell operating companies to own and operate two-way radio services.[58]

Technology. When it first allocated spectrum bands for cellular service, the FCC also established specific technical standards for all licensees. Relying on experimental cellular experience in Chicago and Baltimore and on comments from industry, the FCC required common modulation, signaling technology, and channel bandwidth to promote interoperability across different geographic markets. Today, propelled by rapidly increasing congestion, cellular suppliers are testing several new types of analog (FDMA) and digital (TDMA and CDMA) multiple-access systems. But now that the market is established, the FCC has refrained from prescribing any particular second-generation technology. Instead, it will rely on market forces both to determine the preferred system and to ensure compatibility with customers' existing terminal equipment.

---

56. Pacific Telesis subsequently spun off its own cellular entity and renamed it Airtouch, Inc.

57. L.A. TIMES, Aug. 26, 1990, *cited in* MICHAEL K. KELLOGG, JOHN THORNE & PETER W. HUBER, FEDERAL TELECOMMUNICATIONS LAW § 4.45 (Little, Brown & Co. 1992).

58. Gautam Neik & Daniel Perl, *FCC Allows Phone Companies to Own Dispatch Services, Lifting Nextel Streak*, WALL ST. J., Mar. 8, 1995, at B6.

The rapidly evolving technology of personal communications, including second-generation cordless telephones, advanced two-way paging, and microcellular systems for office buildings, will allow firms to compete for additional segments of the current cellular market. Basic engineering trade-offs are required to serve high-speed mobile units as well as very lightweight portables. Wireless personal communications markets will contain a variety of systems offering different features and prices. Ultimately, if prices decline and sufficient spectrum is available, radio-based cellular and cordless telephony is likely to become a competitive substitute for access to the public telephone network and a genuine alternative to the access bottleneck of the local exchange carrier.

Equal Access. The FCC has not required mobile carriers to offer equal long-distance access, which would allow customers to presubscribe to a preferred IXC that they can access automatically with one-plus dialing. The commission's reasoning has been that an IXC does not confront a bottleneck in obtaining access to customers, as it can negotiate with two mobile carriers, either of which could provide the connection.

Nevertheless, the MFJ court imposed line-of-business restrictions and equal access requirements on the wireline carriers owned by the Bell operating companies, which make up about half of all cellular operators. Thus, subscribers to a cellular system operated by one of those companies do have the opportunity to designate the IXC of their choice for their long-distance calls. The MFJ court more recently allowed the Bell companies to resell interexchange service in markets where the IXCs have competing suppliers of access to mobile switches. The waiver required that the Bell company have an equal access plan, that it offer and market local and interexchange services separately, and that it purchase interexchange service from at least three sources.[59]

As they are not subject to an equal access requirement, the nonwireline carriers have not usually offered presubscription. Instead, they have purchased all interexchange services from a

---

59. *RHCs Win Waiver for Wireless Interexchange Service; Competitive Access Opportunities Seen as Critical*, TELECOMM. REP., May 1, 1995, at 1.

single carrier at volume-discount rates and used those cost savings as a marketing advantage. In that environment subscribers can still route calls to another carrier by dialing that carrier's 10XXX access code. But as a condition of the Justice Department's approval of its 1994 acquisition of McCaw Cellular, AT&T agreed to offer all McCaw subscribers equal access to all IXCs.

Pricing. The duopoly structure of the cellular industry has resulted in prices high enough to bestow large economic rents on cellular system owners. From prices reported paid for those cellular systems that have changed hands, the NTIA has estimated the aggregate value of urban cellular radio licenses nationwide at some $46 billion to $80 billion.[60] A portion of that valuation is attributable to duopoly rents. To capture the anticipated higher capital market valuation accorded cellular firms and to gain freedom from MFJ restrictions, one regional Bell operating company, Pacific Telesis, spun off its cellular and other wireless operations to create an independent company, AirTouch, Inc. AirTouch is free to engage in the manufacture of subscriber paging and cellular equipment and to offer wireless services across LATA boundaries.

The FCC does not regulate prices for cellular service, and most state utility commissions have also refrained from such regulation. Until recently, tariffs were formally regulated only in about five states. Thus, regulation has been light compared with that of conventional LEC telephone service. That is compatible with the view, expressed by the FCC in 1984, that its licensing policy had "resulted in a highly competitive market structure in which two carriers with different histories and different approaches vie with one another in the market place."[61] The effectiveness of competition is also emphasized by Shew,[62] who points out that prices in cellular duopoly markets are lower than in monopoly markets, and that in markets that moved from monopoly to duopoly,

60. U.S. DEPARTMENT OF COMMERCE, U.S. SPECTRUM MANAGEMENT POLICY: AGENDA FOR THE FUTURE 90 (Special Publication 91-213) (National Telecommunications and Information Agency, February 1991).

61. *Cited in* KELLOGG, THORNE & HUBER, *supra* note 57, at 650.

62. Shew, *supra* note 53, at 12.

prices fell from 1985 to 1991 relative to a sample of all cellular markets. In contrast, price regulation (including the requirement to give advance notice of price changes) of cellular telephone services seems to have had no effect or may even have increased prices. Shew finds that rate-of-return regulation has been particularly damaging.[63] Interestingly, he also finds that a formal state prohibition on price regulation is even worse. Knowing that they do not have to fear price regulation appears to help cellular operators either to collude (under a duopoly) or to exercise their market power (when they enjoy a monopoly). Since state regulation of cellular services has been preempted by the 1993 Omnibus Budget Reconciliation Act, such a formal prohibition now exists for all states.

Prices for cellular terminal equipment have benefited from considerable competition. In vying for subscribers, cellular service providers have found it attractive to bundle the service itself with related services or equipment. Thus, the entry price for a new cellular customer typically consists of the cost of a handset or installed mobile set plus the fixed monthly service charge. Retailers compete by offering a package: a handset at a low price (as little as one cent for some basic models) bundled with a minimum number of months of cellular service. The FCC initially opposed but has now eliminated its restriction on such bundling, provided the equipment is also offered separately on a nondiscriminatory basis.[64]

Cellular operators generally interconnect their mobile telephone switching offices directly to an IXC and thus bypass the LEC network and avoid paying access charges to the LEC for long-distance service. Purchasing interexchange service at bulk rates, the cellular carriers can offer subscribers long-distance calling rates that are discounted from the retail rates a wireline subscriber would pay. The total per-minute price, however, also includes the per-minute rate for cellular airtime and therefore exceeds the price of a wireline long-distance call.

63. *Id.* at 69.

64. Bundling of Cellular Customer Premises Equipment and Cellular Service, CC Dkt. No. 91–34 (May 14, 1992).

Pricing of interconnection between the cellular carrier and the LEC remains a disputed issue. The LECs take the position that they should be compensated for completion of calls originated by a cellular subscriber and terminated on LEC networks. Nonwireline cellular carriers argue that as cocarriers they should be reciprocally compensated for wireline calls that are made to a cellular subscriber. In its August 1996 local competition order (see chapter 8), the FCC has required mutual compensation for transport and termination of traffic between commercial mobile radio services (CMRS) providers and the LECs.[65] Mutual compensation can be based on proxy rates established by the FCC, forward-looking economic costs established by the state regulator, or a bill-and-keep arrangement.

Personal Communications Services

The rapid growth of cellular telephone, cordless telephone, and paging services strongly suggests a large potential demand for additional wireless communications services. Personal communications services (PCS) are now understood to encompass a family of service applications based on wireless access to network services. That definition includes a host of new wireless services such as wireless PBX, wireless local area networks, and "wireless tails" to replace portions of the local loop, as well as enhanced cellular, paging, and cordless telephone services.

Federal action was required to allocate radio spectrum for PCS. The FCC held initial public auctions for narrowband PCS in July 1994, and the principal auction of 120 MHz of wideband PCS spectrum began at the end of 1994. At the conclusion of the auctioning of the first ninety-nine licenses, three companies had emerged as major PCS licensees.[66] Wireless Co. L.P., a consortium consisting of Sprint Corporation and three large cable television companies, won about one-third of the licenses. That consortium will now be able to offer long-distance and local

---

65. *Implementation FRAO, supra* note 33, ¶ 1007.

66. *Broadband PCS Auction Nets $7.7 Billion; AT&T, Sprint, Bell Companies Win 70 of 99 Licenses,* TELECOMM. REP., Mar. 20, 1995, at 3.

telephony along with video services. The second major licensee is AT&T, which along with its McCaw subsidiary will now be able to offer wireless local services throughout the country. AT&T is, however, lacking in cable television capacity.[67] The third licensee, PCS Primeco L.P., is a partnership of three regional Bell operating companies and AirTouch. That consortium will now also be able to offer wireless services virtually throughout the country.

The auction raised about $7.7 billion from the winning bidders. The next auction, for the "C" block of PCS frequencies, raised $10.2 billion when it concluded in May 1996.[68] That represents a major commitment to market entry, even if entrants have to invest several times that amount in additional facilities. The pattern of winners suggests that at least three new wireless local telecommunications systems are likely to emerge nationwide. In about half of the country that group includes the current LECs, whereas in the other half the LECs will be additional competitors.

Economies of Scope. A personal radio handset can gain access to the network in any of four possible ways: by accessing indoor private and public base stations, by accessing outdoor base stations, by accessing private indoor office base stations as a cordless phone, or by accessing a public vehicular mobile base station. The infrastructure to support those different types of access offers opportunities to existing telephone, cellular, cable television, and competitive access providers to supply elements of the necessary technology. Building on their existing infrastructure, each type of carrier can provide some functional elements at low incremental cost and thus achieve important economies of scope between PCS and existing carrier services.

Economies of Scale. Total costs per PCS subscriber are potentially affected by the amount of spectrum used by the operator, the

---

67. That may be one reason why AT&T has been seeking an association with Time Warner. *See Wall St. Sees Time Warner in AT&T Deal,* N.Y. TIMES, May 15, 1995, at D1.

68. *"C" Block PCS Auction Raises $10.2 Billion,* TELECOMM. REP., May 13, 1996, at 4.

service penetration, and the density of the population in the service area. Reed[69] finds that, at a 10 percent penetration rate, costs per subscriber are insensitive to the amount of spectrum allocation in a range between 10 MHz and 25 MHz, and only slightly higher if only 5 MHz are allocated. If only a 2 MHz allocation were available, however, a PCS system would be required to double its switching costs, and its transport costs would rise substantially as well. Evidently, a large amount of spectrum is not necessary to supply a PCS system that uses microcells ranging from 1/4 to 1 mile in radius.

For a single PCS provider and a 5 MHz allocation, economies of scale are largely exhausted at subscription penetration rates of 20 percent. When more spectrum is available, cell sizes can be larger and can reduce fixed costs and exhaust economies of scale at somewhat lower rates of penetration.

LEC Ownership and Interconnection Issues. A fundamental policy issue has been whether the LECs will be permitted to operate PCS systems in their own service territories or will instead be limited to the role of a carrier's carrier, providing infrastructure services to independent PCS companies. The FCC resolved this issue by setting upper limits on the amount of spectrum that one entity may own: 45 MHz for combined licenses for broadband PCS, cellular radio, and specialized mobile radio, and 40 MHz for broadband PCS ownership alone. In addition, the FCC's cross-ownership rules limit the percentage share of a PCS system in a major trading area that a cellular carrier in the same area may own.

The LECs are obligated to provide interconnection on request to any commercial mobile radio service operator.[70] The FCC decided that it was premature to impose an obligation on a CMRS operator to interconnect directly with another system. Because two CMRS systems can interconnect indirectly through a LEC, direct

69. DAVID P. REED, PUTTING IT ALL TOGETHER: THE COST STRUCTURE OF PERSONAL COMMUNICATIONS SERVICES (FCC Office of Plans and Policy Working Paper 28, Nov. 1992).

70. Implementations of Section 3(n) and 332 of the Communications Act, Regulatory Treatment of Mobile Services, CMRS Second Rep. & Order, General Dkt. No. 93-252, 9 F.C.C. Rcd. 1411, 1497–98 (1994).

interconnection does not constitute a bottleneck. Instead, the issue is whether a CMRS operator, by refusing to provide direct interconnection to a competitor, would raise the rival's costs. The commission will use a market power analysis to address that issue and to determine whether to require interconnection in specific cases.[71]

Interconnection to personal communications services raises many of the same issues that have been confronted in interconnecting cellular providers to the public network. In addition, some PCS firms will seek interconnection at intermediate points in the local loop (for example, at the serving area interface; see figure 3–2). Thus, the demand to further unbundle local access into components of the local loop will arise much as it has for competitive access providers.

Some PCS services, especially voice telephone, are expected to require extensive intelligent network services to provide personal number service, messaging, and mailbox service. A mobile PCS service might use several intelligent network components to connect to databases containing the home and visiting location registers of PCS subscribers, authentication checks, and equipment identity registers. There are clear opportunities for LECs, IXCs, and cellular firms to supply database and network management services to PCS operators. The FCC foresees economies of scope for the LECs in supplying PCS as a result of selective use of wireless tails in the distribution system and wireline transport from cell sites to PCS control centers.

Prospects for Wireless Service. Until very recently, a genuine division of labor prevailed between federal and state regulation of cellular services. The FCC regulated spectrum and entry; the states regulated rates and service conditions. No jurisdictional cost separation has been required (other than that wireline carriers set up their cellular operations as separate subsidiaries).

71. Interconnection and Resale Obligation Pertaining to Commercial Mobile Radio Services, Second Notice of Proposed Rulemaking, CC Dkt. No. 94-54 (Apr. 5, 1995).

Much of the delay in introducing cellular services resulted from the extended deliberations over the number of competing licenses to be provided. The decision to allow two licenses per area was a compromise in which the FCC rejected not only AT&T's monopoly suggestion but also more competitive market structures. One may speculate that state rather than federal licensing might have been faster, but it might have had questionable impacts on market power, standards, and compatibility. Also, with the benefit of hindsight, we can see that state regulation of cellular telephone services has at best done no harm. By now, state regulation of wireless services has essentially vanished. Given the prediction that wireless services will soon compete head-on with landline services, such competition is likely to fundamentally affect the states' ability to regulate LEC services as well.[72]

With the acquisition of new portions of spectrum, a number of firms and consortia have now gained the ability to offer various wireless telecommunications services, which could range from high-priced digital mobile telephone services that would be largely complementary to basic residential telephone services, to low-priced, stationary PCS services that would represent head-on competition for traditional LEC services.

LEC ENTRY INTO VIDEO SERVICES

The residential video market is today supplied by broadcast television stations, cable television operators, direct broadcast satellite services, and "wireless cable" systems (video delivery over a wireless multichannel, multipoint distribution service). The LECs have been searching for ways to expand into that market for some time. As was noted in chapter 2, the LECs have been pursuing a

---

72. In recent years the United States has fallen behind some other countries in applying the most modern cellular technology. But the United States was the first country to implement cellular technology and now has a large installed base, which stands in the way of converting to a digital system. Also, because of technical developments and the availability of additional spectrum, the United States has not yet run into serious congestion problems. The United Kingdom is currently operating with both analog and digital cellular radio.

variety of alliances and joint ventures with cable television operators outside their home regions and overseas.

The LECs have well-established service relationships, including physical wireline connections to their customers, that appear to give them advantages over the IXCs and other telephone carriers in entering the video market. But the traditional LEC distribution technology, consisting of a star network radiating from a central office switch over twisted-pair copper wires dedicated to each customer, is poorly suited to supplying the much greater bandwidth required to distribute a number of television channels that will be viewed simultaneously by many consumers.

The LECs could pursue either of two alternative paths to overcome the technical limitations of their current networks. One approach is to expand the bandwidth and performance of the existing physical network by means of technical innovations that can deliver video signals over the telephone wires now reaching their customers. Steady advances in data compression, signal processing, and electronics have brought such capability within sight. As of this writing, asymmetrical digital subscriber line (ADSL) systems are capable of transporting several video channels and a voice telephone channel from the central office to the subscriber, and simultaneously allowing the subscriber to send low-speed data back. But those systems cannot be used with local loops that have loading coils or other network devices attached; such devices are often used to deliver telephone service to telephone subscribers more than two miles from the local telephone central office. Nor is it clear whether the data compression systems used with ADSL systems will be able to provide satisfactory quality for fast-moving images such as those in sports events.

The second alternative is to build a new, broadband network to the subscriber's premises. The early designs for LEC video networks envisioned "fiber-to-the-home," with a fiber-optic link replacing the twisted-copper pair. Subsequent field trials have persuaded the LECs that such architecture, when combined with the requirement to provide emergency power to customers' equipment, is excessively costly, except perhaps in new housing developments. Instead, broadband network design has now been modified to provide "fiber-to-the-curb": a fiber-optic connection would extend from a central LEC location to a neighborhood distribution point, where the optical signal would be converted to electrical form and delivered via coaxial cable to the customer's premises.

Which approach to video distribution will be more effective is far from clear. Bell Atlantic announced plans to provide video services over conventional cable, whereas Pacific Bell and U S West are developing large-scale combined fiber-optic and coaxial networks. Reassessments of those technologies have led Bell Atlantic to withdraw its application for facilities authorizations that would use ADSL systems, and have led other LECs to scale back their fiber-to-the-home designs. In the meantime, some LECs have begun to acquire wireless cable operators because they view wireless cable as an interim technology that will enable them to enter the video market until fixed broadband technology matures. They also have started building their own conventional cable television networks.

In time, a variety of interactive video services may replace the downstream-only distribution of television programming over simultaneous multiple channels. Interactive services could range from on-demand delivery of movies and preproduced programming, with user controls for pause and rewind, to video library search services, interactive instruction, and personal videoconferencing. Interactive services place substantially greater capacity requirements and technical demands on the distribution network and require high-capacity switching and retrieval systems that are not yet well developed.

The entry of LECs into video markets within their home regions will pose familiar regulatory issues, which are treated elsewhere.[73] The LECs will invest in new transport and switching equipment to deliver video services; much of that equipment will also be used to supply switched telephone services and dedicated data and video links. Large common costs of facilities will challenge regulators to monitor LEC pricing to avoid cross-subsidies to the new services. Vertical integration by a LEC into the supply of video programming raises the concerns of cost shifting from unregulated programming

---

73. *See* LELAND L. JOHNSON, TOWARD COMPETITION IN CABLE TELEVISION (MIT Press and AEI Press 1994).

to regulated telephone services and of discrimination against competing program suppliers.

LEC Entry into InterLATA Services

Large LECs, in particular GTE and the regional Bell operating companies, are trying hard to integrate vertically into the interLATA long-distance business, from which the regional Bell operating companies under the MFJ, and GTE under its separate decree, had been banned until the passage of the Telecommunications Act of 1996. That move is part of an industrywide trend toward vertical reintegration. There appear to be several reasons for this move.

First, there are likely to be vertical economies of scope from using geographically integrated networks. In the case of the LECs, those scope economies would call for offering long-distance services throughout their own service territories.

Second, carrier-customer relationships could be strengthened through one-stop shopping arrangements. The LECs could build on the strength of their brand names. Again, that consideration would favor the LECs as regional long-distance carriers.

Third, vertical integration generates symmetrical reciprocal relationships when it comes to interconnection agreements. Such agreements will become important both with rivals and with integrated companies in adjacent regions. Although today the LECs have the upper hand in interconnection agreements because they control the bottleneck access to most subscribers, that will no longer be the case once cable television, PCS, competitive access providers, and other companies have their own customer access for telephony. We conjecture that symmetrical relationships are likely to reduce the fierceness of competition, something from which both the LECs and new entrants may benefit. At the same time, if less fierce competition is expected, the incentives to enter increase and will negatively affect total profits.

Fourth, the LECs could leverage market power from their dominant position in the local markets into the competitive long-distance market. That is the basis for the line-of-business restriction in the MFJ. But even if that reason was valid in 1984, it is unlikely to be valid now. In the past decade the interexchange market has grown substantially. It now includes at least three large, financially strong players with digital networks; those players are not going to vanish if the regional Bells enter that market. Furthermore, the incentives for the regional Bells to cross-subsidize new markets from their dominant market positions have been substantially reduced by the move away from rate-of-return regulation. Last, regulatory safeguards that facilitate entry into local markets reduce the dominant LEC positions on which leveraging theory builds in the first place.

GTE and the regional Bell companies adopted various strategies to escape their line-of-business restrictions on offering interLATA long-distance services. Those strategies included seeking termination of the MFJ, lobbying for a change in the Communications Act of 1934, and addressing individual petitions to regulators, the Department of Justice, and the MFJ court. In 1995 Ameritech had achieved an agreement with the Justice Department that would enable it to offer limited interexchange services in the Chicago, Illinois, and Grand Rapids, Michigan, areas. That plan, delayed by passage of the Telecommunications Act of 1996, now helps Ameritech to satisfy the competitive checklist requirement of the act. Indeed, the Ameritech plan has paved the way by showing that the desire of the LECs to enter long-distance markets can ultimately help competitive entry into local markets.

Initially, the relationship of local competition to LEC integration into long-distance services was one of conflict, because the LECs tried to hold such entry hostage to a lifting of their restriction from entering long-distance services. That went so far that at least one state in the region served by U S West tried to defer equal access for intraLATA long-distance services until the interLATA restriction was lifted. The Telecommunications Act of 1996, however, has made accommodation of local entry the quicker way for the regional Bells to gain legal access to long-distance markets.

CONCLUSIONS

The LECs' retail markets are under attack on several fronts. The first line of attack, and the most advanced, has been facilities-based entry in intraLATA toll markets. Since those markets are like small long-distance markets, the regulatory and technological problems of market entry here are very much like those already mastered for the interLATA markets. There are currently three differences. First, equal access still needs to be fully implemented. Second, the LECs are at the same time local-loop access providers and intraLATA toll competitors. Third, the long-distance transport and switching portions of the supply cost are small relative to the local-loop portion.

As a result, the LECs retain substantial competitive advantages in the intraLATA toll market. Those advantages will eventually diminish as equal access becomes widespread. Interexchange carriers will then be able to market all long-distance services, intraLATA as well as interLATA, on a presubscription basis to the LECs' local service subscribers. And as wireless services continue their rapid growth, suppliers who integrate cellular or PCS wireless service with long-distance service will challenge the LECs for a growing share of the intraLATA toll market. But the LECs are likely to continue to hold advantages resulting from their fixed network architecture. Nevertheless, it is doubtful whether intraLATA toll services will continue as sources of subsidies for residential subscriber access. That will only be possible if intraLATA access charges continue at high levels, something that is likely to be economically and politically less feasible over time.

The second line of attack is nonswitched local services. There the competitive access providers have made heavy inroads, made possible in part by their election to be subject to federal rather than local regulation. Competitive access providers often have the advantage of *de novo* entry with the optimal technology and architecture and without the burden of public service obligations. As a result, those companies have become formidable competitors, which can now use their base in nonswitched local services to attack the LECs along the third front.

That third front is switched local services, the core of the LECs' business. The LECs already face competition in that area from resellers and, at a modest level, from competitive access providers, cable television companies, and the IXCs. As multiple PCS licensees begin operation, wireless services are expected to expand well beyond the high-value market initially served by cellular systems and to compete directly for much larger segments of the switched local service market. Since the LECs themselves are heavily involved in wireless services and in cable companies outside their own service territory, they have already started to compete with each other in the switched local services market. In their own service territory the LECs hold several main advantages over entrants:

- They have a ubiquitous sunk network that includes vast databases and access to residential homes and to the existing residential phone numbers.
- They have very strong local name recognition.
- They have been able, up to now at least, to use cross-subsidies and contribution elements from access charges (the residual interconnection charge and the carrier common line charge) to subsidize local residential subscribers.

The first of those advantages will for some time make the LECs indispensable as local bottleneck providers of access to consumers and databases. But that advantage does not rule out entry by others, provided the LECs have to sell a complete set of interconnection services to competitors at cost-based or reciprocal rates. Some LECs, such as Ameritech and Rochester Telephone, have initiated their own strategies to become wholesale providers of network services that entrants can purchase and combine with their own complementary services to satisfy retail customers. Thus, the LECs' sunk cost advantage would hold for the wholesale but not for the retail market. Also, market growth and changes in the cheapest or most preferred access technology may undermine the LECs' sunk cost advantage.

The Ameritech and Rochester plans suggest that economies of scale and scope from integrating wholesale and retail services either have been reduced in recent years or were never so large as claimed. Although the network bottleneck at the wholesale level may be substantial, the plans may further indicate that those LECs fear erosion of that bottleneck once new facilities-based entrants duplicate the LECs' access to final consumers. Without such entry, market dominance may shift to the wholesale markets, and the regulation of integrated firms may continue to be a problem. As explained in the next chapter, that is something the Telecommunications Act of 1996 attempts to alleviate.

The LECs' second advantage, name recognition, is shared by some entrants, such as the large cable television companies and the IXCs; competitive access providers, on the other hand, may have to join forces with better-known entrants to induce residential consumers to switch to their services.

The third advantage, cross-subsidization, is already vanishing as a result of competition in the other markets served by the LECs. The LECs still receive large contributions from intrastate and interstate switched access charges, but there is pressure to reduce those as well.

Although competition for switched local services is still hampered by entry prohibitions or entry regulation in many states, the Telecommunications Act of 1996 and the FCC's local competition order, which we examine in the next chapter, are now pushing rapidly toward opening those markets nationwide. We can therefore expect that intense competition in switched local service will develop throughout the country. At the same time, the LECs will enter interLATA long-distance markets and markets for video services. Those moves correspond to reciprocal moves by the IXCs and cable television companies to create large integrated carriers that will directly compete with each other in all three markets.

8

The FCC's Local Competition Order

IN AUGUST 1996 the FCC adopted its First Report and Order concerning "Implementation of the Local Competition Provisions in the Telecommunications Act of 1996."[1] Issued a week in advance of the six-month statutory deadline set by the act,[2] the 688-page order is possibly the most extensive and explicit set of economic guidelines the commission has ever produced. In its thoroughness and careful citation of authority from the 1996 act, the order anticipated the legal challenges that several parties have subsequently raised with some success.

The order breaks new ground in several respects. It implicitly reorganizes the relationships and responsibilities of federal and state regulators. It enunciates specific costing and pricing methodologies that the states must use to establish rates. And it provides for default rates for state regulators who cannot complete timely cost studies.

The FCC's order characterizes the 1996 act as forging a new partnership between federal and state regulators.[3] The order expands the applicability of national rules to historically intrastate issues and of state rules to historically interstate issues. The FCC establishes uniform national rules for some issues. The states, and

---

1. Implementation of the Local Competition Provisions in the Telecommunications Act of 1996, First Rep. & Order, CC Dkt. No. 96-98 (Aug. 8, 1996) [hereinafter *Implementation FRAO*].

2. Telecommunications Act of 1996, Pub. L. 104-104, 110 Stat. 56 (Feb. 8, 1996) [hereinafter *Telecommunications Act*].

3. *Implementation FRAO*, *supra* note 1, ¶ 2.

in some instances the FCC, administer those rules.[4] The order relies heavily on the states to develop the specific rates and procedures, consistent with the FCC's general rules, which do reflect the experiences of those states that have already endeavored to promote local competition. Nevertheless, the shift from an environment of rates based on jurisdictionally separated accounting costs to one of nationwide uniform costing and pricing methodologies that allows for state-specific data is unlikely to be accomplished without friction.

Under the 1996 act, incumbent local telephone companies and new entrants may voluntarily agree to terms and conditions for interconnection and access to incumbent LEC network elements without regard to the FCC's rules, provided only that the agreements are registered with the relevant state public utility commission and that they do not discriminate against third parties nor conflict with the public interest.[5] If parties cannot reach agreement, however, the FCC has put in place a baseline of terms and conditions for all arbitrated agreements between local telephone companies and new entrants. The FCC's rules are intended to reduce delay in arbitrations and to lower transaction costs.

The 1996 act envisages three paths of entry into the local telephone market—full facilities-based entry, purchasing of unbundled network elements from the incumbent local exchange carrier, and resale of the incumbent's retail services. The order prescribes certain minimum points of interconnection necessary to permit full facilities-based carriers to choose the most efficient points at which to interconnect with the incumbent LEC's network. The order further establishes a minimum list of unbundled network elements that incumbent LECs must make available to new entrants, upon request. Finally, the order sets forth a methodology for states to use when applying the statute's "avoided cost standard" for setting wholesale prices with respect to retail services.

The FCC establishes a methodology for states to use in setting rates for interconnection and the purchase of unbundled elements. In its most central economic decision the FCC concludes that a pricing

4. *Id.* ¶ 24.
5. *Telecommunications Act, supra* note 2, § 251(c).

methodology based on forward-looking economic costs is most consistent with the goals of the 1996 act. The order extensively describes the principles and methodologies that the parties, arbitrators, and states are to use when creating and reviewing "total element long-run incremental cost" (TELRIC) studies that will serve as the basis for states to establish rates for interconnection and unbundled elements. Prices are to be set at TELRIC plus a reasonable share of forward-looking joint and common costs. For those states that do not elect to apply that methodology in time for their arbitration process, the FCC also establishes default proxies that a state commission may use to resolve arbitrations that must be completed before a TELRIC study is conducted.

The FCC's landmark order is the first of three fundamental actions that will bring competition to the telecommunications market. The second and third will be universal service and access charge reform. The 1996 act requires federal and state regulators to develop a new system of funding universal service that is explicit, predictable, sufficient, and competitively neutral, and the FCC, with the help of a new Federal-State Joint Board on Universal Service, is to complete work on that system by May 8, 1997. Because the FCC's rules in the order conflict with the current access charges, the commission has stated that it will complete access charge reform no later than it issues a final order on universal service. To avoid undue tariff arbitrage and disruption of incumbent LECs' ability to support universal service, new entrants purchasing unbundled elements will continue to pay a portion of certain access charges until no later than June 30, 1997.

KEY ISSUES

In the following subsections we summarize the key issues addressed in the order.

Interconnection

The 1996 act requires incumbent LECs to provide interconnection—the physical linking of two networks for the mutual exchange of traffic—to any requesting telecommunications carrier at any technically feasible point.[6] The interconnection must be at least equal in quality to that provided by the incumbent LEC to itself or its affiliates and must be provided on rates, terms, and conditions that are just, reasonable, and nondiscriminatory.

The order identifies as the minimum list of technically feasible points of interconnection: the line side of a local switch; the trunk side of a local switch; the trunk interconnection points of a tandem switch; the central office cross-connect points; the out-of-band signaling (SS7) transfer points; and the points of access to unbundled elements.[7] (See chapters 3 and 6.) The order indicates that if two carriers have interconnected at a point, such a point will likely be technically feasible in other LEC networks.[8]

Telecommunications carriers may request interconnection to provide telephone exchange service, exchange access service, or both. The incumbent LEC must provide interconnection to any requesting telecommunications carrier, including interexchange carriers and commercial mobile radio service providers.

Access to Unbundled Network Elements

In an extension of the concepts of open network architecture and expanded interconnection, discussed in chapter 6, the act requires incumbent LECs to provide requesting telecommunications carriers nondiscriminatory access to network elements on an unbundled basis at any technically feasible point on rates, terms, and conditions that are just, reasonable, and nondiscriminatory.[9] The order identifies seven such network elements, which we describe in chapter 3: network interface devices, local loops, local and tandem switches (including all software features provided by such switches), interoffice transmission facilities, signaling and call-related database facilities (including the Advanced Intelligent Network), operations support systems and information, and operator and directory assistance facilities.

6. *Id.* § 251(c)(3).
7. *Implementation FRAO, supra* note 1, ¶ 212.
8. *Id.* ¶ 198.
9. *Telecommunications Act, supra* note 2, § 251(c)(3).

Not all those elements represent bottlenecks. The entrant can acquire some, like signaling, from providers other than the incumbent LECs. The FCC determined, however, that the bottleneck characteristic is irrelevant because the act requires that competitive LECs be enabled to combine network elements from incumbent LECs. Such combination would be impossible if elements had to be acquired from an outside party. States may require incumbent LECs to provide additional network elements on an unbundled basis, and it is likely that facilities-based entrants using new technologies will seek to have local loops unbundled further into at least distribution and feeder elements.

Incumbent LECs must provide access to network elements in a manner that allows requesting carriers to combine such elements as they choose, and incumbent LECs may not impose restrictions on the use of network elements. The act requires incumbent LECs to provide physical collocation of equipment necessary for interconnection or access to unbundled network elements at the incumbent LEC's premises, except that the incumbent LEC may provide virtual collocation if it demonstrates to the state commission that physical collocation is not practical because of technical reasons or space limitations.[10] With minor modifications, the order adopts the FCC's physical and virtual collocation requirements from the Expanded Interconnection proceeding (see chapter 6).[11]

Pricing Methodologies

Under the act, negotiated agreements reached between incumbent LECs and entrants can take effect without regulatory intervention. They must only be registered with the relevant state public utility commission within ninety days of their conclusion, and they must not discriminate against third parties and not be against the public interest.[12] Experience to date, however, indicates that the pricing

10. *Id.* § 251(c)(6).

11. Expanded Interconnection with Local Telephone Company Facilities, CC Dkt. No. 91-141.

12. *Telecommunications Act, supra* note 2, § 252(e)(2)(A). The agreements must, however, follow the FCC's pricing requirements to satisfy the competitive criteria of the act (§§ 271–272) for RBOC entry into long-distance

of interconnection, unbundled network elements, and transport and termination of interconnected traffic often cannot be resolved by private negotiations, and the act then requires the states to arbitrate. The FCC has moved aggressively to instruct the state commissions on costing and pricing methodologies that are to be used to resolve pricing disputes.

The FCC's approach is to specify, in detail, the economic methodology that states must apply when analyzing cost studies and developing prices. But to head off delays that may result from conducting state-specific studies, the FCC also establishes interim "proxy rates" that states may adopt before completing their cost studies. The proxy rates were developed from generic forward-looking cost models of local exchange networks and rates established in several states that have conducted forward-looking cost studies.

The 1996 act requires the states to set prices for interconnection and unbundled elements that are cost-based and nondiscriminatory and that may include a reasonable profit.[13] The order instructs the state regulators to set arbitrated rates for interconnection and access to unbundled elements pursuant to a forward-looking economic cost pricing methodology.[14] The FCC has concluded that the prices that new entrants pay for interconnection and unbundled elements should be based on the local telephone companies' total element long-run incremental cost of providing a particular network element, plus a reasonable share of forward-looking joint and common costs. Because of its central importance, we examine that standard in detail below.

If states are unable to conduct a cost study and apply an economic costing methodology within the established period for arbitrating interconnection disputes, the FCC has set default ceilings and ranges for the states to apply, on an interim basis, to interconnection arrangements. The FCC establishes a default range

markets within their regions. For a discussion of those criteria, *see* PAUL W. MACAVOY, THE FAILURE OF ANTITRUST AND REGULATION TO ESTABLISH COMPETITION IN LONG-DISTANCE TELEPHONE SERVICES 200–12 (MIT Press and AEI Press 1996).

13. *Telecommunications Act, supra* note 2, § 252(d)(1).

14. *Implementation FRAO, supra* note 1, ¶ 625.

of 0.2–0.4 cents per minute for switching, plus access charges as discussed below; a ceiling of 0.15 cents per minute for tandem switching; monthly rental ceiling rates for local loops in each state, with rates to be disaggregated into three cost zones, largely on the basis of network density; and default ceilings for most of the other unbundled network elements to be derived from interstate access and interconnection tariffs. States will determine, among other things, the appropriate depreciation rates and risk-adjusted cost of capital. The FCC has, however, set an initial standard by determining that the rate it uses for cost of capital is currently 11.25 percent annually.

Access Charges for Unbundled Switching

The order does not alter the collection of access charges paid by an interexchange carrier under Part 69 of the FCC's rules (see chapter 6) for exchange access service obtained either directly or through service resale.[15] Because access charges are not included in the cost-based prices for unbundled network elements, and because certain portions of access charges currently support the provision of universal service, until the access charge reform and universal service proceedings have been completed, the order continues access charge recovery when a carrier uses an incumbent LEC's unbundled switching element for interexchange traffic.

For this traffic incumbent LECs will recover the carrier common line charge and a charge equal to 75 percent of the residual transport interconnection charge for all interstate minutes traversing the incumbent LECs' local switches for which the interconnecting carriers pay unbundled network element charges. That provision expires at the earliest of: June 30, 1997; the FCC's issuance of final decisions in the universal service and access reform proceedings; or, if the incumbent LEC is a Bell operating company, when that company is authorized to provide in-region interLATA service.

---

15. "Part 69" is a section of the FCC's accounting rules that govern the computation of access charges. *See* MTS and WATS Market Structure, 93 F.C.C.2d 241, 309–13 (1983).

Resale

The 1996 act requires all incumbent LECs to offer for resale at wholesale rates any telecommunications service that the carrier provides at retail to subscribers who are not telecommunications carriers.[16] Resale will be an important entry strategy both in the short term for many new entrants as they build out their own facilities and for small businesses that are unlikely to purchase unbundled elements or build their own networks.

States may impose "cross-class" restrictions on reselling, for example, to prohibit resale of residential service to business customers or Lifeline or other means-tested service to ineligible end users.[17] Such restrictions would enable states to maintain non-cost-based rates for groups of end users that would otherwise be quickly eroded by resale arbitrage. An incumbent LEC must, however, give the reseller the wholesale discount in addition to volume discounts where the volume discounts are based on the aggregate traffic of the reseller, not that of the reseller's individual customers.

The 1996 act's pricing standard for wholesale rates requires state commissions to identify what marketing, billing, collection, and other costs will be avoided or are avoidable by incumbent LECs when they provide services wholesale, and to calculate the portion of the retail rates for those services that is attributable to the avoided and avoidable costs. The order establishes a minimum set of criteria for avoided cost studies and allows states broad latitude to select cost methodologies consistent with their own ratemaking practices for retail services. If a state elects not to implement the methodology, it may, on an interim basis, set a discount between 17 percent and 25 percent from retail prices.

The FCC defines avoided costs as those that an incumbent LEC would no longer incur if it were to cease retail operations and instead provide all its services through resellers.[18] All

---

16. *Telecommunications Act, supra* note 2, § 251(c)(4). In addition, all LECs, including nonincumbents, have to allow resale of all their services, including those sold to other network providers. *Id.* § 251(b)(1).

17. *Implementation FRAO, supra* note 1, ¶ 962.

18. *Id.* ¶ 911.

telecommunications services offered to end users must be available for resale at a wholesale discount, including Centrex, optional plans, and contract services. Promotional rates for up to ninety days are not subject to discount.

The order requires an incumbent LEC to provide resale services to competitors under the same terms and conditions it enjoys itself.[19] Reaching agreement on the details of those conditions could be contentious. Ordering systems, exchange of customer account data, and on-line monitoring are examples of service conditions that resellers will push to obtain. Resellers will also seek to have their own brands applied to incumbent LEC-supplied services—both on-line information, directory, and assistance services and in-person installation services.

Transport and Termination

The 1996 act requires that charges for transport and termination of traffic be cost-based and reciprocal.[20] The order directs state commissions, during arbitrations, to set symmetrical prices based on the incumbent LEC's forward-looking costs and to use the same TELRIC methodology developed for interconnection and unbundled network elements.[21] The order defines *transport* as the transmission of terminating traffic from the interconnection point between the two carriers to the terminating carrier's end-office switch (or equivalent facility) that directly serves the called party.[22] The order defines *termination* as the switching of traffic at the terminating carrier's end-office switch (or equivalent facility) and delivery of that traffic from that switch to the called party's premises.[23]

The order requires the structure of compensation for transport and termination to follow that established for switched access (see chapter 6). Thus, incumbent LECs will be compensated for tandem

---

19. *Id.* ¶ 970.
20. *Telecommunications Act, supra* note 2, § 252(d)(2).
21. *Implementation FRAO, supra* note 1, ¶ 1054.
22. *Id.* ¶ 1039.
23. *Id.* ¶ 1040.

switching, for transport between the tandem and the end office, and for end-office switching. But those payments must be based on TELRIC costs, plus reasonable allocations of forward-looking common costs. There are no payments for use of the local loop.

For states that have not conducted a TELRIC cost study, the order establishes proxy rates to be used until such a study has been completed. The order sets a default range of 0.2 to 0.4 cents per minute for end-office termination, and a state may select a rate within that range. The FCC finds significant evidence in the record in support of the lower end of the range.[24] In addition, for termination through a tandem switch, the order sets a default ceiling for the tandem switching component at 0.15 cents per minute.[25] Finally, for transport from the tandem switch to the end office, the order calls for states to be guided by the price proxies established for unbundled transport network elements.[26] The order allows states to require bill and keep as a method of payment for transport and termination as long as traffic in each direction is approximately equal.[27]

Other Provisions

The order determines that cellular, broadband PCS, and commercial mobile radio services (CMRS) providers are telecommunications carriers and therefore are entitled to reciprocal compensation arrangements for interconnected traffic.[28] CMRS providers offer telephone exchange services and therefore may request interconnection from incumbent LECs. CMRS providers will not, however, be classified as LECs at this time.[29]

The order establishes procedures for nondiscriminatory access by cable television systems and telecommunications carriers to poles, ducts, conduits, and rights-of-way owned by utilities or LECs, including several specific rules as well as more general

24. *Id.* ¶¶ 811, 1060.
25. *Id.* ¶¶ 824, 1061.
26. *Id.* ¶ 1061.
27. *Id.* ¶ 1113.
28. *Id.* ¶¶ 993, 1008.
29. *Id.* ¶ 1004.

guidelines to facilitate the negotiation and mutual performance of fair, procompetitive access agreements.[30] Additionally, an expedited dispute resolution process is provided when good-faith negotiations fail.[31]

In a separate order on number portability the FCC established a set of criteria for an acceptable system of permanent number portability and required the LECs to implement permanent number portability in the 100 largest metropolitan areas by the end of 1998.[32]

The 1996 act provides for exemption or modification of the interconnection requirements for rural and small telephone companies under certain circumstances.[33] The order places the burden of proof for such treatment on the LECs.[34]

THE ECONOMIC BASIS FOR THE PRICING METHODOLOGY

Cost Standards

The economic centerpiece of the FCC's order is the requirement that states set prices for interconnection and unbundled network elements based on a forward-looking, long-run incremental cost methodology, with similar provisions for transport and termination of interconnected traffic.[35] The FCC provides the following rationale for using forward-looking economic costs to establish prices:

> In dynamic competitive markets, firms take action based not on embedded costs, but on the relationship between market-determined prices and forward-looking economic costs. If market prices exceed forward-looking economic costs, new competitors will enter the market. If their forward-looking

---

30. *Id.* ¶¶ 1151–1186.

31. *Id.* ¶¶ 1217–1231.

32. Telephone Number Portability, First Rep. & Order & Further Notice of Proposed Rulemaking, CC Dkt. No. 95-116, FCC 96-286 (July 2, 1996).

33. *Telecommunications Act, supra* note 2, § 251(f)(1)–(f)(2).

34. *Implementation FRAO, supra* note 1, ¶ 1263.

35. *Id.* ¶¶ 625, 1054.

economic costs exceed market prices, new competitors will not enter the market and existing competitors may decide to leave.[36]

The commission further asserts:

[T]he prices for the interconnection and network elements critical to the development of a competitive local exchange should be based on the pro-competition, forward-looking, economic costs of those elements. . . . Such pricing policies will best ensure the efficient investment decisions and competitive entry contemplated by the 1996 Act.[37]

TELRIC. The FCC's cost standard is TELRIC, total element long-run incremental cost. That standard requires that the costs of each network element be measured on a forward-looking basis and account for the long-run incremental costs of the entire network element, including all setup and capital costs attributable to that element.[38]

Before this order, the FCC used a similar term: *TSLRIC*, total service long-run incremental cost. TSLRIC is essentially the same concept as TELRIC—it is the forward-looking, long-run incremental cost of an entire service (for example, local residential exchange service). The new term, *TELRIC*, emphasizes that the cost and pricing methodology will be applied to network elements rather than to services that are normally produced by using the outputs of several elements.

Several key cost concepts make up the TELRIC methodology. *Forward-looking* costs are estimated on a prospective rather than historical basis. They focus on the technological possibilities available today to new suppliers, as well as to expanding incumbents. *Long-run* costs are estimated assuming that all of the firm's costs become variable or avoidable. *Incremental* costs are additional costs (usually expressed as a cost per unit) that a firm

36. *Id.* ¶ 620.
37. *Id.* ¶ 705.
38. *Id.* ¶ 690.

will incur when it expands output to produce an additional quantity of a good or service. The increment that forms the basis for a TELRIC study is the entire quantity of the network element provided.

Common Costs. TELRIC, because it is the incremental cost of a *single* network element, does not include the common costs of a firm that produces multiple network elements or other products. Common costs are those costs that are incurred in producing multiple outputs (or services) that are not eliminated unless all those outputs (or services) are not produced. Some costs may be common to two or more network elements (or services), and other costs may be common to the entire set of a firm's outputs.[39]

There should be fewer common costs when costs are calculated at the network component level (TELRIC) than at the final service level (TSLRIC), because network elements largely correspond to distinct network facilities, whereas services usually share the use of one or more network elements.

Pricing Standards for Unbundled Network Elements

The order requires that LEC prices for interconnection and network elements be set to recover TELRIC plus a reasonable allocation of forward-looking common costs.[40] States should conduct cost studies to establish the magnitude of those costs from the basis of an

39. Regulatory discussions of common costs have used several different, sometimes inconsistent, terms for costs that are shared by two or more outputs. The term *shared costs* has sometimes been applied to costs common to a subset of at least two, but not to all, of the firm's outputs. In that usage, common costs are then only those costs that are shared among the entire set of a firm's outputs. *Joint costs* are costs shared by two or several outputs produced in fixed proportions. The FCC's order makes clear that its use of common costs is consistent with economic theory and applies to costs that are shared among proper subsets of the firm's outputs as well as to costs shared over all outputs.

40. *Implementation FRAO, supra* note 1, ¶ 682.

efficient network, starting from the incumbent's existing wire-center locations.[41]

The FCC relied on two cost models for which nationwide data are available to set proxy rates—the benchmark cost model (BCM) and the Hatfield model, version 2.2.[42] Both models are based on detailed engineering and demographic assumptions. The FCC applied a scaling factor to the local loop element rates produced by those models, using the average of rates adopted by six state commissions that had conducted long-run incremental cost studies.[43] The FCC will more fully investigate various long-run economic cost models as the basis for setting proxies for network elements.[44]

In the order the FCC provides substantial guidance for determining what will constitute a reasonable allocation of common costs, and the incumbent LEC has the burden of proof of establishing the specific nature and magnitude of common costs.[45] The commission requires that common costs be directly attributed, to the greatest extent possible, on a causal basis.[46] In particular, shared costs that carriers have often assigned to common cost accounting categories but that vary directly with individual products or network elements should be directly attributed. In addition, the commission orders that costs common to a subset of elements be allocated to only that subset[47] and that common costs be allocated

---

41. *Id.* ¶ 685.

42. Benchmark Cost Model: A Joint Submission by MCI Communications, Inc., NYNEX Corporation, Sprint Corporation, U S West, Inc. (December 1995), submitted by MCI Communications, Inc., Sprint/United Management Corp., U S West, Inc., CC Dkt. No. 96-98 (July 24, 1996); The Cost of Basic Network Elements: Theory, Modeling, and Policy Implications (Hatfield 2) (Hatfield Associates March 1996), submitted by MCI, CC Dkt. No. 96-98 (March 29, 1996); Hatfield Model, Version 2.2, Release 1 (Hatfield Associates March 1996), submitted by AT&T and MCI, CC Dkt. No. 96-98 (May 16, 1996).

43. *Implementation FRAO, supra* note 1, ¶ 794.

44. *Id.* ¶ 790.

45. *Id.* ¶ 695.

46. *Id.* ¶ 682.

47. *Id.* ¶ 694.

on a reasonable basis.[48] Reasonable allocators are deemed to include those that are proportional to directly attributable costs and those that allocate not more than a small share of common costs to bottleneck elements. But, forgoing allocative efficiencies to protect entrants against possible discriminatory behavior, the FCC determined that common costs should not be allocated on the basis of demand elasticities for elements. The FCC orders that the set of network elements taken together recover the common costs attributable to the wholesale network.[49] But network element prices should not include retailing costs.[50] The upper bound for the price of any element is its stand-alone cost, and in most cases the price should be less than that.[51] Finally, the FCC orders that prices should not allow recovery of the same common costs multiple times from different elements.[52]

The commission has provided specific instructions that cost studies are to attribute several types of shared costs and to allocate common costs—for example, the costs of shared maintenance facilities and vehicles, conduit for transport and local loops,[53] payroll, back-office operations related to line technicians,[54] and certain administrative expenses.[55]

The cost study methodology ordered by the FCC effectively requires that the study be conducted as though the LEC were split into virtually separate subsidiaries: a wholesale subsidiary and a retail subsidiary.[56] That view of the incumbent's network corresponds to our discussion in chapters 6 and 10.

In specifying the TELRIC-plus methodology for pricing interconnection and unbundled network elements, the FCC explicitly rejects including three types of costs: embedded costs, opportunity costs, and universal service subsidies. The commission rejects

48. *Id.* ¶ 696.
49. *Id.* ¶ 698.
50. *Id.* ¶ 694.
51. *Id.* ¶ 698.
52. *Id.*
53. *Id.* ¶ 682.
54. *Id.*
55. *Id.* ¶ 691.
56. *Id.* ¶¶ 694, 698.

embedded costs because historic costs are not forward-looking. States are prohibited by the act from conducting traditional rate-of-return proceedings to establish rates.[57] The FCC asserts that prices based on embedded costs would be procompetitor (typically favoring the incumbent LEC) rather than procompetition.[58]

The commission rejects so-called opportunity costs, which have been advocated under the rubric of the efficient component pricing rule (ECPR, chapter 4),[59] because the ECPR would set the price of an input equal to the incremental cost of the input plus the opportunity cost that the incumbent carrier incurs when the new entrant provides services instead of the incumbent. The opportunity cost, computed as revenues less all incremental costs, represents both profit and contribution to common costs of the incumbent at the existing level of retail prices. The FCC asserts that opportunity-cost pricing will not be cost-based, will discourage competition, and will provide no mechanism for forcing retail prices to their competitive level.[60]

The commission rejects universal service subsidies because such charges will not be cost-based.[61]

Pricing of Transport and Termination

The same cost standards and pricing methodology that are established for interconnection and unbundled network elements are to be applied for transport and termination between incumbent LECs and other telecommunications carriers, including CMRS providers.[62]

The order requires compensation for transport and termination to be reciprocal.[63] Furthermore, in general, rates should be

---

57. *Telecommunications Act, supra* note 2, § 252(d)(1).

58. *Implementation FRAO, supra* note 1, ¶ 705.

59. For an extensive description of the ECPR, *see* WILLIAM J. BAUMOL & J. GREGORY SIDAK, TOWARD COMPETITION IN LOCAL TELEPHONY (MIT Press and AEI Press 1994).

60. *Implementation FRAO, supra* note 1, ¶¶ 709–710.

61. *Id.* ¶ 713.

62. *Id.* ¶ 1054.

63. *Id.* ¶ 1089.

symmetrical. There are, however, two exceptions to the requirement of symmetrical compensation. First, a state regulator may establish higher rates if a nonincumbent LEC proves, on the basis of a forward-looking economic cost study, that its transport and termination costs are higher than the incumbent's. Second, a state regulator should establish distinct rates that paging services may charge for transport and termination based on forward-looking costs incurred, since those costs may not be accurately represented by LEC costs.[64] Accordingly, those rates should not be based on default proxies designed for LECs because they may not accurately represent the termination costs in a paging network.

To comply with those compensation principles, states have three options for setting transport and termination rates. A state may establish rates based on forward-looking economic cost studies; it may adopt rates consistent with proxy rates; or it may order bill-and-keep compensation arrangements.[65] If state regulators establish transport and termination rates that vary according to whether the traffic is routed through a tandem or directly to an end-office switch, they are to consider whether new technologies used by an entrant perform functions similar to a tandem switch or whether the entrant's switch serves a geographic area comparable to the area served by the incumbent LEC's tandem switch. In such cases, calls terminating on the new entrant's network should be priced the same as the transport and termination rate for the incumbent LEC's tandem switch.[66]

Under the first option, forward-looking cost studies should be based on the same methodology that is established for unbundled network elements. Termination rates should include an allocation of forward-looking common costs that should be relatively low—no greater proportionately than that allocated to local loops. Rates should not include any opportunity cost.[67]

Under the second option, if rates are set on the basis of default proxies, traffic handed off at the end-office switch should be priced

64. *Id.* ¶ 1093.
65. *Id.* ¶ 1090.
66. *Id.*
67. *Id.* ¶ 1058.

between 0.2 cents and 0.4 cents per minute. For traffic handed off at a tandem switch, an additional rate of not more than 0.15 cents per minute applies. Proxy rates for interoffice transport should be based on interstate direct-trunked transport rates. States that have already adopted end-office termination rates (other than ones based on a full forward-looking cost study) that are no higher than 0.5 cents per minute may keep such rates in effect pending review of a forward-looking cost studies.[68]

Under the third option, a state may impose bill-and-keep arrangements if the state regulator determines that traffic flows are roughly balanced and are expected to remain so. A state may presume that traffic is roughly balanced, unless a party rebuts the presumption.[69]

Pricing of Resale

The order establishes a default wholesale rate between 17 percent and 25 percent below retail levels.[70] Similar to the procedure established for interconnection and unbundled network elements, state regulators are required to use a rate within the default range if they have not completed an avoided cost study.[71] Each state must then set wholesale rates based on an avoided cost study within a reasonable time.[72]

The 1996 act requires that wholesale rates be based on existing retail rates minus avoided costs.[73] The cost standard for resale pricing is thus generally different from the TSLRIC methodology the FCC adopted for interconnection and unbundled network elements. But TSLRIC studies would be appropriate in states where the retail rates have been established by using a TSLRIC method.[74] An avoided cost study must include direct costs and indirect or

---

68. *Id.* ¶ 1060.
69. *Id.* ¶ 1113.
70. *Id.* ¶ 910.
71. *Id.* ¶ 932.
72. *Id.*
73. *Telecommunications Act, supra* note 2, § 252(d)(3).
74. *Implementation FRAO, supra* note 1, ¶ 915.

shared costs and may also include a portion of contribution, profits, or markup.

The FCC used a model submitted by MCI, with some modifications, to establish the default resale discounts. The modified model analyzes two categories of avoided costs, using publicly available Universal System of Accounts data: (1) marketing, billing, and collection costs, and (2) common costs allocated to avoided cost activities.[75] The directly avoided costs include call completion and number services and all but 10 percent of product management, sales, product advertising, and customer services. General overhead and general support expenses are allocated to avoided cost activities in the same ratio as the LEC's direct expenses to total expenses.

ASSESSMENT AND DISCUSSION

The order builds on experience gained in a number of states and in particular on plans like the Ameritech and Rochester plans discussed in chapter 7. The FCC, however, has attempted to establish a unifying approach for the country and a systematic framework on some of the issues.

The methodology the FCC adopted for the pricing of interconnection, unbundled network elements, and transport and termination services is a further development of the approach we have previously proposed with colleagues for interconnection policies in the European Union.[76] The endorsement in the FCC's order for those principles substantially widens the consensus that forward-looking, long-run incremental costs of complete services and network elements are the appropriate basis for efficient pricing.

The FCC considered three alternatives in arriving at a cost methodology that would best generate incentives for efficient investment by new entrants. If network component prices were based on the most efficient network architecture, sizing, technology,

---

75. *Id.* ¶ 891.

76. JENS ARNBAK, BRIDGER M. MITCHELL, WERNER NEU, KARL-HEINZ NEUMANN & INGO VOGELSANG, WITH THE COLLABORATION OF GODEFROY DANG N'GUYEN & BERND ICKENROTH, NETWORK INTERCONNECTION IN THE DOMAIN OF ONP (WIK and European-American Center for Policy Analysis, Nov. 1994).

and operating decisions, then currently feasible prices would simulate conditions in a highly competitive marketplace. Such rates, however, could discourage competition from facilities-based entrants, who would have the use of the incumbent's existing network at rates based on the cost of a hypothetical least-cost, efficient network.[77] Alternatively, prices could be based on the costs of the incumbent's existing network design and technology. That approach would rely essentially on an embedded cost methodology that allows incumbents to recover costs of inefficient or obsolete design and technology but perhaps provides the greatest incentive for entrants to invest in facilities.[78] Third, prices could be developed on the basis of the most efficient technology deployed at the incumbent LEC's current wire-center locations. The FCC concluded that such a benchmark would most closely represent the incremental costs incumbents expect to incur in making network elements available to new entrants.[79] The last approach can be seen as a choice that balances incentives to encourage facilities-based competition by new entrants with recovery by an efficient incumbent of its incremental costs.

The FCC has recognized the need to mark up TELRIC to account for common costs and has gone some distance to indicate what would constitute a "reasonable" markup. Here, too, the FCC's approach parallels a proposal we have developed—in the context of interconnection policy in the United Kingdom—to limit markups above TELRIC to not more than a proportionate share of common costs.[80]

By prescribing TELRIC as the required methodology for determining costs, the FCC will place economic models of forward-looking, long-run incremental costs at the center of the debate over practical methods of measuring economic costs. Some of the first applications of engineering-economic models of telephone networks

---

77. *Implementation FRAO, supra* note 1, ¶ 683.

78. *Id.* ¶ 684.

79. *Id.* ¶ 685.

80. Bridger M. Mitchell & Ingo Vogelsang, *Markup Pricing for Interconnection: A Conceptual Framework, in* OPENING NETWORKS TO COMPETITION: THE REGULATION AND PRICING OF ACCESS (David Gabel & David Weiman eds., Kluwer Academic Publishers 1997).

to pricing focused on the structure of long-distance and local rates.[81] Subsequently, some states[82] and the United Kingdom[83] have developed "generic" models of forward-looking, long-run incremental costs. In this proceeding the FCC relied on a TELRIC model developed by Hatfield Associates[84] and long-run incremental cost studies in six states to establish the proxy rates set out in the order.

We can expect that debate over both the methodology and data for TELRIC models will for some time occupy both the FCC, which will open a proceeding on the topic, and state commissions.

The FCC's rules on wholesale rebates for resale apply an approach to avoided costs that is conceptually similar to TSLRIC. Avoided costs are deemed to be the difference in cost between an incumbent LEC with and without the provision of retail services. Also, avoided costs include a portion of common and fixed costs. Despite that similarity in approach, the result for the same service built from network elements as opposed to acquired wholesale is likely to differ even in the absence of scope economies. The source of the difference is the different pricing treatment the act affords to network elements and resale of retail services. It is not clear that such different treatment will lead to efficient investment decisions, but it is likely to create opportunities for arbitrage.

At one margin, entrants face the choice of purchasing unbundled network elements and combining them with their own local-market facilities to produce retail services or, alternatively, purchasing the incumbent's wholesale services and combining them with retailing

---

81. *See* Stephen C. Littlechild, *Marginal Cost Pricing with Joint Costs*, 80 ECON. J. 323 (1970).

82. *See* Bridger M. Mitchell, *Incremental Costs of Telephone Access and Local Use, in* MARGINAL COST TECHNIQUES FOR TELEPHONE SERVICES: SYMPOSIUM PROCEEDINGS (W. Pollard ed., National Regulatory Research Institute, January 1991); *see also* Robert M. Bowman, *U S WEST Switching Cost Models, id.*

83. OFTEL, *The Methodology to Calculate Long-Run Incremental Costs* (study prepared for OFTEL by National Economic Research Associates) (Office of Telecommunications (London) March 1996).

84. Hatfield Associates, *Documentation of the Hatfield Model, Version 2.2, Release 1* (Hatfield Associates May 16, 1996).

activities. If an incumbent LEC's actual avoidable costs are less than the 17 percent to 25 percent wholesale proxy discount prescribed by the FCC, entrants will tend to emphasize reselling. That could also lead to inefficient replacement of the incumbent LEC's retail business by its wholesale business, as could occur if retail customers perceive no costs of switching to the other telecommunications carrier. Conversely, if the proxy wholesale discount is smaller than the actual avoidable costs, for example, because of an incumbent's inefficiencies, entrants could be inefficiently encouraged to invest in network facilities when their actual efficiencies are in the retailing activities.

For a potential or actual entrant (competitive LEC), the need to exchange traffic with the incumbent LEC directly affects the entrant's net costs of providing local service. Traffic that the competitive LEC originates and delivers to the incumbent for termination incurs a direct cost determined by the transport and termination rates it must pay the incumbent. And traffic that the entrant terminates increases its costs, which may be offset by reciprocal compensation.

In requiring symmetric reciprocal compensation for transport and termination of interconnected traffic, the FCC has struck a compromise between encouraging competitive entry and distorting investment and consumption decisions. The rate paid by carrier C (a competitive LEC) for termination of its traffic to carrier I's (an incumbent LEC) customers, and the corresponding rate paid by I to have its traffic terminated to C's customers, affect decisions at a number of margins. Those include the entry of C into the local exchange market, the choice of architecture and technology by entrant C, the choice of point(s) of interconnection for C and I, marketing to customers with particular calling patterns, and the calling volumes of customers as affected by retail rates for local service. In general, a single reciprocal transport and termination rate paid by each carrier, or two reciprocal rates based on whether both tandem and end-office, or only end-office, switching is used to terminate traffic, will be insufficient to induce efficient choices by each carrier at each of those margins.

On the basis of the objective of fostering efficient competition and the likelihood that facilities-based entry decisions are most strongly affected by the transport and termination compensation arrangements, we suggest two guiding principles that should be followed as far as possible. First, the compensation arrangement should not make an entrant's ability to collect a level of revenue sufficient to cover its costs of providing transport and termination for interconnected traffic depend on what network architecture it chooses and on whether that architecture is similar to that of an incumbent LEC. Second, the compensation plan should not depend on relative prices for specific transport and termination elements that are based on cost details of incumbent LEC networks but do not apply to the entrant's network. Compensation arrangements that are consistent with those principles are payments to entrants that are independent (exogenous) of its actual costs of supplying transport and termination—fixed payments, fixed payments per unit of traffic, and bill and keep.

The FCC's rules on pricing and other issues are certain to generate expectations on the outcome of negotiations between incumbents and new entrants and will furnish the new entrants with bargaining power. The rules achieve that by establishing default positions for state regulators acting as arbitrators, by requiring incumbent LECs, who possess asymmetric cost information, to make it available in negotiations, and by placing strong burdens of proof on incumbents, for example, to justify assignments of common costs.

The parties to negotiations can take the FCC's rules as starting points for achieving more efficient outcomes for themselves. For example, the FCC does not prescribe peak-load pricing of usage. But the fact that something comparable to a most-favored-nation clause applies, according to which individual parts of any agreements have to be made available to other partners of the incumbent LEC,[85] limits the likelihood that efficient outcomes will be reached by trading off against each other countervailing advantages in different parts of agreements.

The basis for the division of labor between the FCC and the state public utility commissions so far has been the distinction between interstate and intrastate traffic. FCC Chairman Reed Hundt believes that such differentiation is out of date. In his view the

---

85. *Telecommunications Act, supra* note 2, § 252(i).

differentiation between local and long-distance services and between voice and other services needs to be replaced by the notion that "a minute is a minute is a minute."[86] Consequently, a new division of labor should evolve that is characterized by three criteria: simplified administration, the availability of human and financial resources, and the presence of geographical differences that require different regulatory approaches. The order defines new, evolving, state-federal regulatory relationships by putting the state public utilities commissions in charge of both intrastate and interstate aspects of the act. Simultaneously, the order establishes FCC rules for intrastate aspects. For example, the FCC objects to state rules that place requirements on competitive LECs that the act places only on incumbent LECs. It appears, however, that the state public utilities commissions can continue their traditional regulation of end-user rates.

The order can be criticized for being extremely detailed in its provisions on all aspects of the relationships between incumbent LECs and other carriers. In fact, the act requires most of that detail. Thus, the only question is whether the FCC or the state commissions should provide the detail. Since the act has charged the FCC with implementation guidelines on all those issues, any fault is more that of the act than of the FCC. The critique does, however, bring out the facts that the act may not be easily implemented and that implementation will likely require many actions by all participants.

In October 1996 the courts stayed the pricing provisions of the FCC's order, and they are unlikely to be reinstated before the state public utilities commissions successfully arbitrate on their own terms a large number of agreements between incumbent LECs and new entrants. Are aggressively procompetitive parts of the FCC's order ineffective now, and will competition be delayed? First experience leads us to believe that not to be the case. So far, state regulators have moved ahead with arbitration decisions and followed the FCC's pricing methodology or established prices within the ranges provided by the FCC's proxies.

---

86. *Hundt Looks Towards "Radical" Overhaul of Regulatory Regimes, Major Business Moves*, TELECOMM. REP., July 15, 1996, at 4.

9

Local Telecommunications Regulation and Competition in the United Kingdom

SO FAR OUR ANALYSIS of the development toward local competition has concentrated entirely on U.S. markets, policies, and institutions. The United States has been a leading force and prime influence in the development of competition in telecommunications worldwide, but other countries have also advanced new ideas and methods that may in turn suggest new policy directions for the United States to follow. New Zealand, for example, has replaced telecommunications regulation almost entirely with antitrust policy, and Australia has embarked on an innovative (although still untried) policy on universal service obligations. Rather than pick the best policy initiatives from a range of such countries, however, in this chapter we provide a case study of the United Kingdom, the country that has the longest experience outside the United States with a number of new regulatory methods of dealing with local competition, incentive regulation, and interconnection. U.K. policies have already influenced some regulatory changes in the United States; the U.K. experience is also of interest because U.S. telecommunications companies are heavily involved in that country.

When the U.K. government formed British Telecommunications (BT) as a public enterprise in 1980 and 1981, it abandoned the traditional concept of a postal, telegraph, and telephone (PTT) administration by severing the ties between telecommunications and postal services. At the same time, the government allowed limited entry into the telecommunications market. The government largely liberalized the market for customer premises equipment, permitted resale of private lines for enhanced services (called value-added network services, or VANS, in Britain), and licensed network entrants. In 1983 the government protected the first network entrant for fixed link services, Mercury Communications, Ltd. (MCL), against further market entry (along with BT itself) through a seven-year duopoly policy. But the government exempted limited entry into telephony by cable television operators (as network providers to BT and MCL) and mobile services providers—themselves a duopoly—from that policy.[1] In 1984 the government converted BT into a public limited company and divested 50.2 percent of its shares. That divestiture was accompanied by innovative regulation, including regulation of interconnection agreements. BT was left intact and vertically integrated. In 1989 the government permitted simple resale of private lines, and in 1991 the duopoly review opened the telecommunications market to many additional network entrants. Over the period from 1991 to 1993 the government sold its remaining shares in BT.

INSTITUTIONAL AND MARKET CONDITIONS

We begin with an overview of institutional and market conditions in the U.K. telecommunications market that stresses the diversity of the sector despite BT's dominance of the market. We then describe in some detail the U.K. regulatory framework and the way in which price-cap regulation of BT has worked.

Market Structure and Entry Conditions

From 1880 onward many independent private and a few municipal telephone companies provided telecommunications service in the United Kingdom. At first the government restricted the size of the geographical areas companies could serve, but in 1884 the government allowed them to operate anywhere in the country, to connect exchanges by trunk wires, and to connect their exchanges to post offices to send and deliver telegrams. There was, however, no interconnection of their networks for telephone traffic.

---

1. Also, so-called specialized satellite service operators were licensed in 1988 and 1989.

The major independent companies amalgamated in 1889 and formed the National Telephone Company (NTC). As a result of public complaints about inefficiency, high costs of service, and the proliferation of overhead cables, in 1892 the government decided to purchase the trunk lines of the NTC and to have the Post Office extend and develop the trunk system. Along with that transfer, in 1896 interconnection was established between Post Office customers in one area and NTC customers in another, but there was no interconnection between customers in the same area.

In 1899 new legislation permitted municipal authorities to establish telephone services, and a number of them applied for licenses. Except for the city of Kingston-upon-Hull, all subsequently surrendered their licenses, and either the NTC or the Post Office took over providing services.

In 1905 an agreement was reached whereby the Post Office would purchase the assets and business of NTC when the latter's license expired. Thus, by the beginning of 1912 a virtual monopoly had been established under state control. The telephone system of Kingston-upon-Hull remained independent, however.

Between 1912 and 1980 any regulatory regime changes in the U.K. telecommunications sector occurred under full state ownership and with an unchallenged monopoly. But the Post Office was converted from a department of state (a ministry) to a public corporation through the 1969 Post Office Act. With that exception regulatory regime changes were mostly implicit rather than explicit. After the Conservative Party's electoral victory in 1979, however, the regulatory situation changed drastically. Since then regulatory reform has come to be viewed as part of a troika along with privatization and the emergence of competition.

The British Telecommunications Act of 1981 converted BT's monopoly rights for network services to an exclusive privilege and allowed the government to issue licenses to other network operators. As noted above, in 1980 and 1981 BT was separated from the Post Office and became a public corporation in its own right. That major organizational step occurred while the British economy and its telecommunications industry were weak. Long queues of consumers wanted new telephone line connections. The delayed modernization of the telephone network caused poor service quality. Like AT&T at the time of its monopoly, the telecommunications division of the

British Post Office was production-oriented rather than market-oriented. Despite the waiting lines, BT's objective was to provide universal basic service rather than to serve customers' demands for new and better services. Customers had difficulty obtaining the newest equipment.[2] During the 1970s the telecommunications division had been coordinating a cartel of British equipment manufacturers, which were developing a digital telephone exchange called "System X." That policy of favoring domestic suppliers substantially delayed implementation of the new technology. In 1981 and 1982 BT relinquished its leadership of the manufacturing cartel, and the cartel was reorganized. Since then, the focus of U.K. telecommunications policy has shifted away from the manufacturing and export of equipment toward the improved provision of services that would lead foreign multinationals with large telecommunications needs to set up their European headquarters in the United Kingdom. According to Beesley and Laidlaw, that change in emphasis led to the focus on liberalization of the U.K. telecommunications market.[3]

In the late 1970s, long before privatization became an issue, there was an emerging debate about liberalizing competition in telecommunications. Referring to the successful U.S. experience, a report by an expert commission in 1977 recommended the liberalization of customer premises equipment, but the Labour government then in power ignored the report. In contrast, in the 1979 Conservative government the industry minister, Sir Keith Joseph, advocated competition in telecommunications markets. He commissioned Michael Beesley of the London Business School to analyze the potential for competition in customer premises equipment, enhanced services, and the network itself. Beesley's 1981 report recommended that the government allow unrestricted resale of leased line capacity and permit BT to set prices for leased lines freely but in a nondiscriminatory fashion.[4] The report also

2. Michael E. Beesley & Bruce Laidlaw, The Development of Telecommunications Policy in the UK, 1981–1991 (1992) (unpublished manuscript, on file with authors).

3. *Id.*

4. MICHAEL E. BEESLEY, LIBERALISATION OF THE USE OF BRITISH TELECOMMUNICATIONS' NETWORK (HM Stationer's Office 1981).

backed network entry. BT claimed that such liberalization would force it to increase sharply telephone line rental charges, connection charges, and charges for local calls because of the reduced availability of cross-subsidies from international and long-distance calling. Thus, the pattern of cross-subsidization appears to have been similar in extent to that in the United States at the time.

The government feared that such a change in price structure would burden residential customers in favor of business users. Consequently, in the British Telecommunications Act of 1981 the government did not follow Beesley's recommendations. It did, however, allow for some entry into the enhanced services market (which was further liberalized in 1987). More important, the act terminated BT's monopoly in customer premises equipment (with the exception of rental of the first phone on an exchange line, for which BT's monopoly only ceased in 1985) and allowed for licensed network entry.

The government issued the first license, based on the 1981 act, to MCL in 1982 for fairly restrictive operations. The government issued a second and broader license, based on the British Telecommunications Act of 1984, to MCL on November 5, 1984. Cellnet and Vodafone, mobile service providers, received licenses in 1985.

In 1983 the government declared a seven-year duopoly policy under which no new competitors to BT and MCL's landline services would be allowed to enter. In 1991, after review of the duopoly policy, the market was opened for new licensees. Since then, the government awarded more than 150 licenses.

According to Armstrong and Vickers,[5] the U.K. government chose to emphasize regulation of conduct rather than of structure in the telecommunications industry. Consequently, BT was left intact after privatization, as an integrated company offering local, trunk, and international services nationwide (again with the exception of local services in Kingston-upon-Hull); BT continues to dominate the British telecommunications market with a domestic market share of

---

5. Mark Armstrong & John Vickers, Competition and Regulation in the British Telecommunications Industry (1990) (unpublished manuscript, on file with authors).

90 to 95 percent. In addition, BT dominates the small but growing market for interconnections, which consists of all telecommunications services transactions between networks. All other telecommunications operators—including those with which BT is in direct competition—have to use BT's network to complete calls. As a vertically integrated nationwide provider of local, long-distance, and international services, BT competes directly with the same operators to whom it provides interconnection services.

Several structural provisions of the Telecommunications Act of 1984 relate directly to competition. The main vehicle for regulating BT is the license, a contract with the government now required of all telecommunications operators. Consequently, the act reduces BT to a licensed public telecommunications operator (PTO). BT holds a twenty-five-year, renewable license. The company is allowed to engage in enhanced services, cellular telephony, and apparatus (customer premises equipment) and other equipment supply, as long as it keeps separate accounts that show that it does not cross-subsidize those activities from its telephone network service business. BT does, however, face some restrictions in the services it may offer, for example, in new mobile technologies such as personal communications networks and in combining its own local cable television operations with its telephone network.

With regard to conduct, the main competitive provisions in BT's license include a universal service obligation, a nondiscrimination requirement, a prohibition against cross-subsidizing specific activities such as its apparatus business, and requirements to purchase equipment by competitive tender and to interconnect with other PTOs.

Major Telecommunications Operators

The main providers of telecommunications services in the United Kingdom are fixed-link operators and mobile operators. BT remains the dominant fixed-link operator.

British Telecommunications. After its conversion to a public limited company in 1984, BT was sold to private shareholders in three tranches of about 50 percent in 1984, about 28 percent in 1991, and the remainder in July 1993.

In 1994 BT had 156,000 employees (reduced from 246,000 in 1990 through streamlining and network modernization), 27 million lines installed, 35 billion inland calls, revenues of £13.7 billion, and £2.8 billion in before-tax profits.[6] BT offers a full range of telecommunications services except cable television (prohibited until 2001, but the company plans to offer video on demand) and mobile (although the company owns 60 percent of Cellnet). BT is a global player and seeks to enter foreign markets by using interconnection agreements in foreign countries. BT owns 20 percent of MCI Communications and reached an agreement in November 1996 to acquire the remainder. At the end of 1995 BT provided 90 percent of domestic calls and 70 percent of international calls in the United Kingdom. But BT still served about 95 percent of all subscriber lines.[7]

Mercury Communications Ltd. MCL was founded in 1981 as a consortium to build a figure-eight-shaped fiber-optic network connecting thirty cities and with an initial license restriction to a 3 percent market share in voice telephony. Within a year of receiving its license, however, the government dropped the market share limitation and in November 1983 initiated a seven-year duopoly policy to protect both BT and MCL from further market entry for fixed-link services (except for cable television companies). After a slow start, MCL experienced impressive growth. MCL is currently owned by Cable & Wireless (80 percent) and Bell Canada (BCE, 20 percent). MCL therefore has access to ample financial resources.[8]

In its 1992–1993 fiscal year MCL had a 10.5 percent market share by revenue, 1.16 million installed lines for 400,000 public telephone customers, total revenues of £1.2 billion (up from £170 million in its 1988–1989 fiscal year), operating revenues from public telephone services of £829 million (including £406 million in international revenues), and a net book value of fixed assets of

6. BRITISH TELECOMMUNICATIONS PLC, REPORT AND ACCOUNTS (1994).
7. OFTEL, Pricing for Telecommunications Services from 1997 (Dec. 1995) (consultative document), annexes at 12.
8. BCE invested £480 million in the company in 1992 to acquire a 20 percent equity share. BCE is also engaged in U.K. cable television franchises in which Cable & Wireless took an equity share.

£1.68 billion.[9] MCL is largely a long-distance telecommunications company that provides local telephone services only to business customers. The largest component of its operating revenues comes from business customers with direct fiber-optic or microwave connections to MCL. The second-largest share is from large, indirectly connected business customers (using automatic least-cost routing over MCL's network for long-distance and international calls), and the third is from indirectly connected residential and single-line business customers. Indirectly connected customers access MCL through the networks of other local carriers, mostly BT. MCL does not provide its own lines for residential and single-line business customers. Most residential customers use telephones equipped with a push button that directs the call over the MCL network, or telephones equipped with a "Mercury Smart Socket" that automatically connects with MCL. In that way customers avoid having to dial three-digit access codes. They use MCL for long-distance and international calls while continuing to pay line rentals to BT and to use BT for local calling. MCL charges its residential customers a flat annual fee plus long-distance call charges.

Kingston Communications, Ltd. (Hull). The Hull telephone department, now Kingston Communications, Ltd. (Hull), serves a city of 375,000 people with 128,000 lines. It offers local telephone services at rates below BT's, yet unlike BT, it seems to be profitable in that area, either because Kingston is more efficient or because Hull's high population density allows for less costly provision of services than can be achieved in the country as a whole. Hull's customers split long-distance calls fairly evenly between BT and MCL.[10]

Cable Television Companies as Fixed-Link Operators. Until the duopoly review in 1991, cable television companies were restricted in their telecommunications operations to voice services provided

9. MERCURY COMMUNICATIONS LTD., BUSINESS REVIEW 1992–93: THE DIMENSIONS OF GROWTH 2 (1993).

10. ELI NOAM, TELECOMMUNICATIONS IN EUROPE 117–18 (Oxford University Press 1992).

for BT or MCL, or to nonvoice services. A cable operator could not, without specific authorization, switch local calls and had to sign an interconnection agreement with BT or MCL for national or international routes. In practice, cable operators mostly used MCL but felt that those arrangements heavily favored MCL. The duopoly review resulted in cable companies' receiving permission to offer switched services and to interconnect at will with either BT or MCL.

Telephone lines supplied by thirteen U.K. cable companies have grown from fewer than 2,300 before 1991 to more than 1 million at the end of 1995.[11] That is more than 3 percent of total direct lines in the United Kingdom. That rapid growth can probably be attributed to a 15 percent price advantage over BT. Most new subscriptions come jointly with those for cable television. For example, in 1994 NYNEX CableComms had about 71,000 customers, 79 percent of which also were buyers of NYNEX's telephone services. Cable companies find their lower telephone prices profitable, whereas BT claims to take a loss with its subscription rates. The reason for that difference seems to be that the incremental cost of providing telephone services is low for a cable television company, provided that the twisted copper telephone wiring is installed at the same time as the coaxial television cable. Currently, only about 4 percent of U.K. households have cable television. Cable companies, which currently enter or pass slightly fewer than 25 percent of British homes, thus have substantial further market potential, as their networks are authorized to pass 70 percent of homes. On the other hand, by 1994 cable television companies had failed to show any overall profits so far.[12] Since over 70 percent of households signing up for cable television also sign up for cable telephony, the competitive threat to BT is substantial as cable penetration rates increase.

Unlike the United States, the United Kingdom has no general restrictions on foreign ownership for telecommunications (and radio)

---

11. OFTEL, *supra* note 7.

12. *British Telecom Struggles to Fend Off Strong Sales Pitches by US Companies,* WALL ST. J., Aug. 26, 1994, at A6.

services. Some of the cable television companies therefore have foreign equity participation or are wholly foreign owned.

Details of the network architecture of one company, NYNEX CableComms, illustrate how some U.K. cable operations are able to supply both cable and telecommunications services efficiently. NYNEX CableComms[13] uses optical fiber for the trunk parts of its network, coupled with coaxial cable for television distribution and twisted copper cables for telecommunications distribution to the end user. The network is designed to supply cable television, residential telephony, and a full range of business telecommunications services. Although the cable television portion of the network is in principle hierarchical, starting from a central office that receives the broadcasting signals and descending to the set-top boxes of individual subscribers, the network is actually designed as a fiber-optic ring, starting and ending at the central office. At the next level the network is divided into units of approximately 2,400 homes, in each of which is located a so-called AM node. Each unit is further subdivided into four areas of 600 homes, the AM node, and three distribution nodes. Each distribution node is then ultimately divided into block nodes of sixty homes or fewer, depending on housing density.

The optical fiber trunk cables leave the central office with 144 fibers each. They are slimmed down as they extend farther from the central office. Each AM node receives twelve fibers, four of which are reserved for television and eight for telecommunications. Currently, only two fibers are actually used for each service; the remainder are held in reserve. From the AM node downward, television signals are carried on coaxial cables, and telecommunications signals first on fiber and then, from the distribution node onward, on twisted copper cables. The drop cable from the block node to the subscriber's premises uses a composite ("siametic") cable with one coaxial portion and two twisted pairs.

An important consequence of that network architecture is that the incremental costs of providing telephone services in addition to cable television are quite low. The same is not true for cable

13. NYNEX CableComms, NYNEX CableComms Network Architecture and Equipment (undated) (unpublished manuscript, on file with authors).

television companies in the United States, which did not start out providing telephony. Thus, some of the U.K. cost experience with cable television companies providing telephone services does not fully carry over to the United States.

Wireless Operators. In the area of wireless telecommunications, two early entrants now provide cellular mobile radio telephone services nationally to more than 2 million subscribers each (using analog and digital technology). Those companies, Vodafone and Cellnet (which is 60 percent owned by BT), until recently had to retail their services through service intermediaries. Each company has two networks (analog and digital) overlaid on each other. Currently, no standard dual handsets are available for both analog and digital service.

In addition, there are two recently established wireless personal communications network operators that use digital technology in the 1.7 to 1.9 GHz band. Hutchison Microtel is owned by Hutchison Whampoa of Hong Kong. In early 1996 it provided services to 400,000 customers under the brand name Orange. Mercury Personal Communications, operating under the brand name Mercury One-2-One, is a 50–50 partnership of Cable & Wireless and U S West. Originally, there were three PCN licenses in use. Mercury One-2-One emerged from a network-sharing agreement with the Unitel consortium so that Mercury Personal Communications could give up its own (the third) license.[14] Mercury One-2-One uses a low-price strategy to compete both with the other wireless operators and with the fixed-link carriers, but so far it has been somewhat less successful in attracting customers than its three competitors and, in particular, in generating cash flow.

Until very recently, all mobile operators had to obtain their fixed links from other PTOs. But Vodafone and Cellnet, in December 1993 and March 1994, respectively, were licensed to

14. In total the U.K. government allocated the band from 1710 to 1880 MHz for PCN (two 75 MHz bands with a 20 MHz guard band). Each PCN operator has two 25 MHz bands reserved for its use; both Mercury One-2-One and Hutchison have used 15 MHz of each of their two bands so far. With the freeing of the third license, some of the remaining spectrum is now occupied by emergency service microwave users, and some is left vacant for future use.

provide certain of their own fixed links and offer landline services. Mercury One-2-One obtains lines from BT and MCL but also builds its own transmission facilities using microwave. Most of the transmission network connecting its cells and switches is self-built.

COMPETITION AND REGULATORY POLICY

Regulatory Framework and Licenses

Entrants in the market for telecommunications network services must acquire a license and must usually enter into interconnection agreements with other PTOs. As long as the entity that is now BT remained state owned, telecommunications regulation was performed quite informally by the secretary of state for trade and industry. It was only upon BT's divestiture in 1984 that regulation became a formal element in U.K. telecommunications. The Telecommunications Act of 1984 created the position of director general of telecommunications, who heads the Office of Telecommunications (OFTEL). The powers and duties of the director general are defined in the Telecommunications Act, in the licenses, and in the Competition and Services (Utilities) Act of 1992. The last of those allows the director general to monitor directly the relationships between the PTOs and their customers. The director general has substantial power and can make most decisions on his own authority. The first director general, Sir Bryan Carsberg, gave few explanations for his decisions, so it was difficult for affected parties to learn for future negotiations. His successor, Don Cruickshank, provides explanatory annexes to his determinations and seeks interaction with the industry. OFTEL had 147 employees in December 1993.[15]

The main vehicle of telecommunications regulation is the license, required of all operators of public telecommunications systems, including BT. Licenses for the major telephone operators have been issued for an initial twenty-five years (cable television companies receive licenses of either fifteen or twenty-three years). BT's license may only be terminated with ten years' notice, after

15. OFTEL, ANNUAL REPORT 67 (1993).

fifteen years have passed, or at other times, for specific reasons such as noncompliance with license conditions.

The license, dealt with in section 7 of the Telecommunications Act, may be issued either by the secretary of state for trade and industry after consultation with the director general of telecommunications, or by the director general "with the consent of, or in accordance with a general authorization given by" the secretary. As of September 1993, no such authority had been given.[16] In contrast, license modifications and monitoring of license compliance are primarily the responsibility of the director general. The director general has the authority to issue orders, enforceable in U.K. courts, to secure compliance. As of September 1993, no major orders had been issued.[17] License changes have to follow a well-specified formal process.[18] If the director general and the licenseholder cannot agree on a license amendment, the Monopolies and Mergers Commission (MMC, one of two principal U.K. competition policy authorities) is brought in. Also, the secretary can block a license amendment if a threat to national security is perceived, or can refer to the MMC any agreement for a license modification reached between the director general and the licensee.

The operator of a telecommunications system may be licensed as a PTO. Such classification facilitates acquiring wayleaves (rights-of-way) and imposes some duties, such as reaching certain penetration levels (as is required of MCL) or providing universal service (required of BT). Licenseholders must also publish prices, terms, and conditions of service and may not discriminate. According to OFTEL, BT's license obligations include: a requirement to meet all reasonable demand for basic telephone services, including rural areas; a requirement to provide public call

16. *See* Mercury Communications Ltd., *Mercury in the United Kingdom, in* CABLE & WIRELESS ANNUAL REPORT TO THE UNITED STATES SECURITIES AND EXCHANGE COMMISSION ON FORM 20-F 1992/93 (Sept. 10, 1993), at 17.

17. *Id.*

18. Pablo T. Spiller & Ingo Vogelsang, *The United Kingdom: A Pacesetter in Regulatory Incentives, in* REGULATIONS, INSTITUTIONS, AND COMMITMENT (Brian Levy and Pablo T. Spiller eds., Cambridge University Press 1996), at 79.

boxes (pay phones), unless certain criteria have been satisfied; a prohibition against discriminatory prices and conditions against certain persons or groups, including people in rural areas; a requirement to provide a residential low-user scheme; a requirement to provide special facilities and priority treatment for the hearing impaired and the sick; and a requirement to provide free public emergency call services.

Wireless operators (as well as fixed-link operators for their microwave and satellite transmissions) need an additional license under the Wireless Telegraphy Act of 1949, and cable television companies require licenses under the 1990 Broadcasting Act (replacing the 1984 Cable and Broadcasting Act).[19] Mobile operators pay a license fee, presumably for scarce spectrum. Cable television operators providing telephony do so under a 1984 Telecommunications Act license, which requires them to provide telecommunications services in their franchise area without undue discrimination.

Non-PTO licenses are easier to get than PTO licenses, and their terms are quite liberal. They apply to private networks such as public utilities, closed user groups such as banks, or simple resale of international private lines. Self-provision licenses refer to private networks and closed user groups (such as cooperatives), whereas telecommunications service licenses refer to provision for others.

Since 1991 (after conclusion of the duopoly review), the government can issue licenses fairly freely for the provision of services over fixed links. The government will consider applications on their merits against the provisions in the 1984 Telecommunications Act. Any requests conferring rights to install equipment on or over public or private land are scrutinized to ensure that the potential disruption is justified. By December 1995, 150 operator licenses had been granted.[20] Several of the new licensees were granted the status of public telecommunications

19. Cable television operators are also regulated by an independent television commission, which reviews content and access for broadcasting (15 percent of programming must be open to independent producers) and cross-media ownership.

20. OFTEL, *supra* note 7, at 5. Over 100 of those licenses are for cable television operators, who can offer telephone service.

systems. They include, among others, Ionica (for a national radio-based network), Energis Communications Ltd. (a subsidiary of the National Grid that plans to offer long-distance services), City of London Telecommunications Ltd. (COLT, which is building a metropolitan-area network service within a thirty-kilometer radius of central London), and MFS Communications Ltd., a subsidiary of the U.S.-based MFS Communications, which is building a sixteen-kilometer-radius fiber-optic network in the London financial district.

An exception to the opening of the telecommunications market to new entrants, however, is that BT and MCL continue to be barred from transmitting television and radio-based signals for their own account at least until 2001. That does not, however, prevent BT or MCL from owning equity in companies that offer such services or from transmitting such signals for others. Also, the Independent Television Commission, in September 1993, issued a statement that it would not require a local delivery license for nonsimultaneous video on demand. Only a "programme service licence" would be needed. That appears to allow BT to provide point-to-point but not broadcast entertainment over its network. BT had been running trials, using asymmetric digital subscriber line (ADSL) technology.

The main network entry barrier in the United Kingdom appears to result from BT's sunk investment in its local loop and, until recently, from regulatory restrictions on BT's retail rate rebalancing, although the influence of the latter is hard to evaluate. BT's sunk local-loop investment makes its incremental costs of gaining new customers or keeping old ones lower than the incremental costs to most new entrants of gaining customers. BT's restrictions on rate rebalancing have kept BT's installation and quarterly subscription rates below the costs of most entering rivals. In 1996 those restrictions were lifted.[21]

---

21. *BT Agrees to Removal of RPI + 2% Constraint*, OFTEL NEWS, Feb. 1996, at 20.

Competition Policy

The director general of telecommunications shares responsibilities with the director general of fair trading (section 50 of the Telecommunications Act) in applying the Fair Trading Act of 1973 and the Competition Act of 1980 to the telecommunications industry. Also, instead of a narrow referral to the MMC on a license change, the secretary of state for trade and industry may make wide referrals on competitive issues. Such a wide referral would entitle the MMC to look into such questions as whether BT's dominant market position is counter to the public interest and whether the company should therefore be split up. The secretary of state for trade and industry, may, however, reject the commission's recommendations on such matters (as has happened in the case of British Gas).

In addition to the Restrictive Trade Practices Act of 1976, further competition law applying to telecommunications operators is contained in their licenses. For example, condition 13 of BT's license disallows provisions in interconnection agreements that are restrictive (collusive) under the Restrictive Trade Practices Act, unless the director general of telecommunications, in a determination, has explicitly consented to such a provision. Both BT and MCL have nondiscrimination clauses in their licenses. The director general of telecommunications is currently attempting to broaden BT's license conditions dealing with competition policy as a step that would permit deregulating more of BT's services.[22]

Regulation of British Telecom

The decision to privatize BT immediately triggered the question of how to deal with BT's monopoly power.[23] Although some parts of the telecommunications market appeared to be geared for vigorous competition, it was clear that in others BT's monopoly was unassailable. Thus, not only did the power of BT over entry and

22. OFTEL, *supra* note 7, at 6.
23. This section and the next are based on Spiller & Vogelsang, *supra* note 18.

emerging competitors need to be addressed, but also BT's ability to raise prices to consumers. In October 1982 the Department of Industry commissioned Stephen Littlechild to report on two proposals for regulating BT's prices: rate-of-return regulation on the U.S. model versus an incentive scheme designed by Sir Alan Walters, then the economic adviser to Prime Minister Margaret Thatcher. Walters's "output related profits levy" (ORPL) would simply be a tax inversely related to BT's output growth, and there would have been no further price regulation of BT's outputs.

Although novel, the ORPL scheme appeared to have some drawbacks both in theory and in its practical application.[24] Littlechild rejected both the ORPL and rate-of-return regulation, the latter on theoretical grounds and because of its unfavorable U.S. track record. Instead, in his 1983 report, Littlechild suggested what he called a "local tariff reduction scheme." Under that scheme only BT's local telecommunications services would be subject to price regulation. The scheme defined a basket of regulated services whose prices on average would be allowed to grow at the rate of inflation minus an unspecified adjustment factor (X). Inflation would be measured by the retail price index (RPI); hence the scheme bore the name "*RPI – X*" and was later called price-cap regulation in the United States. Within the regulated basket, BT would be allowed to rebalance its prices as it chose, as long as the *RPI – X* constraint held for the average of all prices in the basket, expressed as a chained Laspeyres price index.[25] The regulatory scheme would be fixed for five years, after which either BT would be deregulated or

---

24. A theoretical analysis of the ORPL is found in the appendix to STEPHEN C. LITTLECHILD, REGULATION OF BRITISH TELECOMMUNICATIONS' PROFITABILITY (Department of Industry Feb. 1983). *See also* Stephen Glaister, *Regulation Through Output Related Profits Tax,* 35 J. IND. ECON. 281 (1987).

25. A Laspeyres price index uses base-period quantities as weights. By not including consumer adjustments to changed prices, it is a conservative measure that underestimates the effects of price increases. A chained index changes the base period from time to time. Thus, it consists of many subindexes that are linked in such a way that the current period of one subindex becomes the base period for the next. In that way the relevant base-period consumption bundle is never excessively different from the consumption bundle for the current period.

the regulator would revisit the scheme. In addition to his regulatory scheme, Littlechild proposed a number of steps that would have opened up the telecommunications market to more competition.

Although the government did not follow Littlechild's extensive suggestions on competition policy, his regulatory scheme, with some modifications, became part of BT's license. The modifications concern in particular the contents of the regulated basket, which were extended to include BT's long-distance calling services. Thus, when regulation started in 1984, the basket included outputs accounting for slightly more than 50 percent of BT's total sales: the only major outputs excluded were international telephone services, leased lines, and apparatus. BT's connection charges for new subscribers were also excluded from the regulated basket. Within the $RPI - X$ constraint BT may change its prices after giving 28 days' notice. The $RPI - X$ scheme is subject to a sunset provision restricting it to a specified number of years. After an initial five-year period the scheme was renewed for an additional four years. Agreement on the current four-year period, which began in 1993, was reached by the director general of telecommunications and BT in August 1992. Any renewal or change in the price regulation regime automatically requires a change in BT's license.

The inclusion of long-distance services in the basket actually increased BT's ability to rebalance its prices, because reductions in long-distance rates could now be offset against increases in other rates. Thus, paradoxically, the regulation of additional services under price caps gave BT more rather than less freedom. Since BT expected competition from MCL mainly in long-distance services, that inclusion appreciably increased BT's effective ability to compete. At the same time, rebalancing would have allowed BT to move toward subsidy-free and allocatively more efficient prices. But to constrain the amount of rebalancing, in 1984 BT voluntarily agreed to limit annual increases in exchange line rentals to $RPI + 2$ percent.

Initially, after privatization, BT's leased line rates remained unregulated. BT used that pricing freedom to raise prices sharply. For a long time leased lines had failed to break even, because in the 1970s prices for such leases had been kept down in conjunction with general price controls by the Labour government then in power. The argument at that time had been that costs for industries that were themselves subject to price controls could and should be held down by not increasing prices of publicly provided inputs. After 1983 price increases for leased lines moved BT toward compensatory rates, but their steepness triggered political pressure from consumers. In response to that pressure, in 1989 a separate price-cap basket for leased lines was formed with an *RPI* − 0 constraint. Accordingly, leased line rates on average could go up only with inflation, and rebalancing could occur only within the basket of leased lines.

The government had prohibited simple resale (of leased line capacity for uses other than enhanced services) until 1989 because of BT's unbalanced price structure. In the early 1980s permitting simple resale might have led to uneconomic bypass and would have forced BT to raise its leased line rates more drastically than the government would have liked. By 1989, however, BT's price structure had been substantially rebalanced so that the director general felt it safe to allow simple resale of BT's domestic leased lines. Simple resale of international leased lines followed in October 1990.

Development of the Price-Cap Regime

For the period from 1984 to 1989 OFTEL had inherited from BT's privatization process the *RPI* − 3 formula for price regulation of services constituting about 50 percent of BT's output in value terms. Prices for the other 50 percent remained nominally subject to competition. Privatization started with an average real price decrease for the regulated basket of 3.1 percent, slightly better than the regulatory requirement of *RPI* − 3. But the average nominal change combined 7 percent *increases* for exchange line rentals, offpeak calls in general, and local and short-haul long-distance calls with a decrease of about 12 percent for peak and standard national long-distance calls. That price restructuring, which all the experts had expected, came as an unwelcome surprise to the average British telephone customer, who actually faced average telephone rate increases well above *RPI* − 3.

BT easily coped with the *RPI* − *X* constraint, as its increasing profitability after privatization indicates. The 3 percent adjustment factor for the years 1984 through 1989 had originally been put forward by Littlechild as a plausible number, but that seems to have become a focal point in subsequent negotiations.[26] In 1989 Beesley and Littlechild[27] stated that, within a range, any value of X set before the initial flotation of BT's shares would have been acceptable, because investors would have automatically adjusted BT's initial share price. The burden (or benefit) of that adjustment would have been on the Treasury. Clearly, with the benefit of hindsight, 3 percent looks quite generous. On the other hand, BT's long-run rate of productivity improvement had been only about 2 percent. Thus, although *ex ante* 3 percent did not appear to indicate soft regulation by the government, it ended up helping to strengthen the government's sales efforts for BT shares. That means that financial experts rightly expected that BT could increase its profits under the *RPI − 3* regime. Three reasons can be given for their expectation. First, because of rapid technical advances in telephone lines and switching equipment, BT's input prices increased more slowly than the RPI. Second, BT's price restructuring under price caps would increase its profits.[28] Third, and most important, BT was viewed as a firm with great potential to improve its productivity once freed by privatization.

U.K. regulation of telecommunications is not bound by any specific rate-of-return considerations. Sir Bryan Carsberg made it clear in his 1986 report that, under *RPI − X,* BT would be allowed to earn more than its cost of capital. Lip service has been paid to the same principle in the 1988 and 1992 reviews of the price-cap regime. Nevertheless, over time BT's achieved and prospective

---

26. An *RPI − 3* price cap for a local telephone service basket only, as originally suggested by Littlechild, would have been much tougher on BT than the *RPI − 3* for the enlarged basket actually implemented.

27. See Michael E. Beesley & Stephen C. Littlechild, *The Regulation of Privatized Monopolies in the United Kingdom,* 20 RAND J. ECON. 454 (1989).

28. Under the Laspeyres price index approach used by Littlechild, consumers in the aggregate would at the same time be better off by more than 3 percent per year. *See* Ian Bradley & Catherine Price, *The Economic Regulation of Private Industry by Price Constraints,* 37 J. IND. ECON. 99 (1988), and Ingo Vogelsang, *Price Cap Regulation of Telecommunications Services: A Long-Run Approach, in* DEREGULATION AND DIVERSIFICATION OF UTILITIES (Michael A. Crew ed., Kluwer Academic Publishers 1989).

rates of return have in practice become pivotal in the determination of the X factor and the scope of price caps. Also, in his 1986 report Carsberg noted his ability to change BT's license at any time (that is, before the sunset provision of the current formula takes effect) if BT's rate of return became excessive.

From the beginning of *RPI − X* regulation BT did not fully exhaust its legal potential for price increases. Thus, the claim that the deterioration of service quality in 1987 was a way of avoiding the stringency of price-cap regulation appears unfounded, in particular given that labor disputes and strikes in 1986 and 1987 provide a credible alternative explanation of the quality problems. Nevertheless, BT's quality performance gave rise to enough bad publicity that, to regain public good will, the company agreed to a price moratorium from 1987 to 1989. It also gave Carsberg an opportunity to prove his regulatory and negotiating skills: he made BT agree to contractual guarantees on the speed of repairs. In case of delays BT agreed to pay penalties to the affected customers. In addition, BT was obliged to resume detailed reporting on its quality of service, and OFTEL initiated its own quality observation and reporting.

The First Price-Cap Renewal. In January 1988, well before the expiration of the *RPI − X* provision in BT's license in 1989, OFTEL began its price regulation review. In the consultation process there was overwhelming support for an extension of the general *RPI − X* regime, with some variation on issues such as the basis for setting the X factor.[29] At the same time, the director general of telecommunications took up with BT the calculation of BT's rate of return, its productivity performance, and its future investment and employment plans. To that end, OFTEL developed a quantitative financial model for BT and, in particular, of a hypothetical "regulated company" within BT.[30] With that model OFTEL

29. OFTEL, Responses to OFTEL's Consultative Document on the Future Regulation of British Telecom's Prices (Sept. 1988) (Working Paper No. 3).

30. Martin Cave, Recent Developments in the Regulation of Former Nationalised Industries (1991) (HM Treasury Working Paper No. 60).

simulated the effects of regulatory changes under different scenarios. The assumptions for the model and for the different scenarios were clarified with BT. After deciding on a basic set of assumptions and determining their impact on BT's profits, its capital employed, and other variables, the director general of telecommunications proposed an X factor of 4.5 percent for a slightly enlarged main basket for the four years starting in 1989. Operator-assisted domestic calls were added to the basket. BT was allowed to carry forward unused price increase potentials within the four-year period, but not beyond. The $RPI + 2$ rule on telephone rentals was continued and extended to business rentals, and subscriber connection charges were subjected to a rule of $RPI + 2$, outside the basket. Finally, BT committed itself to offering discounts to subscribers with low calling volumes.[31] Although the tightening of the X factor from 3 percent to 4.5 percent may look like punishment for superior productivity performance (as indicated by BT's substantially improved profitability since privatization), it was actually softer than BT's own most recent pricing decisions at the time.[32] In the face of a steeply rising retail price index, BT, by not increasing its regulated prices at all, had realized an $RPI - 4.4$ in November 1987 and an $RPI - 5.9$ in November 1988.[33]

The Duopoly Review. Over the seven-year duopoly period (1984 to 1991) BT had become a more formidable competitor in two major respects. It had invested heavily in a modernized and expanded network, and it had restructured its prices. Because of its pricing policy and its large share of residential customers (who predominantly call during offpeak hours), BT also had much better load characteristics than MCL. On the other hand, BT had not fully

31. For all those changes, *see* OFTEL, The Control of British Telecom's Prices (July 1988) (statement issued by the Director General of Telecommunications).

32. The majority of responses to OFTEL's consultative document had suggested a continuation of $RPI - 3$. OFTEL, *supra* note 29, at 4.

33. K. MEEK, TELECOMMUNICATIONS PRICE CONTROL IN THE UK (International Institute of Communications 1988), *cited in* LELAND L. JOHNSON, PRICE CAPS IN TELECOMMUNICATIONS REGULATORY REFORM (RAND Note N-2894-MF/RC, 1989).

realized its potential for productivity improvements and was probably still cross-subsidizing switched customer access and analog leased lines. At the same time MCL had made heavy inroads in BT's sales to large business customers, in international telecommunications, and in digital leased lines. By the time of the duopoly review in 1991 MCL was actually starting to attract small business and residential customers in appreciable numbers. It was clear for the first time that MCL was realistically aiming for more than just a market niche. BT had been trying to respond to MCL's success among big business customers by offering quantity discounts, but OFTEL prevented the firm from doing so.

The duopoly review led to further liberalization of the U.K. telecommunications market. Somewhat surprisingly, the outcome of the review also included changes in BT's price-cap regulation. Those changes were partly the result of BT's desire to compete more flexibly with MCL and with new entrants. Price-cap-related changes included a more generous $RPI + 5$ for most business rentals, rebates to subscribers with low calling volumes, and the possibility to introduce volume discounts for bulk users, provided that BT obeyed an $RPI - 0$ constraint for median residential bills. Volume discounts for bulk users would make BT more competitive in the market for big business, which MCL was coming to dominate. Rebates to subscribers with low calling volumes would effectively establish "lifeline" rates for customers who would not otherwise benefit from competitive price restructuring.

Most strikingly, international services were now added to BT's price-cap basket, with the X factor increased from 4.5 percent to 6.25 percent and an immediate reduction in international rates by 10 percent. The inclusion of international services under regulation can be viewed as compensation for initially excluding international services from facilities-based entry by firms outside the BT-MCL duopoly. At BT's privatization, it had been thought that international call prices would become competitive very quickly, once MCL entered. But BT's profit contributions from international calls increased sharply since 1988, even though MCL had established itself as a viable company. Consequently, whereas in October 1990 Carsberg had sought a separate basket for international services, he has now made them part of the main basket. That was clearly in BT's interest because it allowed the company more flexibility in price rebalancing.

The Second (Official) Price-Cap Review. In January 1992 the director general of telecommunications initiated the review process for the third round of price regulation. There was a general consensus among all parties consulted that price caps should be continued for at least four to five years and that the basic *RPI – X* approach should be kept intact.

After an exchange of submissions and responses, BT expected to be consulted on the director general's proposal for the new price caps.[34] Instead the director general informed BT's management of his new price-cap decision only the night before he was to announce it at a press conference on June 2, 1992. He made it clear that if BT did not agree to his proposed license amendments, he would make a referral to the MMC under very broad terms, which, according to BT, could have included the possibility of splitting BT into several companies. The decision left BT with only two choices: accept the decision or submit to referral to the MMC. Carsberg may have been motivated toward that strategy by MCL's complaints that it had not been specifically consulted during the duopoly review. But the time factor may have influenced the director general to go forward with a proposal without consulting BT any further. Because of the sunset nature of the *RPI – X* provision in BT's license, if he did not make an amendment, BT could start pricing at will. Carsberg wanted to leave enough time for the option of a referral to the MMC. A case before the commission would take six or more months, and the director general wanted to avoid having the decision come at a time when the pricing clause in BT's current license would be about to expire.

In terms of its content, the director general's decision stayed within the *RPI – X* concept. But price regulation on BT became substantially more stringent and was expanded in scope. For the

---

34. BT's response to the consultative document contained the following statement: "It is . . . expected that further discussions with Oftel will take place covering the detail of BT's proposals and their financial impact." BRITISH TELECOMMUNICATIONS PLC, PRICING FOR CHOICE 3 (Mar. 1992).

general basket, the X factor increased to 7.5 percent. The stringency of the price cap was further enhanced by not giving BT credit for additional volume discounts to large users and by including connection (installation) charges in the basket. Rebalancing within the general basket was now also restricted by an $RPI + 2$ constraint on exchange line rentals (including multiline business connections) and an $RPI - 0$ constraint on all other services in the basket. The tariff for low-volume callers was extended to a larger set of subscribers. For the leased line basket the X factor stayed at zero, but no rebalancing was allowed. Since BT had to reduce some of its leased line rates in response to competition, that meant an effective rate of $RPI - 3$ for leased lines (according to BT representatives we interviewed). BT was particularly stunned by the director general's insistence on the firm's adopting new accounting rules, to be based on current costs and with separations for BT's different activities (as already existed for the water industry). Nevertheless, after substantially more than the two weeks of deliberation originally granted by the director general, BT decided not to contest his recommendation for a license amendment.

BT's favorable decision has to be seen in the context of the director general's threat to refer the company to the MMC. Bringing a case before that body was a credible threat, because BT would have to reveal hitherto proprietary information. In addition, the case would take up precious executive time. Moreover, BT's license condition would for a while become uncertain, the uncertainty of the outcome would affect the firm's share price, and the outcome itself might prove catastrophic if the commission found that BT had to be divested into several companies.

As of this writing, three years into the new price-cap regime, BT's profits have stabilized. So far, BT has been able to counteract the 7.5 percent real price reductions through productivity improvements. In June 1996, the director general of telecommunications proposed a new, more limited price-cap regime for 1997 through 2001 that will cover just 80 percent of residential users and a small fraction of commercial customers. Thus, in the future only about 25 percent of BT's revenues will be subject to price caps, and the director general intends to abolish retail price regulation after the year 2001. In the meantime, the cap may be severe for BT, because the customers covered by price caps from

1997 are those for whom BT would like to raise prices in real terms. In fact, for the residential users covered by the cap, the X factor will increase from the 2.7 percent they experienced in the past to 4.5 percent.[35]

Results of Price-Cap Regulation. In the first ten years of BT's price-cap regulation a monotonic trend has developed. The process has become more public (no more negotiations behind closed doors); regulation has expanded (from covering about 55 percent of BT's revenues in 1985 to about 64 percent in 1995); and it has moved in the direction of rate-of-return regulation and has become more stringent.[36] In fact, the escalation of the X factor from $RPI - 3$ to $RPI - 7.5$ over a number of iterations is quite remarkable. From an optimistic perspective that shows the success of price-cap regulation in helping improve BT's productivity while maintaining a consistently high rate of return, even in the midst of recession in the United Kingdom. That clearly leaves some room for stringency. A more pessimistic perspective, however, focuses on two problems. One is that small residential customers (including the median customer) have seen their bills drop fairly little in real terms. Because of BT's price rebalancing, business and larger residential users have been the prime beneficiaries of the price-cap regime. Thus, without price rebalancing the increase in the X factor would hardly have been viable. The other problem is that $RPI - 7.5$ cannot possibly be maintained in the long run. Thus, the possibility of overshooting raises the specter of a return to the declining profitability experienced in the mid-1970s. Nevertheless, the aggressiveness of the U.K. regulator may contain lessons for the United States in an environment of emerging local competition.

The effect on local competition of ten years of regulation of BT has been that BT has lost comparatively little of its dominance of the local access market. By restricting price rebalancing, the regulator has helped keep entry into residential access unattractive to most would-be competitors. But cable television companies are

---

35. OFTEL, Pricing of Telecommunications Services from 1997 (June 1996) (statement).

36. *See* OFTEL, *supra* note 7, annexes at 5.

now gaining ground quickly, and business users have begun to bypass BT's long-distance and (within downtown London) urban services. The increasingly aggressive price-cap regime has, however, forced BT to become a leaner competitor and has made prices less attractive for entrants.

THE MARKET FOR INTERCONNECTION

Legal Rights Concerning Interconnection

Interconnection is addressed in the specific conditions that are part of all PTO licenses. Those conditions, which provide a detailed and sometimes complicated framework for interconnection agreements, are in many respects similar. Reflecting changes made after 1984, however, condition 13 in BT's license is substantially longer than in all other PTO licenses and contains some items, such as the recently abolished access deficit contributions (see below), that have been conspicuously absent from MCL's license.

Condition 13 requires BT to enter into interconnection agreements with other providers of telecommunications services so that any customer of any licensed operator can call any customer of any other licensed operator. BT must provide points of connection in sufficient capacity and number to enable the interconnector to convey messages via BT's system in a way that meets all reasonable demands. In addition, BT must offer interconnectors the freedom to choose points of interconnection to optimize the routing of long-distance calls. Condition 13 has other requirements to ensure that BT provides effective interconnection services.

BT is not required to provide interconnection if doing so is not reasonably practicable for BT, given the state of technical development or any other matter that appears relevant to the regulator. In addition, BT is not required to provide interconnection if doing so would cause death, injury, or property damage for BT or any person engaged in BT's business, would impair BT's or any other system's quality of service, or would require adjustment or modification of the applicable systems.[37]

---

37. The applicable systems are defined in annex A of BT's license. In a

If BT and the other service provider fail to reach a satisfactory agreement within what the regulator considers a reasonable period, either party may ask him for a determination on specific points of disagreement. That determination is binding. Also, the regulator may implement interconnection agreements whether they are based on his determination or reached by voluntary agreement.

Condition 13 further provides specifically for the determination of interconnection charges. In particular, the interconnector must pay BT on a per-call basis in cases where the interconnector's customer (including another operator) expects to be billed by the interconnector for the conveyance of calls of the type concerned. That demand appears to establish a close relationship between the method of charging for interconnection services and for retail services. It may, however, contradict another postulate of condition 13, according to which interconnection charges should take account of BT's cost patterns. Such tension could occur if BT's retail rates are not themselves based on costs.

Until very recently, interconnection charges had to cover BT's fully allocated costs of conveying a message calculated on a historical cost basis, including a full contribution to relevant overheads. In addition, interconnection charges had to allow for the applicable rate of return to the relevant capital employed and had to include a contribution to BT's access deficit, the access deficit contribution (ADC), suggested by the efficient component-pricing rule. The first two elements in the interconnection charge establish U.S.-style rate-of-return regulation as the basis for interconnection charges. That is in somewhat surprising contrast to the way in which U.K. retail markets in telecommunications are regulated.

Although the ADC was incurred as a result of insufficient connection and rental charges, it was to be recovered on a per-minute basis through calls from customers of interconnecting operators, and separately for local, national, and international (both incoming and outgoing) calls. The presumed rationale for that method was that the opportunity cost to BT was a per-minute cost.

nutshell, they comprise BT's telecommunications network. The definition delineates the boundaries of the systems and excludes wireless networks for mobile telecommunications.

BT itself recovered part of the access deficit from its own retail usage categories, and therefore the ADC was a compensation for profit forgone by selling to competing operators instead of selling directly to consumers.

The director general of telecommunications had considerable discretion to partly or fully waive ADCs. There were four criteria for such a waiver. First, the waiver had to refer to periods before July 1, 1997 (a date that coincides almost exactly with the expiration of BT's current price-cap formula). Second, the waiver did not apply to calls made under an equal access arrangement. Third, the waiver only applied to market shares of at most 10 percent for (most) interconnecting parties and only applied as long as BT's share in the market in question did not fall below 85 percent. That meant that the ADC in any case had to be paid on incremental market shares by which either the interconnector itself exceeded 10 percent or by which BT fell short of its 85 percent. But the regulator had some additional discretion as to the amount of ADC to be paid on those increments. Only if an interconnector's market share exceeded 25 percent did the interconnector have to pay the full ADC. Defining the relevant markets for which those shares applied was partly up to the regulator.[38] Fourth, the regulator had to find the interconnector worthy of such a waiver. Worthiness, according to condition 13, depended on such considerations as the average call volumes per line of the interconnector relative to those experienced by BT. That was supposed to prevent carriers from targeting customers with high calling volumes.[39] Certain mobile operators, and to some extent cable television firms providing telephone services, were exempt from ADCs, irrespective of market share.[40] Furthermore, the regulator was entitled to grant waivers if BT did not fully utilize its leeway to reduce the access deficit by rebalancing its rates. Also, for BT's fiscal years 1992 and 1993 the

38. The regulator's discretion in defining markets is limited by the call categories covered by the agreement and geographically by the area in which the interconnector is licensed to operate. *See* ¶ 13.5A.5(d) of BT's license.

39. Mark Armstrong & Chris Doyle, Network Access Pricing 74 (1993) (unpublished manuscript, on file with authors).

40. NYNEX CableComms, A Year in Perspective—1992 Reviewed 8 (undated).

ADC could have been lowered had BT not achieved benchmark efficiency (using the efficiency levels of the U.S. regional Bell operating companies as the benchmark).[41]

Condition 13 also deals with the reciprocal charges BT has to pay to the interconnector. Such charges must cover the interconnector's costs, in a manner quite similar to conveyance charges in the other direction.

Charges for the establishment of a connection between BT and the interconnector cover the provision of dedicated capacity at a point of (inter)connection, but not transmission capacity (which is recovered through conveyance charges). The costs are shared according to the proportion in which BT and the interconnector each bill customers originating calls conveyed over that point of connection. The proportions are derived from forecasts of the capacity required to convey such calls.

To sum up, the provisions on regulatory determinations leave interconnection issues primarily to private negotiations between the parties involved. The regulator comes in only when the negotiations fail. In practice, however, a regulator's influence seems to dominate certain aspects of interconnection agreements. As Cave has pointed out, "because new entrants typically rely on interconnection with the dominant firm, at prices usually determined by the regulator, entry changes the nature of regulation rather than eliminating the need for it."[42]

The BT-MCL Interconnection Agreement of 1986

Although MCL had reached a draft interconnection agreement with BT as early as 1982, protracted disputes about both the terms of interconnection and its actual implementation required regulatory intervention in 1985, so that the parties did not reach a full-fledged agreement until March 1986. That agreement has set a highly

---

41. The regulator undertook comparisons between BT and certain of the regional Bell operating companies to find out whether BT's productivity indicators lagged theirs. He was satisfied to find that they did not.

42. CAVE, *supra* note 30.

influential precedent for other agreements.[43] Most of what is publicly known about the 1986 agreement comes from the regulator's determination of terms and conditions of October 11, 1985.[44] A major emphasis of the 1985 determination was on the timing of interconnection. That was an important issue because MCL wanted to gain access to customers quickly, whereas BT's interest appeared to have been in delaying interconnection. Given the lack of actual experience with implementing physical interconnection, a number of paragraphs in the determination laid out precise timetables for interconnection and threatened consequences for noncompliance. The determination also specified exchanges for interconnection and let MCL choose one of BT's international gateways for international calls.

According to Armstrong and Doyle,[45] the technology of the U.K. telecommunications system played a key role in the interconnection negotiations. In the mid-1980s BT used a predominantly analog technology for both switching and transmission. Because the firm was investing heavily to modernize its network and replace its analog with digital switches, however, it operated with a mixed analog-digital system.

The 1986 agreement established interconnection at the local and trunk levels, referred to, respectively, as 3L and 3J. Interconnection at the local level "was equivalent to MCL being a direct exchange line customer of BT," providing MCL with the normal form of subscriber access. The trunk interconnection occurred "at the junction side of a trunk exchange" (that is, the side to which lines from local exchanges are connected to the trunk network) and thus bypassed BT's local exchange network.[46] Figure 9–1 shows at what level of BT's network that type of interconnection takes place: at the level of local switches, either lineside at switching centers

43. Armstrong & Doyle, *supra* note 39, at 60.

44. OFTEL, Determination of Terms and Conditions for the Purpose of an Agreement on the Interconnection of the British Telecommunications Telephone System and the Mercury Communications Ltd. System Under Condition 13 of the Licence Granted to British Telecommunications Under Section 7 of the Telecommunications Act 1984 (Oct. 11, 1985).

45. Armstrong & Doyle, *supra* note 39, at 61.

46. *Id.*

FIGURE 9–1
MCL'S INTERCONNECTION POINTS WITH BT'S NETWORK

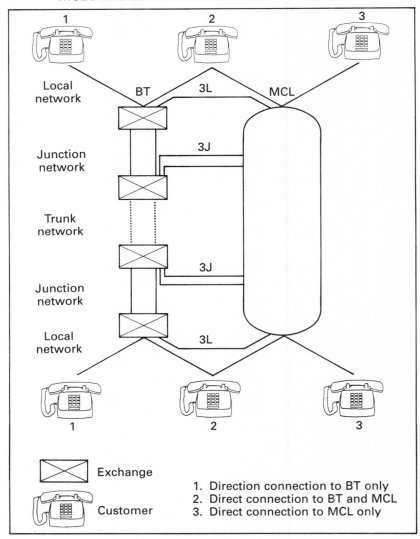

1. Direction connection to BT only
2. Direct connection to BT and MCL
3. Direct connection to MCL only

that are end offices only (3L) or junctionside at switching centers that perform tandem functions (3J).

MCL would have preferred to be assured access at any point of BT's network. That would have given MCL greater flexibility with respect to the size and location of business that MCL was able to accept at the time, and in particular with respect to the planning of its network, which in 1985 was only beginning to take shape. As it has turned out, 3J interconnection at both the originating and the terminating end of a call is the type MCL most frequently employs. The 3L interconnection is far inferior to 3J technically, and MCL uses it only where it has not been able to establish a 3J interconnection point.[47]

To establish trunk interconnection MCL had to pay the sum of the direct cost to BT of providing the interconnection and 50 percent of the "consequential incremental costs" to BT for providing the requested network capacity (whether or not spare capacity is used). MCL had to pay only 50 percent of incremental costs because of the expected additional traffic that MCL customers would generate for BT and because BT expected to have excess capacity in its network for some time.[48]

If, in relation to an exchange, actual traffic exceeds the capacity requested by MCL, MCL must pay 20 percent of BT's consequential incremental costs of the additional facilities, whether there is spare capacity or not. The lower rate of 20 percent discourages MCL from making inflated forecasts of its traffic.[49] It is unlikely, however, to induce MCL to order insufficient capacity, because traffic exceeding ordered capacity may be treated with less priority.

For interconnection at the local level MCL must pay the rental rate BT charges its business customers (without a telephone instrument) for each exchange line BT provides.

Conveyance charges are calculated on a per-minute basis and are differentiated by time of day and by the segment(s) of the other system used (table 9–1). The agreement defines a segment as "that part of a call from the point where the call is received from a customer or handed over to a network to the point where the

47. *See* WERNER NEU & KARL-HEINZ NEUMANN, INTERCONNECTION AGREEMENTS IN TELECOMMUNICATIONS (Apr. 1993) (WIK Diskussionsbeitrag No. 106).
48. Armstrong & Doyle, *supra* note 39, at 62.
49. *Id.*

TABLE 9–1
BT's CALL CONVEYANCE CHARGES TO MCL, 1985 DETERMINATION
(pence per minute and per segment)

Call Type	Rate		
	Peak	Standard	Discount
Single-segment			
Local 3L	2.6	2.3	1.0
Local 3J	2.3	2.0	1.0
Short national	6.0	4.4	2.2
Long national	6.5	5.0	2.4
Two-segment			
Local 3L	2.6	2.3	1.0
Local 3J	2.3	2.0	1.0
Short national	4.6	3.1	1.1
Long national	4.8	3.5	1.4

SOURCE: OFTEL (October 11, 1985).

network hands the call on again or delivers it to the end user."[50] An interconnected call may use one or more segments, and conveyance charges would be incurred accordingly.

According to Armstrong and Doyle,[51] incentives in the 1986 agreement were generally set in such a way that MCL would be induced to build a trunk network quickly. For example, the conveyance charge for calls using BT's local exchanges was set above that for local calls using a trunk exchange. Armstrong and Doyle provide percentage margins of BT retail rates over the

50. *Id.* at 65.
51. *Id.* at 66.

TABLE 9–2
CHARGE MARGINS ON BT's CALL CONVEYANCE CHARGES TO MCL,
1985 DETERMINATION
(percent)

Call Type	Rate		
	Peak	Standard	Discount
Single-segment, MCL-BT			
Local 3L	35	23	0
Local 3J	42	23	0
Short national	40	45	27
Long national	53	50	52
Two-segment, BT-MCL-BT			
Short national (2 × 3J)	54	50	33
Long national (2 × 3J)	67	60	60
Long national (3J + SN)	62	63	70

SOURCE: Armstrong and Doyle (1993, 66).

corresponding domestic conveyance charges to be paid by MCL (table 9–2). Those are highest for long national calls and for two short segments that MCL combines with its own trunk lines to convey long-distance calls.

After their initial determination by OFTEL in 1985, BT's interconnection charges for MCL have followed an *RPI* – 3 formula. That was constructed like a price cap but without the rebalancing feature. As explained above, by about 1990 BT's retail prices in real terms had, for four years in a row, declined at a much faster rate than the *RPI* – 3 (4.4 percent in 1987, 5.9 percent in

1988, and 4.5 percent in both 1989 and 1990). In contrast, BT increased interconnection charges to the extent allowed by the formula, and by 1991 MCL was feeling a squeeze from increases in BT's interconnection rates relative to MCL's own retail prices. Under a specific review clause of the 1986 interconnection agreement, starting in March 1988 either party could ask the director general to modify all or part of the agreement.[52] MCL did so with respect to interconnection charges, and as a consequence from the 1990–1991 fiscal year onward a new (unpublished) adjustment formula was implemented. Since MCL had been pushing for a cost-oriented approach, the new interconnection charges were not indexed against the RPI but instead were based on BT's actual costs. The implicit results for 1990–1991 interconnection charges corresponded to an *RPI* − 9 formula, and for the 1991–1992 fiscal year they corresponded to *RPI* − 11.

The regulator made it clear that, in his view, MCL had initially been receiving entry assistance in the form of favorable interconnection charges, but that such assistance had declined over time.[53] On the other hand, MCL was (and still is) suffering from lack of equal access and the lack of number portability. Consequently, new subscribers of MCL usually also remain BT customers (for their incoming calls).

The BT-MCL Agreement of 1994

The duopoly review had resulted in major changes in BT's and MCL's licenses and had changed market conditions. Also, the price adjustment clause in the 1986 interconnection agreement had proved unworkable. Therefore, in March 1992 BT and MCL entered into negotiations for a new interconnection agreement. The negotiations stalled on call charges and connection payments, and in June the parties agreed to ask the regulator for a determination on those

52. Mercury Communications Ltd., *supra* note 16, at 22.
53. OFTEL, ANNUAL REPORT 3 (1991). In contrast, MCL (according to company officials interviewed) feels that the starting levels for interconnection charges under the 1986 agreement were already excessive and that the *RPI* − 3 price cap from 1985 to 1990 was overly generous toward BT.

issues. That determination was published in December 1993.[54] Subsequently, MCL asked for a declaratory court ruling on the correct interpretation of BT's condition 13; the firm claimed that the regulator had misinterpreted BT's license. But agreements between BT and MCL on the basis of the determination were reached for the time being.

The regulator's determination concentrates on conveyance charges. Payments for the conveyance of calls include: conveyance rates for local and for short and long national calls and a new rate for the use of the Digital Local Exchange (DLE);[55] ADCs payable for local, national, and international calls; and waiver of ADCs for MCL. The calculation of conveyance rates is based on component costs and routing factors. Routing factors are derived statistically for each type of call (local and short and long national) on the basis of samples that measure the use of the network. The routing factors represent average usage of each network element by each type of MCL interconnection segment. The costs of each MCL segment are estimated by multiplying the average cost per minute of use of each element by the ratio of MCL's routing factor to the routing factor for all calls using the network.[56] If routing factors and component costs were calculated perfectly, MCL would have the correct incentives to use BT's network efficiently and would choose to bypass it only where MCL itself could provide cheaper alternatives. But the use of fully distributed costs and the likelihood of sampling errors may have distorted MCL's decisions in favor of an average cost approach. Thus, for example, MCL may have incentives to use

---

54. OFTEL, Determination of Terms and Conditions for the Purpose of an Agreement on the Interconnection of the British Telecommunications Telephone System and the Mercury Communications Ltd. System Under Condition 13 of the Licence Granted to British Telecommunications Under Section 7 of the Telecommunications Act 1984—Interconnection Charges and Explanatory Document 1993 (Dec. 1993) ¶¶ 36–37.

55. Until December 1993 BT offered genuine interconnection only at the trunk level and published no rates for lineside interconnection. MCL now has access further into BT's network, to the end office rather than to the tandem office.

56. OFTEL, *supra* note 54, at 24.

BT for long distances and substitute its own lines for shorter distances.

In calculating BT's costs the regulator excluded a number of BT overheads, such as retail billing and bad debts, marketing and direct advertising, and, remarkably, the chairman's office and related activities, as irrelevant to interconnection (BT had already voluntarily excluded some of those items). Those exclusions amounted to 43 percent of revenue costs less plant maintenance and depreciation.[57] The cost of capital in the calculation was 15 percent, derived by the capital asset pricing method and a formula for the weighted average cost of capital.[58] MCL's rate of return is 26 percent below the rate of return of 20.3 percent originally suggested by BT. Averaging over revenue costs and the cost of capital, the regulator (together with voluntary decisions by BT) can claim to have reduced total costs, as reported in its financial statement, *Financial Results by Services*, to MCL by 35 percent between the 1985 and 1993 determinations.[59] In fact, for the time that had elapsed since MCL had asked for the determination, MCL received a refund of £74 million from BT.

Rates per minute and per segment are given in table 9–3. They are generally lower than the rates in the 1985 determination, but markedly lower for peak periods and longer distances. Hence they reflect some downward adjustment in the overall price level and some rebalancing due to different cost levels and methodologies. The costs of unsuccessful calls (call attempts) are built into those rates in lieu of a separate charge for call attempts.

Charges are to be recalculated annually on the basis of BT's most recent audited *Financial Results by Services*.[60] Thus, there is a built-in dynamic adjustment and possibly a readjustment of rates for the past year. That attempt to circumvent regulatory lag introduces an element of uncertainty into conveyance rates that could have been avoided by putting the difference between the newest year's and the previous year's figures into the current year's

57. *Id.* at 18.
58. OFTEL, BT's Cost of Capital (1992) (consultative document).
59. OFTEL, *supra* note 54, at 26.
60. *Id.* at 7.

TABLE 9–3
BT'S CALL CONVEYANCE CHARGES TO MERCURY, 1993
DETERMINATION
(pence per minute)

Call Type	Rate		
	Peak	Standard	Discount
Local exchange	1.53	1.16	0.67
Tandem local	1.85	1.41	0.81
Tandem short national	2.17	1.65	0.95
Tandem long national	2.73	2.08	1.20

SOURCE: OFTEL (1993).

rates. The price to be paid for such an arrangement would have been a (small) additional allocative distortion in conveyance rates.

The 1993 ADCs on a per-minute basis are shown in table 9–4. The ADCs are a varying percentage of the corresponding conveyance rates, ranging between about 40 percent for local cheap-period calls to about 100 percent for tandem short national calls. International rates in the table range between 2 and 58 pence per minute and average 8.5 pence.

MCL received an ADC waiver on the first 10 percent of its local, national, and international market shares, including MCL calls routed over BT's system. The regulator justified the ADC waivers with reference to the disadvantages MCL faces relative to BT, in particular the lack of number portability, whereas other factors, such as volume of calls per line and economies of scale, appear to balance each other.[61]

---

61. *Id.* at 21. MCL also claims that BT is able to charge higher prices to its retail customers than MCL can. Armstrong & Doyle, *supra* note 39, at 59, argue that BT has some specific advantages, including default carrier status combined with customer inertia, detailed information on the entire customer base, unsurpassed brand recognition, and enormous human resources to

TABLE 9–4
ADCs CHARGED TO MCL, 1993 DETERMINATION
(pence per minute)

Call Type	Rate		
	Discount	Standard	Peak
Local	0.27	0.54	0.71
National	0.94	1.48	1.93

	Charge band						
	1	2	3	4	5	6	7
Outgoing							
Peak	2.10	3.76	9.26	10.03	11.11	12.51	15.73
Standard	2.10	3.76	9.26	9.24	10.66	12.51	15.73
Discount	1.71	3.14	7.83	7.94	9.00	8.95	12.62
Incoming	1.96	3.55	8.60	8.76	9.70	11.48	15.13

	Charge band					
	8	9	10	11	12	13
Outgoing						
Peak	15.07	26.99	29.29	26.94	28.28	58.01
Standard	15.07	26.88	29.29	26.94	28.28	58.01
Discount	12.20	23.03	24.83	25.69	27.19	57.08
Incoming	14.37	25.17	27.22	26.68	28.03	57.77

SOURCE: OFTEL (1993).

For the year ending March 31, 1993, MCL was found to have about 7 percent of the market for local and national calls and 19 percent of the market for international calls. Initially, therefore, the waiver applied fully to local and national traffic. For its

support competitive and regulatory analysis.

international traffic MCL became the first firm actually to have to pay ADCs.

In an annex to the determination the director general refers to his duties and powers under the 1984 Telecommunications Act to promote the interests of telecommunications consumers, purchasers, and other users in the United Kingdom and to promote active competition in the U.K. telecommunications sector, as a consequence of which he sought to use waivers to encourage the development of a wide range of services at the lowest sustainable prices. Waivers should therefore induce BT to achieve greater efficiency on a sustainable basis, help maintain maximum flexibility to meet the demands of changes in the market, and apply to companies providing competition to BT in the local loop, particularly in serving residential customers.

Interestingly, there is no explicit reference to the demand relationship (substitutability or complementarity) of the interconnector's services to those of the incumbent BT. Such a link would be part of both a Ramsey pricing and an efficient component-pricing rule approach to interconnection charges. When an efficient component-pricing rule is used, the opportunity cost of supplying interconnection would be the profit forgone by BT in losing retail output to the interconnector. That loss would be greater the closer substitutes the outputs are for each other. For complementary outputs, however, the opportunity "cost" would turn into a gain.

The OFTEL Initiative on Interconnection and Accounting Separation

U.K. telecommunications providers are now engaged in an extensive discussion, with OFTEL consultation, about competition in their market, with special emphasis on interconnection issues. In March 1994 the director general announced a three-stage program of interconnection and accounting separation.[62] The first stage, which began immediately, used the December 1993 BT-MCL determination as a basis for interim charges for interconnection with

---

62. OFTEL, Interconnection and Accounting Separation: The Next Steps (Mar. 1994) (statement).

BT by other operators. The second stage envisaged a list of standard interconnection charges, a more transparent process for relating costs to charges, and accounting separation of BT's operations into network, access, and retail services. The second stage was targeted on implementing the new list and determining charges for the services included on it. That would require changes to BT's license. The third stage dealt with issues "on which the substance and the timing of conclusions are uncertain." That stage includes items such as alternative cost bases (that is, alternatives to fully allocated historic costs), alternative charging structures for interconnection services (for example, capacity charging), and the future of ADCs. In particular, the regulator expects the outcome of the third stage to influence and to be influenced by the revision of the current price-cap regime in 1997.

Interim Standard Charges (Stage 1). The use of the BT-MCL determination in the first stage comes close to a standard price list for BT services. To arrive at their own interconnection charges, interconnectors other than MCL would simply adapt the MCL rates to their individual circumstances. Annex B of the statement therefore provides a "'Ready Reckoner,' based on the costs determined for the BT/MCL determination, from which other operators will be able to estimate the costs they are likely to face in interconnecting with the BT network."[63] What is particularly important is that the routing factors relevant for the conveyance rates are specific to each operator. Hence, routing factors have to be individually estimated, which can be a tough task for new licensees. Although the routing factors do not normally imply any geographic deaveraging of conveyance rates, they do cause cable television operators interconnecting with BT to pay different conveyance rates depending on their local characteristics.

In terms of pricing method, how do those standard charges compare with the U.S. rate structure for switched access? A first difference is that until now the local ADC is always included in the U.S. residual interconnection charge, whereas in the United Kingdom it was mostly waived and has now been altogether

63. *Id.* at 8.

abolished. A second difference is that in the United Kingdom dedicated lines are the exception rather than the rule. At the same time, transport distance and switching characteristics of calls are not individually traced in the United Kingdom. Access charges are based on average distance and switching profiles of interconnectors instead of on individual calls as in the United States. In contrast, distance and switching characteristics in the United States are not fully reflected in call charges. A third difference is that, in the United Kingdom, time-of-day pricing of access charges follows the pattern of retail rates. In contrast, the access rate structures in the United States have hardly any time-of-day pricing at all. A fourth difference is that, unlike in the United States, the United Kingdom has standard interconnection rates for long-distance and international interconnection services.

The firms interconnecting with BT would like to see interconnection services further unbundled, as is done for the competitors of the LECs in the United States. Those operators presented a list of network components that they wanted separately tariffed. That was based on BT's existing network structure and consisted of five categories: basic switching, transport, features and intelligence, services (for example, database access, directory and operator assistance), and access to (possibly proprietary) interconnection information. Depending on their cost drivers, those categories were further subdivided into elements. The firms also want the choice to use a facility either on a dedicated or on a shared basis.[64]

There is little indication that geographic deaveraging of interconnection charges will occur anytime soon. In his 1993 consultative document the director general had suggested three alternatives for the geographical differentiation of interconnection charges. Those could be calculated on a route-specific deaveraged basis ("actual costs"), or they could be nationally averaged for each network component ("average component costs"), or they could be

---

64. The list and thirteen principles postulated by the other firms for interconnection appear in OFTEL, *The Relationship Between Costs and Interconnection Charges*, PROCEEDINGS OF THE SECOND MEETING (Jan. 11, 1994), at annexes A and B.

nationally averaged by network function ("average function costs"). The present system is based on the third method. For example, routing factors are now related to distance, type of link, and number of lines, and not to density or thickness of line. The actual-cost method is presently infeasible from an accounting perspective and, because it might induce BT to deaverage retail tariffs as well, probably also politically infeasible. The current system certainly has its beneficiaries. For example, the huge London calling area has local rates that are the same as local rates in the rest of the country.

Accounting   Separation   and   New   Interconnection   Contracts (Stage 2). As already postulated in the 1992 price-cap revision, OFTEL has proceeded with its accounting separation of BT into retail, network, and access functions. The purpose of that separation is to allocate BT's costs in a way that properly reflects the division between BT's separated activities and to demonstrate in published audited financial statements that BT's network and ADC charges have not resulted in unduly discriminatory behavior (or an unfair cross-subsidy). Those accounts should follow three principles. First, they should be prepared in accordance with Companies Act requirements, as far as applicable, and should be directly reconcilable to BT's statutory accounts. Second, cost allocation should be in accordance with principles and cost drivers agreed by OFTEL (after consultation with the operators). Third, BT should publish details of its internal transfer charging system.

BT-Network includes all services offered to interconnectors and to BT-Retail. BT-Access includes costs, capital employed, and revenues of BT's provision of installation, phone line rental, and other access services to the business and residential public switched telephone market. Until 1996 BT-Access also shows the ADCs received from BT-Retail and other operators, as well as the part of the access deficit not recovered.[65]

BT-Retail is itself separated into service categories. There are separate financial statements for regulated and for nonregulated services, to demonstrate the absence of cross-subsidies to nonregulated activities. Regulated services include, in particular, the

---

65. *See* OFTEL, *supra* note 62, at 10.

various call categories, directory assistance, and leased lines. The retail accounts are also used to demonstrate that BT charges itself the same conveyance rates as it charges other operators. That corresponds to the imputation required by many state regulators in the United States (see chapter 6). OFTEL requires BT to unbundle services to BT-Retail in such a way that the correspondence with charges paid by interconnecting operators can be seen.

Moving Further toward Competition (Stage 3). In 1994 and 1995 OFTEL pushed the discussion about the future framework for competition a step further by proposing a number of concrete changes and asking opinions on all the relevant issues in a consultative document.[66] Again, interconnection is at the heart of the competitive drive. We mention here only those items where the regulator actually has proposed a change in policy. The first proposed change is a move from historical fully allocated costs to forward-looking incremental costs as the basis for calculating interconnection charges. For the calculation of standard charges OFTEL, in conjunction with BT and the other licensed operators, has helped develop incremental costing methodologies. BT prefers a so-called top-down approach, which starts with its full historic accounting costs, converts those into current costs, and subsequently tries to delete all costs that are not deemed incremental. In contrast, the other operators prefer a bottom-up approach, in which services are built up from their components in an engineering model. From the two approaches OFTEL is seeking consensus results for both incremental and stand-alone costs of services. Second, as part of a proposed price-cap approach to interconnection, incremental costs will serve as lower bounds and stand-alone costs as upper bounds for prices within baskets of interconnection services. Third, OFTEL is seriously considering capacity-based interconnection charges instead of, or in addition to, per-minute charges. Fourth, OFTEL has decided to abandon BT's restrictions on rate rebalancing before the current price-cap regime expires in 1997. OFTEL actually believes that BT will not rebalance drastically at that time. At the

66. OFTEL, Effective Competition: Framework for Action (July 1995) (statement issued by director general of telecommunications).

same time the ADC regime has been abolished. Fifth, OFTEL is considering new approaches to sharing and financing universal service obligations. Overall, OFTEL is now moving from a competitive regime guided by regulation to one that is more guided by competition policy.

CONCLUSIONS

In the United Kingdom, the legal and regulatory framework provided by licenses and by the Telecommunications Act of 1984 is very extensive and extremely specific. Nevertheless, the fact that OFTEL is a small organization compared with the U.S. Federal Communications Commission, with 147 employees in 1993, indicates that U.K. telecommunications regulation is fairly cheap.

A remarkable feature of U.K. regulation is the central role of the regulator. The regulator has substantial authority in shaping regulation and competition, including price-cap regulation, the overall interconnection regime, and specific interconnection agreements.

The first ten years of BT's price-cap regulation have seen the process become more public and regulation itself expand in scope, move in the direction of rate-of-return regulation, and become more stringent. The remarkable escalation of the X factor from $RPI - 3$ to $RPI - 7.5$ over the course of ten years has resulted in a decrease in BT's telephone service rates of 40 percent in real terms, while the company maintains a consistently high rate of return. Because of price rebalancing, however, business and larger residential users have been the prime beneficiaries of the price-cap regime. Thus, without price rebalancing the increase in the X factor would hardly have been viable. Indeed, for the future a price cap of $RPI - 7.5$ cannot possibly be maintained in the long run. Thus, OFTEL's plan to abolish retail price regulation after 2001 reduces the probability of overshooting and of the specter of a return to the declining profitability experienced in the mid-1970s.

The effect on local competition of ten years of regulation of BT has been that BT has lost little of its market dominance of local access. By restricting price rebalancing, the regulator has helped keep entry into residential access unattractive to most would-be entrants. Cable television companies are now gaining ground quickly, however, and there has been some long-distance and (in London) urban bypass of BT by business users. The increasingly aggressive price-cap regime has, however, forced BT to become a leaner competitor and has made prices less attractive for entrants.

Operator license provisions in the United Kingdom leave interconnection issues primarily to private negotiations between the parties involved. The regulator enters the picture only when those negotiations fail. The regulator and OFTEL clearly want to promote competition, however. The other operators know that and therefore expect regulatory rulings in their favor. That is the reason that they take BT's offer of an interconnection agreement as a starting point for going to the regulator. BT believes that the bottleneck services of other operators should also be regulated. Nevertheless, because of BT's current and expected future market dominance, regulation remains asymmetrical. OFTEL (we are told by OFTEL officials whom we interviewed) backs that arrangement. According to BT, one problem of asymmetrical regulation is that the demands of other operators on the regulator are not constrained by the danger that the resulting rules will be applied against the party demanding them. Conditions also need to be specified for the eventual deregulation of BT.

In mid-1995 there were about 150 licensed operators in the United Kingdom, and the Department of Trade and Industry is engaged in discussions with numerous potential licensees. The addition of new providers has yielded the benefits of competition but has also led to inevitable strains on the regulatory process. Regulation has to take into account the diverse interests of a large number of participants. Interconnection is currently an area of great activity and wide-ranging discussion. The discussion on interconnection currently concentrates on several key issues:

- the amount of information that each interconnecting party (BT in particular) should provide about itself to the others and to the public, and the transparency of the regulatory system;
- the identification of the cost of universal service obligations;
- the definition and utility of alternative costing procedures as a basis for interconnection charges;
- the definition of interconnection services, including the unbundling of components and the set of services to be offered; and

• issues not directly related to costs and charges, such as the quality of interconnection services, equal access, number portability, and access to directory information.

In addition, several important interconnection issues have conspicuously failed to create protracted disputes. Those include the types and technical aspects of interconnection, network security and integrity, and interface standards.

Cost allocation is seen as the most critical issue in interconnection agreements.[67] Until very recently, the guiding principle has been fully allocated historical costs, and that principle has initially been included in BT's accounting separation. The use of that cost concept is somewhat surprising, given the openness and economic sophistication with which OFTEL has otherwise addressed interconnection issues. BT's accounting system may have been a constraining factor here. Now that BT is starting to produce current cost accounts, incremental costs become more easily measurable, and the regulator is now implementing an incremental cost approach.

Given the large amount of interconnection activity and revenues that surround special access in the United States, the question arises whether the U.K. treatment of leased lines for interconnection purposes deserves more attention than it has received in the past. For example, MCL's largest source of retail revenues is its directly connected customers. Such customers use dedicated lines that, in part, could also be leased from BT if conditions were right.

Inspired by the efficient component-pricing rule, OFTEL developed the concept of ADCs and tried to make them workable. The result was some very complicated and uncertain decision making. The current practice of waivers resulting from that approach made ADCs quite ineffective. ADCs have therefore been abolished along with BT's restrictions on rebalancing of its tariffs. The question now is, What prices will BT charge without the *RPI* − 2 constraint? That is hard to answer because, as long as the constraint existed, BT had an incentive to price at the constraint (to remain entitled to receive ADCs).

---

67. Interview with OFTEL officials, London (Mar. 1, 1994).

Once OFTEL moves to incremental costs as the basis for BT's interconnection pricing, and now that ADCs have been abolished, the question becomes, How can BT recover common costs through interconnection prices?[68] Here the regulator has decided to allow for proportional markups on BT's average incremental costs.[69] In that way common costs will be distributed in accordance with the incremental cost incurred by all of BT's services to which these common costs apply.

Current interconnection determinations by the regulator amount to rate-of-return regulation of interconnection. A price-cap approach to interconnection charges is under discussion. The question is how it should be related to the retail price cap. That was an issue taken up in comments on a consultative document by OFTEL.[70] On the one hand, there was some frustration with the established relationship (specified in BT's license) between BT's retail prices and its interconnection charges. That relationship clearly affects competitive positions. On the other hand, BT's retail rates are incentive-oriented whereas interconnection rates are of the cost-plus type. Since retail services still account for about 97 percent of BT's network revenues, however, the incentive effects of retail regulation should dominate the incentive effects on network elements used by both retail and interconnection services.

---

68. Bridger M. Mitchell & Ingo Vogelsang, *Markup Pricing for Interconnection: A Conceptual Framework, in* OPENING NETWORKS TO COMPETITION: THE REGULATION AND PRICING OF ACCESS (David Gabel and David Weiman eds., Kluwer Academic Publishers 1997).

69. OFTEL, *supra* note 7.

70. Excerpts of those comments were published in OFTEL, *supra* note 62.

10

Synthesis and Conclusions

THE PRECEDING CHAPTERS have shown that the emergence of
competition in the last ten miles of the telephone network is the
culmination of technological, regulatory, and market changes. In
this concluding chapter we reexamine those driving forces, assess
their likely impact on the continuing development of the
telecommunications sector, and describe the role that public policy
can play.

THE MARCH OF TECHNOLOGY

In the long run, the force of technological development overwhelms
entrenched suppliers and conservative regulatory institutions and
pries open protected markets throughout the economy. In
telecommunications the effects of rapid, unabating technological
change are seen in only a few years' time.

The advent of microwave radio transmission enabled MCI to
bypass AT&T's infrastructure monopoly in the 1970s and to mount
a competitive challenge in the market for long-distance service.
Now equally fundamental changes are under way in the market for
local telephone service.

Rapid advances in all major telecommunications technologies
have constantly expanded the scope for competition in a market long
dominated by the traditional local exchange carriers. Since the 1984
divestiture of AT&T, the thrust of most of those changes has been
to reduce the compartmentalization of telecommunications markets.
The convergence of wireline telecommunications, video distribution,
and computer technologies is creating opportunities for new

suppliers to enter local communications services while at the same time broadening the markets in which the LECs will operate. Distance to the customer becomes less important as fiber-optic technology lowers the incremental costs of high-quality signal transport.

A variety of telecommunications technologies offer access to the switched telephone network. Besides the traditional medium of the LEC's distribution network, telecommunications users can now connect to the public switched telephone network by means of cellular radio, personal communication systems, cable television networks, or a competitive access provider's fiber-optic ring. The demands for that access are likewise varied: by type of traffic (voice, data, or video), by volume (as measured by bandwidth or transmission speed), and by type of user (residence, business, or government; urban or rural).

The significance of those alternative technologies is that other firms can now compete for the LEC's customers without duplicating all the components of the LEC network—provided they can interconnect with the LEC's facilities. A wide range of challengers—including competitive access providers, wireless carriers, cable television systems, and interexchange carriers—are actively entering many of those markets. No single competitor can at present effectively contest the full range of the LEC's product line, however. Network interconnection is therefore the key to effective competition and becomes a central focus of regulatory policy.

THE CHANGING ROLE OF REGULATION

The current state of local telecommunications markets has largely been determined by antitrust and regulatory policies. To take but the most conspicuous example, it was antitrust policy, conducted by the Justice Department and a federal court, that led to the breakup of AT&T and gave birth to the regional Bell operating companies that today dominate—but have also been restricted to—local and short-haul long-distance markets.[1] The broad thrust of those policies has

---

1. United States *v*. American Tel. & Tel. Co., 552 F. Supp. 131 (D.D.C.

been to achieve a fundamental shift from a franchise monopoly, whose overall earnings and service conditions were regulated by federal and state commissions, to a more competitive environment in which a dominant, price-regulated firm is confronted by new entrants in its most profitable markets.

The argument that a tendency toward natural monopoly justifies regulation of the entire telecommunications sector has been convincingly challenged by successful competitive entry in parts of the telecommunications market, and by empirical research on the properties of telecommunications cost functions. That does not mean, however, that other parts of the telecommunications sector cannot be natural monopolies when viewed in isolation or over a short to intermediate time horizon during which the sunk costs of the local telephone loop matter. Hence, regulation may still be justified in those particular areas that constitute bottlenecks—natural monopolies for specific inputs to which competitors need access. The global network externality magnifies the importance of those bottlenecks: the uncompensated spillover benefits that are conveyed to all network customers by the interconnection of such competitors.

The persistence of those bottlenecks means that interconnection will be the major regulatory issue for local telecommunications markets at least as long as they are dominated by the LECs. In addition, regulation of the prices set by the LECs and of public service obligations will persist after entry regulation has been dismantled.

Fears of monopoly leveraging—of a dominant carrier using its market power in one domain to seize an unfair advantage in another, more competitive market—have been used to justify policies to keep the LECs out of long-distance and video markets and to regulate interconnection. Both those policies are attempts to inject more competition into those markets into which the LECs might leverage their market power. We believe, however, that, of

---

1982) (text of the decree), *aff'd sub nom.* Maryland *v.* United States, 460 U.S. 1001 (1983); United States *v.* Western Elec. Co., 569 F. Supp. 1057 (D.D.C. 1983) (approving the plan of reorganization). For a more detailed discussion of that antitrust policy, *see* PAUL W. MACAVOY, THE FAILURE OF ANTITRUST AND REGULATION TO ESTABLISH COMPETITION IN LONG-DISTANCE TELEPHONE SERVICES (MIT Press and AEI Press 1996).

the two, regulating interconnection is more precisely directed at the competitive goal, because it helps competitors without barring the LECs, whose exclusion might actually reduce overall competition. Thus, the policy lesson from monopoly leveraging theory is to reduce entry barriers and other restrictions facing competitors rather than to prevent a monopolist in one market from competing in another.

Regulatory developments since the AT&T divestiture have established conditions favorable to local competition. Regulators have reduced cross-subsidies between the LECs' services and have allowed entry into market segments that have been sources of subsidies. The interconnection regime governing the wholesale market has been improved as a basis for local competition. Unbundling of transport and interconnection services allows competitors to pick and choose which of their own service elements to substitute for those of the LECs, while continuing to use other LEC services as inputs. The FCC's earlier proceedings on expanded interconnection and now the FCC's local competition order make possible a broader palette of service offerings by entrants freed from having to invest in highly capital-intensive facilities.[2] Similarly, resale of LEC services allows full entry with only partial and gradual investment in facilities. By moving away from rate-of-return regulation, many regulators have provided a further basis for competition. The new forms of regulation have given the LECs incentives to lower their costs and thus prepare themselves for competition and have allowed the LECs to start rebalancing their rate structures. That has made partial regulation of LEC services practical and has forestalled the emergence of new, competition-induced cross-subsidies. The LECs in most states now lack both the incentive and the ability to leverage their market power.

The regional Bell operating companies have been regulated by state public utility commissions with respect to their intrastate services, and by the FCC with respect to local interconnection that involves interstate traffic. The interaction of federal with state

2. Implementation of the Local Competition Provisions in the Telecommunications Act of 1996, First Rep. & Order, CC Dkt. 96–98 (Aug. 8, 1996).

regulation, and of antitrust with both, is not always harmonious. When there is conflict, antitrust policy usually dominates federal regulation, while the latter (through federal preemption) usually dominates state regulation—usually, but not always. Protracted interagency disputes can still occur, and inefficiencies can still arise from attempts to separate spheres of influence. That is likely to become a major problem for the implementation of the Tele-communications Act of 1996,[3] which has changed some of the traditional division of labor between the FCC and state regulators. In its local competition order the FCC has attempted to define the new spheres of influence, but that definition will have to withstand legal scrutiny before all players come to accept it.

There are important differences among the various states in their approach to telecommunications regulation. Those differences relate to pricing, the type of regulation, and the status of competition. After the Modification of Final Judgment mandated the breakup of AT&T, the most efficient strategies for state regulators would have been to allow competition in intrastate long-distance services and other areas capable of supporting competition, to rebalance rate structures in favor of business and long-distance rates, and to impose incentive regulation in a manner compatible with partial competition. If all the states had regulated interconnection and access charges for intrastate services in concert with FCC requirements for interstate services, they would have induced interconnecting carriers and service providers to use the same pricing and access arrangements for both state and interstate services. That would have avoided tariff arbitrage by customers between state and federal jurisdictions.

From the perspective of political economy, the same policy moves (except, perhaps, that toward low business rates) would have been advisable after some states had moved first. There might have been some strategic uncertainty initially, as each state waited to see who would test the waters. States often differ in their interests, however, so that there exists a natural avant-garde of states with a greater appetite for regulatory reform.

---

3. Telecommunications Act of 1996, Pub. L. 104-104, 110 Stat. 56 (Feb. 8, 1996).

For some time after the MFJ, states diverged in their approaches to rate structures, rate levels, and local competition. More recently, however, state regulatory policies are again converging. All states are moving away from traditional cross-subsidization: some have made major steps (California) and others have abandoned it altogether (Illinois). Most states have moved away from rate-of-return regulation. One has deregulated altogether (Nebraska). All have moved to accommodate some form of competition at the intrastate level. Full-fledged competition emerged first in Illinois and New York, but a number of other states are following their lead.

Regulator-defined local access and transport areas (LATAs) persist as an increasingly anachronistic hangover from an earlier era in which the LECs had stranglehold grips on virtually all access markets. As we have seen, the partitioning of markets into competitive long-distance and monopoly local services is under ever-increasing tension from alternative access technologies and entry by new suppliers. The abolition of LATAs could result from the Telecommunications Act of 1996.

Regulation remains hampered by a number of institutional constraints.[4] In particular, regulators lack information. In addition, they are constrained by the political process, and are slowed down by due process requirements. Furthermore, they have a limited repertoire of policy tools. Finally, they cannot commit far into the future. As Salinger observed, competition makes regulation more complex and therefore even more difficult than those constraints indicate.[5] Under monopoly, the regulator has only to define the optimal conduct of the regulated firm. Under competition, the additional interrelationships with entrants and firms in related markets have to be taken into consideration. Also, regulators have to deal with a new set of stakeholders besides consumers and the regulated firm. Those new stakeholders bend the regulatory process in a new direction that does not necessarily benefit consumers. That

4. For a lucid exposition of those constraints, see JEAN-JACQUES LAFFONT & JEAN TIROLE, A THEORY OF INCENTIVES IN PROCUREMENT AND REGULATION 1–6 (MIT Press 1993).

5. Michael A. Salinger, The Future of Local Telecommunications Networks (1994) (paper prepared for Charles River Associates conference, Boston).

is, for example, reflected in price floors for the regulated firm, something that would be inefficient under pure monopoly regulation.

How, then, can regulation lead to the best sustainable outcome? Since regulators do not know in advance what that outcome is, they cannot directly aim for it, for example, by picking winners. Rather, from a normative perspective, regulation should keep the process open so that the optimal outcome has the highest probability of winning. That is assured if regulation reduces distortions in the decision making of private agents. Now that legal and regulatory entry barriers are vanishing, the remaining potential sources of distortions are cross-subsidized price structures, network externalities, and monopolistic entry barriers (bottlenecks). Public policy can eliminate the first of those. Over time, regulators should abandon retail rate regulation except in remote areas with sustaining monopolies. As recognized by the Telecommunications Act of 1996, concerns for network externalities and redistribution can be captured through explicit universal service and standardization policies, and monopolistic entry barriers can be overcome through regulation of interconnection that is ultimately built on a model of open access and reciprocity. The role of state regulation in such an approach is to identify local conditions that allow for early deregulation.

The slight danger that such an open market policy entails is that the optimal market structure may actually be a monopoly. In that case the regulatory policies we are advocating might nurture a nonoptimal (competitive) market structure. With a sensible interconnection policy in place, however, the likelihood of inefficient duplicative investment in infrastructure is minimized. Firms are unlikely to commit huge duplicative investments in a natural monopoly industry if they can instead supply the market through interconnection. Thus, although there may be excessive investment (as there is in most competitive markets), there is unlikely to be ruinous competition. Some excessive investment will be compensated by benefits from more competitive pricing and greater product differentiation. In any case, investments will not remain sunk for a long time if innovation and market growth continue at their current pace.

We believe it is more likely that the optimal market structure is a competitive one. Moreover, the downside risk of a policy of fully opening all telecommunications markets to competition is small, even if monopoly should turn out to be the optimal market structure. In contrast, the upside potential from promoting competition is substantial.

Therefore, as the conditions for competition in the telecommunications sector improve, regulation should retreat and be replaced by competition policy. The retreat should begin in the most competitive market areas and move from there to the least competitive. In our view, the last regulatory bastions in telecommunications are likely to be in the areas of universal service obligations and interconnection. Here we agree fully with the emphasis on local telephone competition and universal service found in the Telecommunications Act of 1996.

INTERCONNECTION: OPENING THE NETWORK FOR COMPETITION

The interconnection of LEC networks with other carriers and service providers raises all the principal issues of competition in local telephone markets. The technical conditions of access are most prominent in those decisions regarding collocation of equipment and access to LEC network intelligence functions. Regulatory decisions on the pricing of interconnection determine the relative cost advantages among the LEC's competitors and the LEC's own flexibility to respond to competitive entry. Unbundling requirements determine whether competitive entry is possible without complete duplication of local network facilities. Mixed into those decisions are other objectives of supporting universal service and mitigating the dislocations of rapid rebalancing of rate structures that are not based on cost.

So far, the design of access charges for IXCs in the United States has not been very sophisticated. In switched access, pricing has been by minutes of use (instead of by call attempts or peak traffic contribution); there has been almost no peak-load or two-part pricing. In special access, geographic deaveraging has barely begun.

Carrier common line charges and charges for transport services provided to the IXCs are huge sources of revenues to the LECs. The loss of the contribution those revenues make to meeting the LEC's total network costs, should the IXCs shift to competitive providers or to supplying transport on their own, would have major effects on other services, including residential and business local exchange service. The additional substitution of special access for switched access resulting from expanded interconnection and, even more, the new availability of unbundled network elements reduce the contribution further by reducing the volume of switched access traffic—a service that today is presumably laden with heavy contribution. To resolve the resulting competitive and contribution problems, the FCC plans to reform the access charge regime about the same time that new universal service policies are decided upon.

The FCC's open network architecture initiative initially envisioned a thorough opening up of the local network. But the effect has largely been to unbundle the pricing of separate calling features without fundamentally unbundling the principal components of the local loop. Meanwhile, to advance the technical and practical aspects of opening LEC network features to other suppliers, the interested parties—regulators, carriers, and enhanced services providers—have turned to voluntary industry standards organizations.

"Expanded interconnection" aims to provide all interested parties with direct, nondiscriminatory access to the LEC networks. Progressive states such as New York and Illinois first promoted expanded interconnection. As a consequence, they have seen prices for digital access services fall, service improve, and the diffusion of fiber-optic technology accelerate. As a result of the dual regulation experience from collocation, those innovative states influenced the FCC, which in turn subsequently homogenized state approaches.

Although the proceedings on access charges and expanded interconnection have directly concerned only the wholesale markets in which the IXCs, enhanced services providers, and large businesses seek access, they have strongly affected competition in the retail markets for interexchange and enhanced services and have paved the way for interconnection arrangements involving local competitors. Such arrangements are the prerequisite for local facilities-based competition.

The Telecommunications Act of 1996 envisages three idealized forms of local competition—full network entry by facilities-based competitors, partial network entry (also by competitors with local facilities), and resale. Corresponding to those forms are three ways for competitors to deal with each other and, in particular, with the incumbent LECs. A full network entrant requires interconnection with the incumbent LEC for the completion of its subscribers' calls that terminate on the LEC's network and for terminating LEC-originated calls to its subscribers. A partial network entrant also requires unbundled network elements, such as unbundled local loops, switches, or access to the LEC's signaling network, to fill in gaps in its own local network facilities. A reseller needs to be able to purchase LEC retail services at a wholesale discount. The Telecommunications Act of 1996 and the FCC's subsequent local competition order address those three competitive relationships between entrants and incumbent LECs. The act and the order (though partially stayed) give the entrants substantial new rights and, in particular, favorable cost-based prices and cost-based wholesale discounts. They should, therefore, greatly facilitate entry into the LECs' markets.

COMPETITION IN THE RETAIL MARKETS

LEC retail markets are under attack on several fronts. The first, and the one where competitive penetration is most advanced, is facilities-based entry in intraLATA toll markets. Since those markets are like small-scale, long-distance markets, the regulatory and technological problems of market entry here are very much like those already mastered for the interLATA markets. There are currently three differences. First, equal access still is not fully established. Second, the LECs are both providers of local-loop access and competitors in intraLATA service. Third, the long-distance transport and switching portions of an intraLATA connection are small relative to the local-loop portion.

On the first front, the resulting competitive advantages the LECs hold over facilities-based entrants in intraLATA toll markets will diminish with the advent of equal access. Interexchange carriers will then be able to offer all their long-distance services as an integrated package. They will be joined by cellular and PCS wireless service providers in aggressively going after the LECs' intraLATA market shares. In addition, intraLATA access charges will continue to fall over time. Despite the LECs' advantages from their fixed network architecture, LEC intraLATA long-distance services are therefore likely to lose their importance as sources of subsidies for residential subscriber access.

The second front is nonswitched local services. Here competitive access providers have made heavy inroads, made possible in part by their election to be subject to federal rather than local regulation. Competitive access providers often have the advantage of *de novo* entry with the optimal technology and architecture and without public service obligations. That has made them formidable competitors, able to use that base to attack the LECs on the third front.

That third front is switched local services—the core of the LECs' business. Facilities-based local exchange competition for landline services is still in its infancy, but it is an area of enormous activity by varied and powerful new players. Given the diversity of their approaches and the uncertainty of technological progress, it is hard to predict the eventual depth and breadth of market penetration that those new entrants will achieve. But the United Kingdom's experience with such competition could be indicative. In the United States the LECs face competition for local switched services from resellers and, to a more modest extent, from competitive access providers, cable television companies, and the IXCs. Multiple PCS operators are expected to expand mobile services beyond the initial cellular system markets and to compete directly for much larger segments of the switched local service market. Since the LECs themselves are heavily involved in wireless services and cable companies outside their own service territories, they have already started to compete with each other in the market for switched local services. In their own service territories the LECs hold several main advantages over facilities-based entrants. First, they have a comprehensive sunk network that includes vast databases and access to residences and to existing residential phone numbers. Second, they have very strong local name recognition. Third, up to now at least, they have been able to use cross-subsidies and contribution elements from access charges to subsidize local residential services.

The first of those advantages will for some time make the LECs indispensable as local bottleneck providers of access to consumers and databases. But that will not prevent others from entering, because the LECs are now obliged to sell a complete set of interconnection services to competitors at cost-based or reciprocal rates. Some LECs, such as Ameritech and Rochester Telephone, have adopted their own strategies to become wholesale providers of network services, which entrants could purchase and combine with their own complementary services to meet the needs of retail customers. Thus, the LECs' sunk cost advantage would hold for the wholesale but not for the retail market. Also, market growth and changes in the cheapest or preferred access technology may undermine the LECs' sunk cost advantage. The advantage for entrants from the Rochester and Ameritech plans is quick and fairly risk-free entry. The advantage for the incumbents is that duplication of their access facilities becomes less likely. Such duplication could lead to competition after entry and could totally undermine the incumbent's market position.

The Ameritech and Rochester plans imply that economies of scope from integrating wholesale and retail business are not overwhelming. It may make sense, therefore, to look at the wholesale market for interconnection services and the retail market for telecommunications services as related but separate markets. The main relationship between them, from the perspective of competition policy, is that integrated companies have a decisive advantage in the retail market if they dominate an inefficiently regulated wholesale market. Early experience with the Rochester and Ameritech plans suggests that market dominance in the wholesale markets and the regulation of integrated firms may continue to be a problem. The FCC's local competition order builds on that experience and has strengthened the bargaining position of the entrants to local markets.

The second advantage, name recognition, is shared by some entrants, such as the larger cable television companies and, in particular, the IXCs. Competitive access providers, on the other hand, may have to join forces with other, better-known entrants to induce residential consumers to switch to their services.

The third advantage, cross-subsidization, is already vanishing as a result of competition in the other markets served by the LECs. The LECs still receive large contributions from intrastate and interstate switched access charges, but there is pressure to reduce those and, by May 1997, to find new ways of financing universal service obligations.

Although competition for switched local services is still hampered by entry prohibitions or entry regulation in many states, actions on the regulatory and legal fronts are moving toward an opening of those markets nationwide. In particular, as a result of the Telecommunications Act of 1996, intense competition for switched local services will develop throughout the country. At the same time, the LECs are attempting to enter interLATA long-distance markets and markets for video services. As those moves are reciprocated by the IXCs and cable television companies, the result will be the emergence of large integrated carriers directly competing with each other in all three markets.

The current trend back in the direction of vertical integration, together with that toward integration of telecommunications and video services, is paramount for the development of competition. The latter trend creates a huge new market in which two existing provider groups—the LECs and cable television operators—contest local markets in virtually all parts of the country. The questions here are, Which group has the better position at the starting gate? and, Will both networks coexist in the future?

There are unlikely to be any major diseconomies of scale or scope due to vertical integration. Thus, vertical integration is likely to be a no-lose situation for market participants (as long as they do not overpay for their acquisitions). Vertical integration and integration across services are likely to improve load profiles and internal pricing. Vertical integration also provides firms with the market skills and inside information they need to react flexibly to market changes, and it promotes symmetrical reciprocal relationships between firms in a way that should prove beneficial when they come together to negotiate interconnection agreements. Such agreements will become important both with rivals and with integrated companies in adjacent regions. Whereas today the LECs have the upper hand in interconnection agreements because they control the bottleneck access to most subscribers, that will no longer be the case once cable operators, personal communications services firms, competitive access providers, and other companies have their own access to customers for telephony. It is our conjecture that symmetrical relationships are likely to reduce the fierceness of competition, and that is something from which both the LECs and new entrants may benefit in the form of higher profits. But muted competition would increase incentives to enter, and that could eliminate those benefits. By giving incentives for low interconnection charges, low rates for unbundled network elements, and high wholesale discounts, the FCC in its local competition order has certainly tried to raise the level of competition that can be expected in the local telecommunications market.

EXPERIENCE IN THE UNITED KINGDOM

The past ten years have seen a fruitful cross-fertilization between U.K. and U.S. regulatory practice and market experience in telecommunications. The United States has (to cite one prominent example) adopted the price-cap approach pioneered for British Telecommunications. Conversely, the United Kingdom has adopted the transparency and process orientation of the U.S. regulatory approach and has learned from the U.S. experience in unbundling interconnection services. That cross-fertilization can be expected to continue. The United Kingdom is likely to learn from the U.S. experience with open network architecture and the intelligent network, with collocation, with unbundled network elements, with rate setting for special access, and with spectrum auctions.

What can the United States, for its part, learn from the U.K. experience at this juncture? That learning is likely to concentrate on the following areas:

- The United Kingdom already has substantial experience with facilities-based entry in the local exchange, beginning with Mercury Communications in the London financial district. More relevant for the United States is the practice, increasingly widespread in the United Kingdom, of providing telephone services through cable television networks. Such services have proved themselves able to grow quickly and provide effective competition for BT.
- Equally favorable is the U.K. experience with low-priced wireless services that compete with landline services.
- The price-cap regulation regime in the United Kingdom has gone through more iterations than in any of the U.S. states. Increases in the X factor (the productivity adjustment factor in the price-cap formula) seem to have spurred rather than reduced BT's productivity. The aggressiveness of the U.K. regulator may

therefore hold lessons for the United States in an environment of emerging local competition.

• Price-cap regulation has led to gradual rate rebalancing across BT's services. Rebalancing has been limited through past constraints on subscription and customer connection charges. In contrast, the omission of price floors from BT's price-cap regulation led to problems when BT offered "Sunday specials" that competitors could not profitably meet because of high interconnection charges. That, however, appears to be more of a problem of interconnection charges (and specifically a lack of effective imputation) than of price caps.

• The U.K. experience in regulating a dominant, vertically integrated carrier, which competes and interconnects with nonintegrated rivals, shows that competition and regulation can complement each other in such circumstances. That is relevant for the U.S. trend toward vertical reintegration.

• The United Kingdom's regime of access deficit contributions has been complicated and arbitrary. The regulator almost consistently waived the access deficit contributions, and they were totally abolished before they did any substantial harm to the competitive process. The lesson for the United States here appears to be that such a regime with discriminatory waivers is unlikely to work and indeed would perform even worse within the U.S. legal and regulatory tradition, which lacks a single authority as powerful as the director general of telecommunications in Great Britain.

• In the United Kingdom privately negotiated contracts were intended to become the norm for interconnection agreements, with the regulator as a binding arbitrator. The idea of having the parties themselves negotiate interconnection agreements, with the regulator coming in only as needed to provide binding arbitration, is sound. The U.K. practice, however, shows that such an arrangement is likely to devolve into simple regulation, because the weaker party will fall back on the regulator. First hints at that tendency can be gained from the FCC's local competition order, which has a decidedly regulatory flavor. Private negotiations with regulatory backup remain private only when the parties' interests are complementary—and then the regulator may justifiably have suspicions about anticompetitive agreements' emerging.

- There has been a move toward standardization of interconnection agreements in the United Kingdom. Such standardization can improve the ability of potential entrants to evaluate market opportunities before committing themselves to entry. On the other hand, standardized contracts may stand in the way of organizational innovation.

- Time-of-day rates for interconnection services are the norm in the United Kingdom. The U.K. regime shows that such rates are useful, but they should become more sophisticated than they are now.

- BT has introduced routing factors to determine interconnection charges. Although cumbersome, those factors could be an adequate way of pricing the non-traffic-sensitive part of the incumbent's network to interconnectors.

- The U.K. regulator recently imposed accounting separation as an explicit device for preventing anticompetitive cross-subsidies. Although U.K. accounting separation has some similarities to U.S. cost separations, its purpose is quite different: to make imputation effective and help discover cross-subsidies. That idea, which is also applied in California, may be worth some effort. The United Kingdom's earlier use of a fully distributed costing approach is to be avoided, however—a lesson that is indicated by OFTEL's own move toward incremental costing for interconnection services.

Conclusions

Progress toward local competition in telecommunications can be described as a series of waves of market entry spreading across the communications landscape. In one dimension, that of distance from the customer, competition has been spreading inward from the periphery: from interLATA long-distance to intraLATA and then to local services. In a second dimension, that of customer size, competition began with the largest business customers and then moved to smaller businesses and from there to residential customers. In the third dimension, that of network density, competition has propagated from dense metropolitan areas to smaller cities and thence to rural areas.

In this book we have emphasized the distinction between wholesale and retail markets. The wholesale market consists of two closely related segments, special access and switched access. The retail market is more differentiated, currently into local, long-distance, and wireless services. Telecommunications markets evolve in stages. In the first stage of market development, both wholesale and retail markets are monopolized. In the United States that stage corresponds to the old Bell System before 1970. In the second stage, competition in the first retail market segments, long-distance and wireless services, emerges, but the wholesale market remains largely monopolized. That stage began in the 1970s and continued until the recent FCC decisions on expanded interconnection in the early 1990s. The slower pace of competition in wholesale markets has made retail market competition less than fully effective. In particular, local competition was largely suppressed, and wholesale markets became the target of regulatory action.

In the third and current stage, which was set in motion by passage of the Telecommunications Act of 1996 and the FCC's first local competition order, competition in the wholesale market occurs through bypass and unbundling of wholesale services. Market entry occurs in many guises, but often the entrants are sizable firms that are integrated into related communications services and infrastructure markets. As the U.K. example indicates, that may be the stage to deregulate retail services altogether.

Only a few miles of the communications landscape now remain untouched by that continuing transformation. One can anticipate, within the next decade, a fourth stage in which both wholesale and retail markets become competitively structured. It is likely, but not certain, that the wholesale telecommunications market will then behave like other competitive markets, provided that the costs for retail subscribers of switching suppliers are small. Those costs are diminishing quickly. We are therefore confident that telecommunications competition will easily capture the last ten miles to the customer.

Glossary

Access deficit contribution: Fees paid to British Telecom by interconnection operators as part of an agreement to cover the claimed deficit arising from the regulatory constraint on BT's ability to raise installation and monthly charges for telephone customers.

Access tandem: LEC switching system that concentrates and distributes interLATA traffic originating or terminating within a LATA. Each access tandem provides an IXC with access to more than one end office within a LATA.

Area code: The first three digits in a telephone number in the ten-digit North American Numbering Plan. Most codes designate a geographic area, but some are reserved for nongeographic services: the codes 800 and 888 designate toll-free numbers, 900 is used for kiosk-type services, and 700 for carrier-specific services.

Asymmetrical digital subscriber line (ADSL): Local loop attached to digital compressional encoding equipment that permits simultaneous delivery of a compressed video signal to a subscriber and use of the line for telephone and limited data service.

Asynchronous transport mode: A protocol for very high-speed transport and switching of voice, video, and data communications over common fiber-optic links.

Call externality: The benefit derived by a party for receiving a telephone call without having to pay for it or by making a free call (to an 800 number, for example).

Carrier access code (CAC): The number sequence a caller dials to obtain access to the switched services of a carrier to which the user is not presubscribed. CACs are five digits in the form 10XXX, where XXX is the carrier identification code.

Carrier common line charge (CCLC) or rate: Access charge levied per minute of interexchange calling to recover the non-traffic-sensitive cost of the local loop.

Carrier identification code (CIC): Last three digits of a CAC; identifies an individual carrier in the area serviced by the NANP.

Central office: Usually a local switching system that connects lines and trunks. Sometimes used also to refer to a telephone company building in which switching system and telephone equipment are installed.

Central office code: Three-digit identification number under which up to 10,000 station numbers are subgrouped; also called "NXX" code or "end-office code."

Centrex: Service that permits large customers with many stations to dial from station to station as if within a PBX exchange, even though switching functions are performed in the carrier's central office.

Common-channel signaling: A signaling system (for example, SS7) in which the control signals for all calls travel on a separate digital network that is interconnected with the voice network at switches and other signal transfer points.

Common line: Line that provides transport from a subscriber to an end office.

Common transport: Transport of the switched access traffic of several IXCs over a common facility.

Comparably efficient interconnection: Access to a carrier's basic services that is effectively equal in quality, but not necessarily identical, to the access the carrier itself uses to produce enhanced services.

Competitive access providers: Companies founded to provide special access transport services for interexchange carriers as well as private line services to large businesses and government users, but who now compete directly with local exchange carriers for retail business.

Conveyance charges: Per-minute charges paid by interconnection operators for conveying messages over another operator's network.

Cross-connect: Interconnection of physical cables or electronic circuits to establish a semipermanent, continuous path between two sets of cables or trunks.

Dedicated transport: Transport of the switched access traffic of a single IXC over a single facility that only that IXC uses.

Dialing parity: The ability to route calls, without the use of any access code, to a subscriber's designated carrier, including a LEC.

Distribution frame: *See* Main distribution frame.

DS1 (digital signal level 1): The initial level of multiplexing in the time division multiplexing hierarchy of a telephone network.

DS3: A digital transmission system that carries twenty-eight DS1 channels at 44.736 million bits per second.

Dual-tone multifrequency (DTMF): A tone-signaling method of transmitting address and other information in which a set of dual-tone pulses is used to represent a set of characters.

Efficient component-pricing rule (ECPR): A means to determine charges an interconnecting operator pays to defray both the incremental and so-called opportunity costs incurred by a network operator. That opportunity cost is the profit contribution forgone by the network operator for selling interconnection rather than the retail service for which interconnection is provided.

End office: LEC switching system within a LATA or market area where local loops serving individual customers are terminated for purposes of interconnection at each other and at trunks.

Enhanced services: Telecommunications services other than basic services. Used by the FCC to cover largely the same services that the MFJ court has labeled "information services" (see below). The FCC, however, has classified some protocol conversion services as enhanced, whereas the Justice Department considers them to be basic services.

Equal access: MFJ term denoting the requirement imposed on regional Bell operating companies to provide all IXCs with exchange access and exchange services for access that are equal in type, quality, and price to those provided to AT&T. Can be implemented either by subscriber presubscription to an IXC for one-plus-dialed calls or by 10XXX access dialing codes for nonpresubscribed carriers.

Equal-charge rule: Access-charging rule according to which all interconnecting interexchange carriers pay the same per-minute charge independent of a particular carrier's cost of being interconnected.

Essential facility: A facility controlled by one firm but that is an indispensable input for the firm's competitors.

Expanded interconnection: Interconnection that allows an interconnecting carrier to substitute its own facilities for those of the network with which it interconnects.

Feature group A: Local access arrangement that combines lineside connection to a local switch and a local seven-digit access number.

Feature group B: Local access arrangement that combines a trunkside connection to a local switch via a 950–1XXX access number.

Feature group D: Local access arrangement that combines trunkside connection and one-plus and 10XXX access to an IXC, with optional additional information: automatic number identification, answer supervision, and tandem routing.

Federal preemption: An act by a federal regulator (or Congress) that takes away regulatory jurisdiction from state or local regulators and assigns it to the federal regulator.

Foreign exchange line: A leased line to a distant community that enables callers to dial a number at the local call rate.

Fully distributed costs: Joint or common costs allocated to individual services according to a formula that follows some simple convention and allocates all costs.

Hundred call seconds (CCS): Unit of time equivalent to 100 seconds: thirty-six CCSs in an hour.

Incremental cost: Cost arising from the provision of a specified increment of output. Depending on the problem at hand, the increment can range from a marginal quantity to the whole level of a service or of a network element.

Information services: MFJ term for generating, acquiring, storing, transforming, processing, retrieving, utilizing, or making available information that may be conveyed by telecommunications. Services comprise data processing, electronic publishing, voice answering services, electronic mail, videotext, electronic yellow pages, emergency services, and directory assistance to customers of nonassociated companies.

Intelligent network: Means of control and information processing functions of a telephone network across specialized computer-controlled devices linked by a data network and defined by software that can be customized and modified by the service provider.

Interexchange transport: Transport between local exchange areas. May be intra- or interLATA.

Interexchange carrier (IXC): Common carrier that provides "long-distance" services to the public between local exchanges on an intraLATA or interLATA basis and that is not an end user of the services provided.

InterLATA: Telecommunications services, revenues, and functions originating in one LATA and terminating in another LATA or at another location.

IntraLATA: Telecommunications services, revenues, and functions that originate and terminate within the same LATA.

Lifeline program: Reduced-rate and direct subsidy programs for connection fees, monthly rental, and local calling for low-income, elderly, or other designated groups of consumers.

Link: Pair of wires, or a virtual circuit path, to a LEC switch.

Local access and transport area (LATA): Geographically defined exchange area, created by the AT&T divestiture decree, beyond which a local Bell operating company would not carry telephone calls; generally centered in a metropolitan area.

Local exchange: Generally the first switch to which a customer is connected plus the transport from that customer to the switch. In technical usage, only the first switch.

Local exchange carrier (LEC): Company that provides transport and exchange service within a LATA.

Local loop: Set of services comprising a common line, dial tone (access to local switching), and a telephone number.

Main distribution frame (MDF): Distribution frame used to interconnect cable pairs and line and trunk equipment terminals on a switching system.

Mobile telephone switching office (MTSO): Cellular mobile carrier switching system used to terminate mobile stations for interconnection with each other and with a public switched network.

Modification of Final Judgment (MFJ): 1982 agreement reached between the Department of Justice and AT&T whereby AT&T committed itself to divest its local and regional operating companies. Replaced the 1956 Consent Decree and settled the antitrust case of the United States *v.* AT&T begun in 1974.

Natural monopoly: A market configuration where it is socially optimal that only a single firm supplies a (set of) market(s) (normative natural monopoly) or where single firm supply is the market outcome (positive natural monopoly). Normative natural monopoly is also defined by the property that a single firm can supply the relevant market output at lower cost than any larger number of firms.

Network externality: Costless benefit derived by network subscribers from the addition of new subscribers.

North American Numbering Plan (NANP): Telephone numbering plan used in the United States, Canada, Bermuda, Puerto Rico, and certain Caribbean islands.

Number portability: The ability of a subscriber to retain the same telephone number when (a) subscribing to a different carrier, (b) moving to a different fixed location, or (c) moving between different fixed and mobile telephones.

Numbering Plan Area Code (NPA): Three-digit code that identifies a numbering plan area. Before 1995 NPAs were in N0/1X series; since then in NXX.

NXX code: Code normally used as a central office code but occasionally as an NPA code or special NPA code.

Open network architecture (ONA): Components and services of a telecommunications network to which the network operator and service providers have equal unbundled access at tariffed rates and conditions.

Opportunity cost: The cost in terms of the value of the best alternative forgone.

Outside plant: Part of a telephone system located outside the company's buildings; includes cables, supporting structures, and certain equipment items such as loading coils. (Microwave towers, antennas, and cable-system repeaters are not considered outside plant.)

Personal communications services (PCS): New wireless services, including enhanced cellular, paging and cordless telephone services, and wireless PBX and local area networks.

Physical collocation: Interconnection of a non-LEC supplier's facilities with terminating equipment within a LEC office and where the interconnector has access for installation and maintenance.

Point of presence: Physical location within a LATA at which an access customer establishes itself for the purpose of obtaining LATA access and to which a LEC provides access services.

Point of termination: Point within a customer's premises at which a telephone company's responsibility for providing access service ends.

Port: Means of providing dial tone to a public switched network and a unique network address (telephone number).

Presubscription: The process by which a customer indicates to a LEC a choice of an IXC for interLATA calls.

Private branch exchange (PBX): Customer-owned switch used to connect an organization's internal telephones and to interconnect to a public switched network by trunk to the local exchange and possibly also directly to an interexchange carrier.

Ramsey pricing: Socially optimal regulatory pricing rule under the constraint that a regulated firm can break even. In simplest form Ramsey prices call for markups on marginal costs that are inversely proportional to demand elasticities.

Residual interconnection charge (RIC): A per-minute charge for IXC traffic interconnected to a LEC switched network at a tandem switch. Calculated to preserve a LEC's total revenue from switched access under the interim rate structure beginning in November 1993, after subtracting revenue collected from flat-rate and usage-based rates for switched access to the LEC network.

Serving wire center (SWC): Termination point for subscribers' lines at a central LEC office and a point of interconnection for other carriers.

Shared tenant services: Telecommunications services shared by the tenants of a building. Shared tenant services facilitate pooling of demands and thereby allow participants to lower individual costs and take part in more sophisticated services than if purchased individually.

Signaling system: Facilities and intelligence for routing and billing calls, providing information services, and maintaining a network.

Special access: Dedicated transport link from a customer to an IXC's point-of-presence; used primarily for voice-grade access, WATS access, and DS1 and DS3 access. Includes transport over a local loop via a central office (without switching) and over LEC trunks to a point-of-presence.

Subscriber line charge: Federal monthly charge imposed on telecommunications subscribers for each local exchange line.

Switched access: Transport over a local loop to a central office, where calls are switched and then transported to the point-of-presence of an IXC either via direct trunk or over a trunk to a LEC tandem office and then by direct trunk.

Tandem access: Access by a second carrier to individual subscribers at a local exchange carrier's tandem switch, where calls from several local switches are brought together.

T1: Copper-based digital transmission facility that carries twenty-four voice channels.

Tier 1 LECs: LECs with annual revenues exceeding $100 million.

Tier 2 and tier 3 LECs: Medium and small-sized LECs.

Total element long-run incremental cost (TELRIC): The long-run incremental cost of a network element, including element-specific costs that do not vary with output of the network.

Total service long-run incremental cost (TSLRIC): The long-run incremental cost of a service, including service-specific costs that do not vary with output of the service.

Trunk: In a network, a communications path connecting two switching systems used in the establishment of an end-to-end connection. In selected applications, both terminations of a single trunk may be within the same switching system.

Virtual collocation: Interconnection with terminating equipment that an interconnector cannot access for installation and maintenance but can maintain remotely. Physical interface may be at the main distribution frame or nearby at a digital access and cross-connect system.

Wide area telecommunications service (WATS): Originally, an AT&T tariff for bulk interexchange switched voice service to a defined geographic area.

Wire center: Location of one or more local switching systems; point at which customers' loops converge.

References

"ALTS Members Claim Public Policy 'Victory,' Make Case for Growth Beyond Confines of 'Cap' Label," *Telecommunications Reports,* Nov. 7, 1994, at 7.

"Ameritech Agrees to Offer Reciprocal Compensation," *Telecommunications Reports,* Jan. 16, 1995, at 28.

"Ameritech Attacks MCI Plan to Resell Local Service," *Telecommunications Reports,* Nov. 28, 1994, at 9.

"Ameritech Modifies Universal Access Plan, Pursues Interim Number Portability in Effort to Quell Objections," *Telecommunications Reports,* Feb. 21, 1994, at 25.

Andrews, Edmond, "Ameritech Forcefully Stays Home," *New York Times,* Nov. 22, 1994.

Andrews, Edmond, "MCI Seeks to Be 'Local' in 5 States," *New York Times,* Oct. 4, 1994.

Areeda, Phillip, "Essential Facilities: An Epithet in Need of Limiting Principles," 58 *Antitrust Law Review* 841 (1990).

Armstrong, Mark, and Chris Doyle, "Network Access Pricing" (1993).

Armstrong, Mark, and John Vickers, "Competition and Regulation in the British Telecommunications Industry," Oxford University working paper, 1990.

Arnbak, Jens, Bridger M. Mitchell, Werner Neu, Karl-Heinz Neumann, and Ingo Vogelsang, with the collaboration of Godefroy Dang N'Guyen and Bernd Ickenroth, "Network Interconnection in the Domain of ONP" (WIK and European-American Center for Policy Analysis, under contract to Directorate-General XIII of the European Commission, Nov. 1994).

"ARRC Staff Says Ameritech's 'Universal Access Plan' Is 'Viable' Basis for Local Competition but Lists Concerns," *Telecommunications Reports*, Apr. 11, 1994, at 17.

AT&T, *1993 Annual Report* (1994).

AT&T, *1994 Annual Report* (1995).

AT&T, *1995 Annual Report* (1996).

"AT&T Makes Pledges about 'Nondominance' Plea," *Telecommunications Reports*, Nov. 27, 1995, at 10.

"AT&T, McCaw Cellular Defend Proposed Merger," *Telecommunications Reports*, Dec. 13, 1993, at 20.

Averch, Harvey, and Leland L. Johnson, "Behavior of the Firm under Regulatory Constraint," 52 *American Economic Review* 1052 (1962).

Baumol, William J., and J. Gregory Sidak, *Toward Competition in Local Telephony* (MIT Press and AEI Press 1994).

Baumol, William J., Michael F. Koehn, and Robert D. Willig, "How Arbitrary Is 'Arbitrary'? or, Toward the Deserved Demise of Full Cost Allocation," *Public Utilities Fortnightly*, Sept. 3, 1987, at 16.

Beesley, Michael E., *Liberalisation of the Use of British Telecommunications Network* (HM Stationer's Office 1981).

Beesley, Michael E., and Bruce Laidlaw, "The Development of Telecommunications Policy in the UK, 1981–1991" (1992).

Beesley, Michael E., and Stephen C. Littlechild, "The Regulation of Privatized Monopolies in the United Kingdom," 20 *RAND Journal of Economics* 454 (1989).

Bellcore, *Advanced Intelligent Network (AIN) Release 1 Switch-Service Control Point/Adjunct Application Protocol Interface Generic Requirements*, TA-NET-001126 (May 1991).

Bellcore, *ONA Services User Guide* (Jan. 31, 1992).

Berg, Sanford V., and John Tschirhart, *Natural Monopoly Regulation* (Cambridge University Press 1988).

Blank, Larry, David L. Kaserman, and John W. Mayo, "Dominant Firm Pricing with Competitive Entry and Regulation" (May 1994).

"BOCs Sketch Plans in ONA Annual Reports for Service Based on Advanced Technologies," *Telecommunications Reports*, Apr. 25, 1994, at 33.

Bolter, Walter G., J. W. Connaughey, and F. J. Kelsey, *Telecommunications for the 1990s and Beyond* (M. E. Sharpe, Inc. 1991).

Borrows, John D., Phyllis A. Bernt, and Raymond W. Lawton, "Universal Service in the United States: Dimensions of the Debate," WIK Diskussionsbeitrag No. 124 (Mar. 1994).

Bowman, Robert M. "U S West Switching Cost Models," in *Marginal Cost Techniques for Telephone Services: Symposium Proceedings* (W. Pollard ed., National Regulatory Research Institute, January 1991).

Bradley, Ian, and Catherine Price, "The Economic Regulation of Private Industry by Price Constraints," 37 *Journal of Industrial Economics* 99 (1988).

Braeutigam, Ronald R., "Analysis of Fully Distributed Cost Pricing in Regulated Industries," 11 *Bell Journal of Economics* 182 (1980).

Braeutigam, Ronald R., and John C. Panzar, "Diversification Incentives under 'Price-Based' and 'Cost-Based' Regulation," 20 *RAND Journal of Economics* 373 (1989).

"British Telecom Struggles to Fend Off Strong Sales Pitches by US Companies," *Wall Street Journal,* Aug. 26, 1994, at A6.

British Telecommunications PLC, *Pricing for Choice* (Mar. 1992).

British Telecommunications PLC, *Report and Accounts* (1994).

"Broadband PCS Auction Nets $7.7 Billion; AT&T, Sprint, Bell Companies Win 70 of 99 Licenses," *Telecommunications Reports,* Mar. 20, 1995.

"'C' Block PCS Auction Raises $10.2 Billion," *Telecommunications Reports*, May 13, 1996, at 4.

Cable Television Association, *Independent Television Commission* (May 20, 1993).

"California Says IntraLATA Competition Will Begin Jan. 1," *Telecommunications Reports,* Sept. 19, 1994.

"CAP Seeks Local Services Authority in North Carolina," *Telecommunications Reports,* Oct. 24, 1994, at 15.

Cave, Martin, "Recent Developments in the Regulation of Former Nationalized Industries," HM Treasury Working Paper No. 60 (1991).

Cave, Martin, and Ian Martin, "The Costs and Benefits of Accounting Separation," *Telecommunications Policy* 28 (1991).

Cellular Telecommunications Industry Association, *1995 Wireless Industry Survey Results* (Mar. 25, 1996).

"Cincinnati Bell Inc. Unit Files Protest against Time Warner's Ohio Phone Plan," *Wall Street Journal,* Feb. 21, 1995, at D6.

Cohen, Jeffrey E., *The Politics of Telecommunications Regulation—The States and the Divestiture of AT&T* (M. E. Sharpe 1992).

Cramer, Curtis A., "Local Competition for Telephone Services," 9 *Review of Industrial Organization* 273 (1994).

Donald, Stephen G., and David E. M. Sappington, "Explaining the Choice Among Regulatory Plans in the U.S. Telecommunications Industry," 4 *Journal of Economics and Management Strategy* 237 (1995).

Donaldson, Lufkin and Jenrette, *The Wireless Communications Industry* (Summer 1994).

"Doubt Surfaces about Rochester 'Open Market' Plan; Critics Say Competition Is Sputtering," *Telecommunications Reports*, Aug. 14, 1995, at 7.

Dougherty, Kevin, "Bell, MH Talked about Sharing Superhighway," *Financial Post,* Apr. 14, 1994, at 3.

Economics and Technology, Inc./Hatfield Associates, "The Enduring Local Bottleneck" (1994).

"F.C.C. Approves Waivers for Rochester Unbundling Plan, Supports Local Competition 'Experiment,'" *Telecommunications Reports,* Mar. 13, 1995, at 8.

"F.C.C. Puts Transport in New 'Trunking' Price Cap Basket," *Telecommunications Reports*, Jan. 24, 1994, at 6.

Federal Communications Commission, Industry Analysis Division, *Fiber Deployment Update* (Apr. 1994).

Federal Communications Commission, *Monitoring Report* (May 1993).

Federal Communications Commission, *Statistics of Communications Common Carriers 1992/3*, 7th ed.

"A Focus on the Consumer Supplement: Jones Intercable Company Profile," *Broadcasting and Cable,* Nov. 28, 1994, at 4.

Fox, William, and John W. Mayo, "State Level Telecommunications Policy in the Post-Divestiture Era: An Economic Perspective," Center for Business and Economic Research, College of Business Administration, University of Tennessee, Knoxville (March 1991).

Gabel, David, and D. Mark Kennet, "Economies of Scope in the Local Telephone Exchange Market," 6 *Journal of Regulatory Economics* 381 (1994).

Gabel, Richard, "The Early Competitive Era in Telephone Communications, 1893–1920," 34 *Law and Contemporary Problems* 340 (1969).

Geller, Henry, "Broadcasting," in *New Directions in Telecommunications Policy* (Paula Newberg ed., Duke University Press 1989).

Gist, P., and S. A. Meadowcroft, "Regulation for Competition: The Newly Liberalised Market for Private Branch Exchanges," 7 *Fiscal Studies* 41 (1986).

Glaister, Stephen, "Regulation through Output Related Profits Tax," 35 *Journal of Industrial Economics* 281 (1987).

Greenstein, Shane, Susan McMaster, and Pablo T. Spiller, "The Effect of Incentive Regulation on Local Exchange Companies' Deployment of Digital Technology," 4 *Journal of Economics and Management Strategy* 187 (1995).

Hatfield Associates, *Documentation of the Hatfield Model, Version 2.2, Release 1* (May 16, 1996).

Huber, Peter W., Michael K. Kellogg, and John Thorne, *The Geodesic Network II: 1993 Report on Competition in the Telephone Industry* (Geodesic Co. 1992).

"Hundt Looks towards Radical Overhaul of Regulatory Regimes, Major Business Moves," *Telecommunications Reports*, July 15, 1996, at 1.

Illinois Commerce Commission, Staff Report, *Local Competition and Interconnection*, 1992.

Information Industry Liaison Committee, "Minutes of the Information Industry Liaison Committee," Issue 026 Task Group (Sept. 2, 1993).

"IntraLATA Equal Access Expected Early 1996 in Minnesota; PUC Affirms 'Bona Fide' Request Rule," *Telecommunications Reports,* Oct. 31, 1994, at 13.

"IXCs, CAPs Like Maryland's Local Competition Efforts; Bell Atlantic Suggests Easing Regulatory 'Restraints,'" *Telecommunications Reports,* Aug. 8, 1994, at 12.

Johnson, Leland L., "Price Caps in Telecommunications Regulatory Reform," RAND Note N-2894-MF/RC (1989).

Johnson, Leland L., *Toward Competition in Cable Television* (MIT Press and AEI Press 1994).

"Jones Intercable, Canada's BCE Add Twist to Telco/Cable TV Convergence with Deal to Form Strategic Alliance," *Telecommunications Reports*, Dec. 6, 1993.

"Jones Lightwave, MCI Plan to Test Telephone Service over Cable TV Systems," *Telecommunications Reports*, Nov. 29, 1988, at 10.

"Justice Says Ameritech's InterLATA Service Waiver Is 'More Limited, More Profound,'" *Telecommunications Reports*, May 8, 1995, at 28.

Kaestner, Robert, and Brenda Kahn, "The Impact of IntraLATA Competition on Local Exchange Company Prices," in *Economic Innovations in Public Utility Regulation* (Michael A. Crew ed., Kluwer Academic Publishers 1992).

Kaserman, David L., and John W. Mayo, "Deregulation and Market Power Criteria: An Evaluation of State Level Telecommunications Policy," in *Telecommunications Deregulation—Market Power and Cost Allocation Issues* 65 (J. R. Allison and D. L. Thomas eds., Quorum Books 1990).

Kaserman, David L., and John W. Mayo, "Monopoly Leveraging Theory: Implications for Post-Divestiture Telecommunications Policy," Center for Business and Economic Research, College of Business Administration, University of Tennessee, Knoxville, 1993.

Kaserman, David L., and John W. Mayo, "Regulatory Policies toward Local Exchange Companies under Emerging Competition: Guardrails or Speedbumps on the Information Highway?" (1995).

Kaserman, David L., John W. Mayo, and Patricia L. Pacey, "The Political Economy of Deregulation: The Case of Intrastate Long Distance," 5 *Journal of Regulatory Economics* 49 (1993).

Kellogg, Michael K., John Thorne, and Peter W. Huber, *Federal Telecommunications Law* (Little, Brown & Co. 1992).

Knieps, Gunter, and Ingo Vogelsang, "The Sustainability Concept under Alternative Behavioral Assumptions," 13 *Bell Journal of Economics* 234 (1982).

Kraemer, J., *Telecommunications Industry Program, Competitive Assessment of the Market for Alternative Local Transport* (Deloitte & Touche 1994).

Laffont, Jean-Jacques, and Jean Tirole, *A Theory of Incentives in Procurement and Regulation* (MIT Press 1993).

Larson, Alexander C., and Margaret Z. Starkey, "Unbundling Issues and State Telecommunications Regulatory Policy" (Feb. 16, 1994).

"LECs, Competitors Debate Unbundling, Interconnection Details, Divide over Proposed Compensation, Universal Service Models," *Telecommunications Reports,* Dec. 5, 1994, at 5.

"LECs File New Tariffs for 'Virtual Collocation'; NYNEX, Pacific Telesis Continue Physical Collocation," *Telecommunications Reports*, Sept. 5, 1994, at 1.

"Legislation Earns Widespread Praise from Industry; Companies Announce Plans to Enter New Markets," *Telecommunications Reports*, Feb. 5, 1996, at 35.

Lewis, Bill, "Bell Competitors Square Off in Data Transmission Duel," *Memphis Business Journal,* Oct. 11, 1993, at 3.

Littlechild, Stephen C., *Regulation of British Telecommunications' Profitability* (Department of Industry 1983).

"Local Access Venture Off to a Slow Start," *Network World,* Dec. 19, 1994, at 1.

MacAvoy, Paul W., *The Failure of Antitrust and Regulation to Establish Competition in Long-Distance Telephone Services* (MIT Press and AEI Press 1996).

"The Man Who Would Save NY for NYNEX," *New York Times,* Apr. 3, 1995.

Mathios, Alan D., and Robert P. Rogers, "The Impact of Alternative Forms of State Regulation of AT&T on Direct-Dial Long-Distance Telephone Rates," 20 *RAND Journal of Economics* 437 (1989).

"MCI Fires Five Local Service Salvos," *Interactive Week,* Oct. 10, 1994.

"MCI Goes to War to Promote Local Exchange Competition; Will Spend $2 Billion Building Networks in 20 Cities," *Telecommunications Reports*, Jan. 10, 1994, at 1.

"MCI, Manufacturers Unveil Numbers Portability Solution," *Telecommunications Reports*, May 15, 1995, at 11.

"MCI Metro Filed Applications in Conn., Ohio, and Ore. to Provide Local Telephone Service," *Communications Daily,* Dec. 21, 1994, at 5.

Meek, K., "Telecommunications Price Control in the UK," International Institute of Communication (1988); cited in Leland L. Johnson, *Price Caps in Telecommunications Regulatory Reform*, RAND Corp. Note N-2984-MF/RC, 1989.

Mercury Communications Ltd., *Business Review 1992–93: The Dimensions of Growth* (1993).

Mercury Communications Ltd., "Mercury in the United Kingdom," in *Cable & Wireless Annual Report to the United States Securities and Exchange Commission on Form 20-F 1992/93* (Sept. 10, 1993).

Mercury One-2-One, "Press Information" (Mar. 1, 1994).

"MFS Doesn't Have to Pay Carrier Common Line Fee," *Telecommunications Reports,* Apr. 3, 1995, at 12.

"MFS Plans to Build Networks in Seattle, Oregon," *Telecommunications Reports,* July 11, 1994, at 33.

"MFS Requests 'Co-Carrier' Status in Texas," *Telecommunications Reports,* Aug. 8, 1994, at 11.

Mitchell, Bridger M., "Incremental Costs of Telephone Access and Local Use," RAND Corp. 3909-ICTF (1990).

Mitchell, Bridger M., and Tenzing Donyo, "Utilization of the U.S. Telephone Network," RAND Corp. MR-436-EAC/WIK (Mar. 1994).

Mitchell, Bridger M., and Ingo Vogelsang, "Markup Pricing for Interconnection: A Conceptual Framework," in *Opening Networks to Competition: The Regulation and Pricing of Access* (David Gabel and David Weiman eds., Kluwer Academic Publishers 1997).

Mitchell, Bridger M., and Ingo Vogelsang, *Telecommunications Pricing: Theory and Practice* (Cambridge University Press 1991).

Monopolies and Mergers Commission, *British Telecommunications PLS and MITEL Corporation: A Report on the Proposed Merger* (HM Stationer's Office 1986).

Moss, Mitchell, "Can States Face the Future? A New Agenda for Telecommunications Policy," 9 *New York Affairs* 81.

Montgomery, W. P., "Promise versus Reality: Telecommunications Infrastructure, LEC Investment and Regulatory Reforms" (Aug. 1994).

National Association of Regulatory Utility Commissioners, *Bulletin* 15 (1986).

National Association of Regulatory Utility Commissioners, *NARUC Report on the Status of Competition in Intrastate Telecommunications* (originally published Aug. 26, 1992; updated and republished Nov. 9, 1993).

National Association of Regulatory Utility Commissioners, *1993 Report of the Administrative Director on Litigation* (1993).

National Cable Television Association, *Cable Television Developments* (Nov. 1993).

National Regulatory Research Institute, *Regional Regulation of Public Utilities: Opportunities and Obstacles*, NRRI 92-19 (Dec. 1992).

"NCTA Plans Local Competition Initiative with IXCs, CAPs; Entry Barriers in Six States to Be Targeted," *Telecommunications Reports,* Nov. 14, 1994, at 1.

Neik, Gautam, and Daniel Perl, "FCC Allows Phone Companies to Own Dispatch, Lifting Nextel Streak," *Wall Street Journal,* Mar. 8, 1995, at B6.

Neu, Werner, and Karl-Heinz Neumann, "Interconnection Agreements in Telecommunications," WIK Diskussionsbeitrag No. 106 (Apr. 1993).

"1991 State Regulators' Forum on Regional Regulation," *Public Utilities Fortnightly*, Nov. 1, 1991, at 28.

Noam, Eli, *Telecommunications in Europe* (Oxford University Press 1992).

Noll, Roger G., "State Regulatory Responses to Competition and Divestiture in the Telecommunications Industry," in *Antitrust and Regulation* (Ronald E. Grayson ed., Lexington Books 1986).

Noll, Roger G., "Telecommunications Regulation in the 1990s," in *New Directions in Telecommunications Policy* (Paula Newberg ed., Duke University Press 1989).

Noll, Roger G., and Frances M. Rosenbluth, "Telecommunications Policy in Japan and the U.S.: Structure, Process, Outcomes," CEPR Publication No. 349, Stanford University (1993).

Noll, Roger G., and Susan Smart, "The Political Economics of State Responses to Divestiture and Federal Deregulation in Telecommunications," Discussion Paper 148, Workshop of Applied Microeconomics, Industrial Organization and Regulation, Department of Economics, Stanford University (1989).

"North Dakota Court Upholds IntraLATA Equal Access Ban," *Telecommunications Reports,* Nov. 14, 1994.

NYNEX CableComms, "NYNEX CableComms Network Architecture and Equipment" (undated).

NYNEX CableComms, "A Year in Perspective—1992 Reviewed" (undated).

"NYNEX Gets Limited Waiver to Alter Access Charges: FCC Recognizes Start of Local Competition in N.Y.," *Telecommunications Reports,* May 8, 1995.

"NYNEX, Pacific Telesis Continue Physical Collocation," *Telecommunications Reports,* Sept. 5, 1994, at 1.

OFTEL, *Annual Report* (1991).

OFTEL, *Annual Report* (1993).

OFTEL, "BT's Cost of Capital" (1992).

OFTEL, "The Control of British Telecom's Prices" (July 1988).

OFTEL, "A Framework for Effective Competition" (Dec. 1994).

OFTEL, "Interconnection and Accounting Separation: The Next Steps" (Mar. 1994).

OFTEL, "The Methodology to Calculate Long-Run Incremental Costs," study prepared for OFTEL by National Economic Research Associates (Mar. 1996).

OFTEL, "Pricing of Telecommunications Services from 1997," consultative document (Dec. 1995).

OFTEL, "Pricing of Telecommunications Services from 1997," statement (June 1996).

OFTEL, *The Relationship between Costs and Interconnection Charges, Proceedings of the Second Meeting* (Jan. 11, 1994).

OFTEL, "Responses to OFTEL's Consultative Document on the Future Regulation of British Telecom's Prices," Working Paper No. 3 (Sept. 1988).

"Ohio Action Gives Ameritech Region-Wide Price Regulation," *Telecommunications Reports,* Nov. 28, 1994, at 6.

"Ohio Approves Time Warner AxS Application; Leaves Tough Issues for When LEC Certification Is Sought," *Telecommunications Reports*, Dec. 13, 1993, at 26.

"Oregon Permits ELI to Provide Switched IXC Services," *Telecommunications Report*, Jan. 24, 1994, at 7.

Owen, Bruce M., and Ronald Braeutigam, *The Regulation Game: Strategic Use of the Administrative Process* (Ballinger 1978).

Palmer, Karen, "A Test for Cross Subsidies in Local Telephone Rates: Do Business Customers Subsidize Residential Customers?" 23 *RAND Journal of Economics* 415 (1992).

Parsons, Steve G., and Michael R. Ward, "Vertical Disintegration of the Bell System: The Effects on Access Markets" (Oct. 22, 1993).

Paul Kagan Associates, *Marketing New Media* (Aug. 21, 1995).

"Price Regulation Plan for Ameritech-Illinois Approved," *Telecommunications Reports,* Oct. 17, 1994, at 16.

"Proponents of Rochester Tel Pact Make Case to PSC, Say 'Open Market Plan' Balances Competition, Safeguards," *Telecommunications Reports,* July 4, 1994, at 26.

"Proposal to Merge Bell Atlantic/NYNEX Raises Questions about Fate of Competition," *Telecommunications Reports*, Apr. 29, 1996, at 1.

"RBOC, LEC, and ALT/CAP Market Shares," 3 *Connecticut Research Report on Competitive Telecommunications* (June 1, 1995).

Reed, David P., "Putting It All Together: The Cost Structure of Personal Communications Services," FCC Working Paper 28 (Nov. 1992).

"RHCs Win Waiver for Wireless Interchange Service: Competitive Access Opportunities Seen as Crucial," *Telecommunications Reports*, May 1, 1995, at 1.

"Rochester Tel's 'Open Market Plan' Approved in New York; Telco's Rates Will Drop by $21 Million over Seven Years," *Telecommunications Reports,* Oct. 17, 1994.

Rohlfs, Jeffrey H., Charles L. Jackson, and Tracey E. Kelly, "Estimate of the Loss to the United States Caused by the FCC's Delay in Licensing Cellular Telecommunications"; cited by William B. Shew, in "Regulation, Competition, and Prices in Cellular Telephony," American Enterprise Institute for Public Policy Research working paper (June 2, 1994).

Salinger, Michael A., "The Future of Local Telecommunications Networks: Will Competition Really Emerge?" paper prepared for Charles River Associates conference, Boston (1994).

Sappington, David E. M., and Dennis L. Weisman, *Designing Incentive Regulation for the Telecommunications Industry* (MIT Press and AEI Press 1996).

"SBC, Pacific Telesis Plan First Bell Company Merger in Wake of New Telecom Law," *Telecommunications Reports*, Apr. 4, 1996, at 1.

Schwartz, Gail Garfield, and Jeffrey H. Hoagg, "Virtual Divestiture: Structural Reform of an RHC," 44 *Federal Communications Law Journal* 285 (1992).

"Semiconductor Vendor Level One Has Product to Spur HDSL Development," *Telecommunication Reports*, Jan. 17, 1994, at 29.

Shapiro, Eben, "Time Warner's Orlando Test to Start—Finally," *Wall Street Journal*, Dec. 7, 1994, at B1.

Sherman, Roger, *The Regulation of Monopoly* (Cambridge University Press 1989).

Shew, William B., "Regulation, Competition, and Prices in Cellular Telephony," American Institute for Public Policy Research working paper (June 2, 1994).

Shin, Richard T., and John S. Ying, "Unnatural Monopolies in Local Telephone," 23 *RAND Journal of Economics* 171 (1992).

Sidak, J. Gregory, letter to the authors, Feb. 7, 1995.

Sievers, Mark, "Percentage Interstate Usage: The Case for Occam's Razor and Access Parity," paper presented at the 21st Annual Telecommunications Policy Research Conference, Solomons Island, Md. (Oct. 4, 1993).

Spiller, Pablo T., and R. Gely, "Congressional Control or Judicial Interpretation: The Determinants of U.S. Supreme Court Labor Decisions, 1949–1988," 23 *RAND Journal of Economics* 463 (1992).

Spiller, Pablo T., and Ingo Vogelsang, "The United Kingdom: A Pace Setter in Regulatory Initiatives," in *Regulations, Institutions, and Commitment: Comparative Studies of Telecommunications* (Brian Levi and Pablo T. Spiller eds., Cambridge University Press 1996), at 79.

"Sprint Ventures into Partnership with Cable Company Trio," *Telephony*, Oct. 31, 1994.

Sugawara, Sondra, "A Power Play for the Information Highway?" *Washington Post*, Dec. 28, 1993, at D1.

Sullivan, Kevin R., "Competition in Telecommunications: Moving Toward a New Era of Antitrust Scrutiny and Regulation," in *Future Competition in Telecommunications* (S. P. Bradley and J. A. Hausman eds., Harvard Business School Press 1989), at 123.

"SW Bell to Purchase Two DC-Area Cable Systems from Hauser Commun.," *Telecommunications Reports*, Feb. 15, 1993, at 9.

Tardiff, Timothy J., and William E. Taylor, "Telephone Company Performance Under Alternative Forms of Regulation in the U.S.," National Economic Research Associates (1993).

Taylor, William E., Charles J. Zarkadas, and J. Douglas Zona, "Incentive Regulation and the Diffusion of New Technology in Telecommunications," National Economic Research Associates (1992).

"Telephone Companies Hear Call of New Round of Competition," *Los Angeles Times*, Dec. 30, 1994.

"Teleport Reaches Compensation Agreement with NYNEX," *Telecommunications Reports*, June 27, 1994, at 30.

"Teleport Seeks Switched Service Authority in Michigan," *Telecommunications Reports*, Nov. 21, 1994, at 18.

Teske, Paul E., *After Divestiture—The Political Economy of State Telecommunications Regulation* (State University of New York Press 1990).

"Time Warner Cable: Building Full Service Network," *Telephony*, Nov. 1993, at 51.

"Time Warner Unwraps Full Service Network," *Telephony,* Dec. 19, 1994.

Tye, William B., "Competitive Access: A Comparative Industry Approach to the Essential Facility Doctrine," 8 *Energy Law Journal* 337 (1987).

"UK: Cable Industry Reveals Biggest Ever Rise in Subscription in Final Quarter of 1994," *Computergram,* Feb. 28, 1995.

U.S. Department of Commerce, *US Spectrum Management Policy: Agenda for the Future*, National Telecommunications and Information Agency, Special Publication 91-213 (Feb. 1991).

"US Signal Wins License to Offer Local Services in Michigan," *Telecommunications Reports,* Oct. 24, 1994, at 11.

"U S West Seeks Broad Decree Waiver for Time Warner's Planned Full-Service Network," *Telecommunications Reports*, Dec. 20, 1993, at 10.

Vogelsang, Ingo, "Price Cap Regulation of Telecommunications Services: A Long-Run Approach," in *Deregulation and Diversification of Utilities* (Michael A. Crew ed., Kluwer Academic Publishers 1989).

"Wall St. Sees Time Warner in AT&T Deal," *New York Times,* May 15, 1995, at D1.

"Washington Commission Grants MCI Local Service Request," *Telecommunications Reports,* Nov. 14, 1994, at 10.

Weisman, Dennis L., "Why Less May Be More under Price-Cap Regulation," 6 *Journal of Regulatory Economics* 339 (1994).

"Wisconsin Grants Teleport Authority to Offer Local Services," *Telecommunications Reports,* Aug. 29, 1994, at 3.

Ying, John S., and Richard T. Shin, "Viable Competition in Local Telephone: Superadditive Costs in the Postdivestiture Period" (Dec. 1994).

Case and Regulatory Proceeding Index

Name Index

Subject Index

Regulation, United Kingdom
of British Telecom, 266–69
licensing of telecommunications,
256, 262–64
price-cap regime for BT, 95–96,
269–77
Resale of services
by LECs, 186–87
under Telecommunications Act
(1996), 234–35
Residual interconnection charge
(RIC), 122, 125
Restrictive Trade Practices Act
(1976), United Kingdom, 266
Revenue sharing, state-level
regulation, 97
Rochester Telephone Corporation
Open Market Plan, 193–96
See also Frontier
Communications of Rochester

Separations idea, 80–82
Service creation, 48
Service platform, 48
Service providers, 19–20
See also Access providers
Signaling System 7 (SS7), 26, 43
Special access, 116–18
expanded interconnection for,
153
LEC bundling of services for,
153
lines, 3
pricing, 160
Spectrum licensing, 206–7
Subscriber line charge, 115
Subsidies
by consumer groups, 196–97
in switched local services, 186
universal service, 241–42
See also Cross-subsidies
Switched access
FCC reform of regulation,
166–68
Switches
defined, 38–39, 47
stored-program-control, 146
Switching
high-speed, 27
LEC position in local, 144–45
switched access, 116–19
tandem switched access, 117–19

Switching Cost Information System
(SCIS), 142

Tandem switched access, 117–19
Technology
components of telecommunications, 37–40
effects of changes in, 20–27
fiber optics, 22–23
LEC use of wireless cable, 221
limitations in LEC distribution,
220
of telecommunications networks,
16–17
used for network access, 37–40
Telecommunications
components of network, 10–15
vertical and horizontal integration
of firms in, 15–17, 30–34
Telecommunications Act (1996), 1,
6
collocation rules under, 159
competition determination
checklist, 203–5
effect on regulatory regime, 305
FCC fiat under, 227–29
FCC order related to local
competition, 227–29
FCC price setting methodology
under, 237–45
importance for local competition,
69–70
intraLATA regulation, 181–82
key issues of FCC competition
order, 229–37
provisions for local competition
policies, 62, 84, 106, 152
universal service, 88–89, 93
Telecommunications Acts (1981,
1984), United Kingdom, 253,
255–56, 262, 264
Telecommunications market
post–AT&T Modification of
Final Judgment, 28
Telecommunications market, United
Kingdom
history, 252–54
liberalization, 254–55
players in, 251–52
Telecommunications policy, United
Kingdom, 266